D1591656

THE ROAD TO SUBLIMATION SUCCESS

Harnessing the Power of Sublimation for Outstanding Profits

By

W. David Gross

J. Stephen Spence

THE ROAD TO SUBLIMATION SUCCESS

Harnessing the Power of Sublimation for Outstanding Profits

Cover Design by Todd Till

ISBN 978-1-953921-01-7

First Edition

WHO SHOULD BUY THIS BOOK?

This book should prove valuable to anyone who works with sublimation, is interested in sublimation or most of all, is interested to starting a sublimation business or adding sublimation to an existing business.

The authors have tried to provide both a book introducing the science of sublimation, the necessary steps to starting a sublimation business and a reference book that will be turned to often, even after your business is up and running.

The authors have extensive experience both with sublimation and running a sublimation business, so they provide advice from actual experience, not theory.

Inside, you will find information about selecting a printer, heat press, ink and other necessities to be successful along with sections about the various types of products and in some cases, even how to make them.

You will also find business helps including business plans and formulas for learning what it costs to actually be in business.

In the back of the book, you will find an extensive reference section listing everything from educational sources to Tips & Tricks that will solve many of the problems you might encounter along the way.

Last but not least, you will gain admittance to a website containing Designs 4 U, a library of ready to print awards, plaques, clocks and dozens of other items. All you have to do is change the names and your job is ready to print. This is made possible by their creator, Universal Woods, and originally sold for about $200 and they're yours FREE of charge. All you have to do is download the files you want.

TABLE OF CONTENTS

PART TWO: THE PRODUCTS

PART THREE: PROMOTION

BUSINESS BASICS

APPENDIX

◀ ABOUT THIS EDITION

Thank you for purchasing the *First Edition* of <u>The Road to Sublimation Success</u>! To our knowedge, this is the first "real" book ever published about sublimation and how to start your own sublimation business.

The authors expect there to be many future editions of this book since the sublimation industry is changing and maturing so quickly. Each updated version of this book will be given a new Edition Number such as Edition Two, Three and so on.

This Edition however is the First Edition and although it may never go down in history as an exceptionally valuable book, it is our hope that it will become exceptionally valuable to you as you start up your own sublimation business or add sublimation to your existing business.

Conde Headquarters, Mobile, Alabama

◣ ACKNOWLEDGMENTS

I want to thank my wife Monica along with my kids: Trey, Finch and Victoria and the entire Conde team for making this book happen. Folks like my partners: Tim Lynn and Jere Austill along with Sprite Wood, Jeff Butler, Todd Till and Megan Brewer were invaluable.

Our partners: George Knight, Universal Woods, Sawgrass, Source Substrates and my good friend Steve Spence.

Over the last 25 plus years, I have greatly enjoyed playing the role of sublimation evangelist for our industry as well as being an advocate for bringing new substrates to market. In my first life as an electrical engineer, I helped with the design of some of the world's first monochrome laser printers at QMS. This helped introduce me to digital imaging and ultimately color printing which I fell in love with. I started looking for high value ways to harness the power of color print imaging and fell in love with digital decorating. That is, taking something other than paper and putting color images or graphics on it such as shirts and mugs. This led me to sublimation. With the help of the early pioneers such as Sawgrass and Unisub came the birth of the digital sublimation industry. Yes, many other companies played a role in this revolution that should be given credit, so I apologize now as I am not writing a history book on sublimation; only a guide to grow our industry. So, let's get to it!

David Gross
President/CEO Condé Systems
dgross@conde.com

PREFACE

"Success is walking from failure to failure with no loss of enthusiasm." -Winston Churchill

Down the Rabbit Hole

David Gross

David Gross

Have you ever found yourself perusing the Web and stumble upon an Etsy page, or perhaps it is an eBay store, with beautiful, one-of-a-kind gifts? These could be anywhere from cutting boards to clothing designs, to key chains to coffee mugs...the products now available are endless. More importantly, while browsing have you ever thought to yourself, "Hey! I can do that!" Well, I'm here to shed a little secret... you can! Buckle up, ladies and gentlemen, as we take a trip down the rabbit hole exploring the intoxicating world of sublimation!

The sublimation industry is an ideal business to be a part of because of its very little start-up cost, and for the potential of an excellent return. If you possess the will and the drive, my crew and I can help mold you into a successful businessperson in this ever-growing and ever-changing industry.

Thank you for joining me as we discuss this topic. My name is David Gross. I am an electrical engineer based out of Mobile, Alabama, with over twenty years' experience helping others become victorious in the field of sublimation. My company, Condé Systems, has specialized and perfected the art of producing sublimatable products, as well as supplying all the tools necessary to get you started, or to expand your business.

Condé Systems has become the recognized leader in the personalized products market by offering everything needed to get into the photo gift business including transfer systems, production software, blank imprintables, transfer paper and supplies, and instructional videos. We also offer state-of-the-art printers and printer accessories and heat presses. Screen printers, sign makers, embroiderers, pad printers, engravers, photographers, artists, and home business entrepreneurs can expand their current product offerings by providing their customers full-color, photographic quality gifts and awards. During all stages of product selection, sales, and post sales, Condé offers expert knowledge and superior one-on-one customer support with one of our many reliable staff members to help fully ensure your understanding of the products, the equipment offered, and also the sublimation process.

As evident from this book and the articles I have published on the subject over the many years (which can be accessed on our website, www.Condé.com), I am very passionate about sublimation. From the moment I wake in the morning and have my morning coffee until I go to bed at night, I am always thinking about what new products we can bring to the market as well as what we can do to help people like you become successful.

Think about it. What other income producing activity has a low cost of entry and yet can produce such a diverse range of high value products? And what's even more enticing, is that regardless of whether you buy the most expensive system we offer or the least expensive, the quality of the product stays the same—only size, volume and piece cost are affected.

The sublimation industry is just getting started. Everyday more and more people are jumping on board. Trade shows are designed to join all these people together and showcase the variety and potential of sublimation. These shows are an excellent way of networking while providing a fun and interactive way to meet key players in the industry.

When I am at trade shows, I am always checking out other companies and what they are producing and see how we stack up comparatively. Staying one step ahead and within the times is extremely important to us here at Condé.

I also host many seminars at these trade shows. I love to share what knowledge I have acquired over the years and reach out to people who would like to know more. People like you! When I attend a show, there is always a balanced sense of learning and teaching that occurs. Michelangelo, in the later years of his life, scribbled down the words "ancora imparo," which loosely translates into, "I am still learning." This is a principle that I hold dear, and practice in my personal and business life. If you are done learning, then you are done growing. We can only achieve what we desire through growth!

I understand. Sometimes getting to these trade shows can be hassle. We all have busy lives and it is not always conducive for us to pack up our things and head to Long Beach, California for the weekend! Regardless of whether you are a trade show frequenter, or have yet to attend one, I wanted to write this book to give you all the information to get you started as well as resources to continue you on your journey. It is always beneficial to have a physical model you can look back upon. And, if you walk away having learned something beneficial for you and your business, I'll consider this work a success!

One of the main things I stress in sublimation is that everything has value. In order to be successful in this business, you need to change the way you look at otherwise mundane objects around you. Recognizing a product's potential is key. Even the simplest of items, such as a coffee mug, can be transformed into something with more value, i.e., a picture of the family dog, an inspirational quote, or an appreciation for a hard-working teacher.

Be aware of the products that are useful in your own life and see how you can improve upon them. What organizations are you, or if you have children, are they involved in? Look around you as you read this book. Make a list of the objects that surround you and focus on how you can add value through sublimation.

Chances are, you already have ideas of your own. Constantly challenging yourself, however, allows the wheels to continue to turn, and for your business to stay fresh. So, you made it big in the trophy/award business... What can you do during the off-season to continue your success and reduce the decline in sales? What can you offer your clients that will keep your business in their minds throughout the year and not just part of the year?

Our goal is to make products that people want and are willing to pay lots for, and they will do so because they can trust the product they are receiving will be durable and of the highest quality. It is amazing what just a simple touch of charm and personalization can do to the overall value of a product.

The three keys to value are as followed:

> The Substrate: the blank version of the product we sell.

> The Artwork or Design: the decoration that is sublimated on the substrate.

> Our Sales/Marketing efforts: how you promote and sell the product.

We will discuss these three key areas of value to help maximize your efforts further in this book. The aim is that having a high value will translate to excellent profits.

As we bury ourselves deeper down the sublimation rabbit hole, I can't stress this prevailing thought enough: You can do it! Yes, you, sitting there with this book cupped in your hands. You are capable and full of promise. Already you are heading in the right direction, and we will help you every step of the way.

PREFACE

"Success does not consist of never making mistakes but of never making the same one a second time.   -George Bernard Shaw

THE ROAD TO SUBLIMATION SUCCESS

Steve Spence

Steve Spence

This book has been a labor of love. In the works for over three-years, it has grown from an idea to a monster effort. Still, David and I feel it is time sublimation got a *real* book of its own.

I started with sublimation in 1990 when we used converted photocopiers to print one color at a time. They were awful. Then, in 1997, I tried inkjet sublimation. It was slow, cantankerous and the printers constantly clogged up, but it was color, it looked great and I was hooked!

From there came a career of writing articles for the trade magazines, teaching Sublimation University all over the United States, Canada and even South America. That was a great experience and as time passed, everything got better and faster and cheaper until it was finally perfected.

Yes, "perfected" is the right word. No longer do printers clog up and do weird things no one can explain. No longer do we have to search for products and settle for mediocre quality. Today, there are about 1,000 products available and they work great.

A big part of the maturation of sublimation was due to none other than David Gross and Condé Systems in Mobile, Alabama. Through the years and the various struggles with sublimation inks and printers, David has persisted to hang in there and develop top quality products that work! It hasn't always been easy, but he has always kept a good spirit and never doubted a great future for the sublimation process.

In the writing of this book, David and I have passed it back and forth making changes and corrections so many times I'm not sure who wrote what or when. For that reason, it is written in first person and even we don't know who wrote what.

When I discovered inkjet sublimation back in 1997, I knew it had a glorious future. Today, I know I was right and best of all, it will only continue to improve. For that reason, I present to you – *The Road to Sublimation Success.* Come on, join the fun!

FOREWARD

"Success usually comes to those who are too busy to be looking for it." -- Henry David Thoreau

"OH WOW!"

"Oh Wow!" It's what people say when you open a heat press and they see a sublimated image for the first time. As CEO of Universal Woods for 25 years. (We are the manufacturer of all the UNISUB® and Chromaluxe® sublimation products.) I have heard people from almost every state, and at least 20 different countries, make the same, almost involuntary, exclamation. "Oh Wow!"

It feels like magic.

David Gross and Steve Spence wrote this book to explain the science behind the magic and to teach you how to turn an "Oh Wow!" moment into a thriving business.
They've been doing just that for 25 years.

David is the President and one of the founders of Condé Systems, the largest distributor in the world of sublimation systems and related products. An electrical engineer, he combines deep technical knowledge with a love for sublimation. He has never met a sublimatable product he didn't like. David has shared his knowledge with thousands of people in seminars and in technical support calls over the years.

Steve is the owner of Recognition Concepts in West Virginia, which creates awards and recognition items using sublimation and engraving equipment. He is a minister by training, changed careers over 30 years ago, and now is a leader in our industry. Steve has written extensively for trade publications over the last 25 years. He was the lead instructor for Sublimation University, an industry wide effort launched 20 years ago, to provide weekend seminars for sublimators throughout the United States. He also knows more corny jokes than anyone else I know.

Together David and Steve have helped entrepreneurs like you launch thousands of successful businesses utilizing sublimation technology. This book is designed to further that mission by providing detailed technical information about the how tos (and how not tos) of the sublimation process. More importantly, they share insights, gathered from years of experience and discussions with successful business owners, into how to make money with your sublimation system.

So, enjoy the book. I hope as you read it you will find many moments to think "Oh Wow!"

Paul Neumann
CEO Universal Woods (1994-2020)

GETTING STARTED IN SUBLIMATION 1

"You're always going to miss your chance if you never take a risk." -Unknown

WHY SUBLIMATION?

Why sublimation? It's simple. If you are considering starting your own business or starting a new income stream for your existing business, I can't think of a better choice than sublimation. Here's why:

As the legend goes, someone asked Jessie James why he robbed banks. His answer was, "Because that's where the money is!". Well, sublimation is where the money is as well. As you will see below, the investment is lower than any other business platform I know of and the profit margin is one of the highest. What more could you want?

The investment is low. There aren't many businesses or income streams you can get into for the cost of sublimation. Depending on what equipment you have already, the investment can be as low as a few hundred dollars. Even if you have to start from scratch and go with the best of everything, your investment is still only a little over $3,000. Other businesses like a laser engraver start about $10,000, UV printing about $20,000, embroidery about $10,000, screen printing about $10,000 and direct-to-garment closer to $20,000.

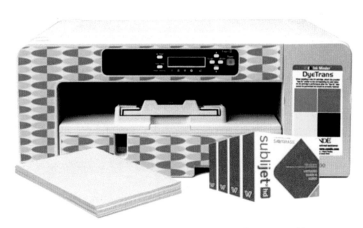

This is the larger size printer. It can print 13' x 51' with its optional by-pass tray.

The return is high. Sublimated products range from 100% to 900% profit, depending on the product. Most small items (key chains, name badges, etc.) range from 600% to 900%. Coffee cups and shirts run about 100% to 300%, depending on the market. How many things can you get that kind of return on?

The technology is easy to learn. Between this book and the Condé website and CondéTV, you have decades of knowledge and experience at your fingertips. And if that isn't enough, just call – we can help with whatever problem you might encounter.

Add a printer and ink to this DK20s press and you are ready to make products.

No big investment for product. Some business plans require you to buy a large inventory of products right from the beginning. Condé has no such

1

requirement. Buy what you want, when you need it. Most products can be ordered in single lots and rarely are we out of stock, so we can be your warehouse. We're just a day or two away.

Expendables such as ink and paper are inexpensive. The cost of a sheet of transfer paper is around 15¢ and the cost of ink about a penny per square inch.

According to countless surveys, personalized products are the number one desired product on the market. You don't have to "sell" your products, just make them available and products will sell themselves.

You are never alone. Condé is always there for you – no matter what. We want to be your partner in business. When you succeed, we succeed.

Well, there you have it. The essentials of the business. Again, I ask, "What other business can you get into for so little and make so much?"

WHY SUBLIMATION?

Low entry cost

Lots of education available for free

High profit margins

Easy to learn

Doesn't require a large workspace

Can be portable

Minimal inventory required

Instant business opportunities from Sawgrass

Sublimatable products sell themselves

Sublimation is fun

GETTING STARTED IN SUBLIMATION 2

"You will get all you want in life, if you help enough other people get what they want." -Zig Ziglar

BRIEF HISTORY OF SUBLIMATION

The earliest evidence of this printing method traces back to 1957 in France. Noël de Plase developed the method of printing for Substrates SA when he observed that dyes sublimate.

The Jet Propulsion Lab in the United States later invented the first ever computer printing machine that used the dye sublimation method. Wes Hoekstra led this project and became known as the father of computer image sublimation. Later works of Hoekstra include toner sublimation. Since then, the technology continued to develop using toners, wax films and eventually inkjet solutions. Sawgrass Technologies is credited with finding a way for the dyes to be suspended within a liquid so the printers that used them would print consistently.

It was not until the early computer days of the 1970s that the first monochrome transfer was developed using specialized ribbons impregnated with sublimation particles. The transfer was printed with a dot matrix impact printer. It was during this time Wes Hoekstra created the first computer output sublimation system as part of an extension of his "image processing work" with the Jet Propulsion Lab in Pasadena California. The JPL is the "leading U.S. center for robotic exploration of the solar system." They specialize in the construction and operation of robotic instruments, but also conduct Earth-orbits and astronomy missions. How's that for an out-of-this-world beginning?

After the electrostatic printer became more affordable for the regular Joe, toner cartridges containing sublimation solids began to appear on the market. They were, however, limited to single color or limited color

One of the very early sublimation printers. This one was single color and used powered toner.

transfers. Thankfully, we have surpassed this Stone Age in sublimation. Today, as we step proudly forth in this Golden Age of sublimation as we print full-color transfers through the use of offset presses and special inks, and this is all done quite economically

Cartridges could be exchanged to change the color being used.

as well!

THE PROCESS: The wonderful world of science!

Sublimation refers to the chemical process of a solid converting into a gas without first passing through the intermediate liquid stage. It also refers to the reverse process of a gas turning into a solid upon cooling.

I know, I know, real exciting stuff, right? But before I lose you, the real fun is to see this process at work. One common example of sublimation is frozen carbon dioxide or "dry ice." As it melts, or sublimates, it returns to a gas. To the amazed wonderment of a child, this transformative effect is magical. We have a similar magical effect! We use a method called Dye Sublimation Transfer. Dye Sublimation Transfer is a process where you take an image that has been created digitally (either by scanning, downloaded from a digital camera or created on your computer), and then print the image using special sublimation transfer inks onto transfer paper, or sublimation release paper. Once the image is on the paper you place it under a heat press on top of your polyester or poly coated item (substrate), and heat until the ink turns to a gas. This process transfers the image onto the item. As the product cools, the dye returns to its solid form, and the design is set.

I fell in love with sublimation over twenty years ago because of the quality of product that could be produced. Sublimation produces permanent full color photographic quality in minutes with no setup and minimum quantity of one. We now have thousands of blank sublimation substrates to choose from—the list is growing even as you read this book.

One of our beloved team members at Condé has a booth at the Flea Market in Mobile selling personalized phone cases and car tags. When a client walks up to his booth, they simply pick out a design from one of his many readily available templates (we provide template resources), and within minutes their personalized phone case or tag is created! If the client chooses to have a picture printed, all they have to do is connect through our team member's Wi-Fi, pick the photo they wish to print in their gallery, choose the printer, and Boom! Their very own customized phone case has been created. This business venture is very quick and easy. And at a reasonable $20 a case or tag, is very profitable. It has become quite normal for this particular team member to sell $2000 worth of phone cases in a single weekend. And this is just a side job!

Sublimation is a great product to offer in flea markets, car shows, carnivals and more. Here a display of phone covers is being shown.

This team member, with the help of sublimation, is indeed a magician! No, he's not pulling a rabbit out of his hat, but he is pulling in a lot of cash with very little cost to him. As you begin to utilize sublimation to your advantage, you will begin to feel like a magician as well. You will be creating workable, wearable, sellable products out of seemingly nothing, while also managing to have a little fun and make lots of money while doing so!

Gone are the days of frantically skimming through Etsy or eBay to find that perfect, last-minute gift. You will have all the necessary tools right at your fingertips to create something totally unique and valuable. And what's not to like about that?

Just a few of the more than 1,000 products you can sublimate.

GETTING STARTED IN
SUBLIMATION 3

*"The most serious mistakes are not being made as a result of wrong answers.
The truly dangerous thing is asking the wrong question."* -Peter Drucker

SUBLIMATION DURABILITY

There has been much discussion as to the durability of a sublimated product, particularly when used outdoors. But durability goes far beyond exterior applications and we will discuss all of them here as candidly as I know how.

The first area we should discuss is scratching. Although sublimation is typically thought of as being highly resistant to scratching, let's explore several different products and see how they measure up and why.

Some substrates are clearly more durable than others. This is because of the hardness of the special coating that is applied to the product. UNISUB products fair by far the best in these tests since the coating used is extremely hard and although they can be scratched if attacked by a knife blade, under normal use, they are almost impossible to damage. This is especially true with the Fiberglass Reinforced Plastic (FRP) products, making them a perfect choice for key fobs and name badges. Being carried in a pants pocket with keys and change will do little to damage such a tag and the only thing that will harm an FRP name badge is when the finding (pin, magnet, etc. on the back comes off). Even washing machines and clothes dryers have little or no affect. What will damage one of these products is leaving it in direct sunlight on the dashboard of a car for an extended period. We'll talk more about that later.

Sublimation metal is available under several brands. The UNISUB brand is hard as nails and will only scratch when physically abused with a sharp object. Other metals will scratch more easily but when used in normal applications, hold up very well.

Ceramic and porcelain tiles vary in durability depending on who coated them and with which coating. A rule of thumb is, the glossier the tile's finish, the more susceptible it is to scratch. Matte finished tiles, when coated by a reputable dealer, are extremely durable.

Sublimation dyes lie just under the surface of whatever coating is used on a product. Except for cloth, all products must have a polyester based coating applied for the sublimation dyes to saturate. A great many coatings have been tried and some are obviously better than others. To insure you are buying a good coating, you must trust the dealer you buy from. A reputable dealer will ensure that only the best coatings are used.

Be especially suspicious of products that are coated in China. A great many products are manufactured in countries all over the world. Many things like keepsake boxes and home décor items are made overseas but the metal plate, ceramic tile or FRP plate is made and coated in the USA. Cups, mugs and steins are among the worst offenders at having poor coatings and uneven surfaces. Although you usually can't see the flaws or recognize the inferior coating, it is there just the same and shows up either during the imprinting process, or when placed in a microwave or dishwasher.

Durability of imprinted shirts and other fabric: Sublimation works on Polyester fabric. For the most part, any Polyester item will sublimate but some may do better than others. The color of choice for all substrates is white. This is because the dyes used in sublimation inks are translucent (you can see through them). Many people do print on light to medium colored shirts with great success. The issue that has to be taken into account is that the color of the shirt will show through the ink and change the colors – a yellow shirt and blue ink will make green, etc. To correct this to some extent, you can print a color chart on each color shirt you are going to work with. The chart will show you how the ink is going to respond to the background color, and you can decide if that is acceptable or not. In the case of spot colors (not photographs), you may want to alter some of the colors to obtain a more desirable outcome.

Once a polyester shirt is sublimated, the colors are permanent. Washing and drying them will not change the colors, nor will wearing them over and over. Likewise, wearing them in sunlight as one typically would, will never cause the inks to fade. If, however, you sublimate a shirt and place it in your showroom window, you will see significant fading in less than three months. You should not be overly concerned about this (just don't put samples in your window), since most swimwear is sublimated polyester. I have heard people remark about a well-used swimsuit and how the chlorine has taken some of the color out. Truth be known, it probably wasn't the chlorine, but the sun was actually the cause.

Fading on hard substrates: Perhaps the biggest of all challenges that has faced sublimation is fading. True enough, given the right circumstances, sublimated products will fade. Usually this is caused by direct sunlight in exterior applications, but it can fade indoors too in some environments.

The method used to keep sublimation from fading is by adding special molecules in the coating used on the product. To date, we have found nothing to put in the ink that will help with this problem. Likewise, one should never cover a sublimated product with wax, polyurethane or plastic. This will actually accelerate the speed it will fade by causing something called migration.

Migration is a phenomenon where the sublimation particles in the ink try to off-gas and can't because it is covered in some way. As a result, the off-gassed molecules bounce off the coating and actually re-sublimate onto the substrate causing a shadow or ghosting effect. People have, for years, experimented with semi-permeable coatings that can be applied over a sublimated product to make it more durable in direct sunlight, but so far, nothing has actually proven to be worth the effort.

Understanding all this, you can better understand why some substrates hold up better to fading than others – it's all in the coating. The most durable UV coating we have is the one used exclusively by UNISUB. It shines far and beyond anyone else's when used outdoors on signs or license plates. My experience has taught me that a UNISUB license plate will hold its color for at least a year and usually about 18 months before showing any significant signs of fading. After that, it fades fairly rapidly until the color is about 25% gone. Then it stabilizes and maintains that color for a long time. Of course, these are not scientific numbers, just my observations. Consequently, I tell my customers to expect about 12-18 months without fading and they are quite happy with that. I would rather tell them a low-ball number than to promise two-years and then have the product fade in 18 months.

When using other hard surfaced substrates by companies other than UNISUB, you can expect the product to fade rather quickly when exposed to direct sunlight for any length of time. Even though the product may sublimate well (and they do), they are not intended for exterior use.

Other situations that may cause fading: Exterior applications are not the only ones that will promote fading in sublimated products. Placing a metal plaque where a sunlight can pass through a window directly onto the substrate is asking for trouble. Environments that have fluorescent lights that give off a lot of UV like grow lights, can cause accelerated fading. These are not things you should be overly concerned about, but it might be wise to advise customers that "direct sunlight takes the color out of almost anything". Suggest they try and hang it where direct sunlight can't get to it. Most people are well acquainted with the fact that sun does fade most anything and this information will serve only as a reminder to the facts of everyday physics.

All in all, sublimated products are extremely durable both from being easily scratched or from fading. 95% of everything you make will never raise the question but once in a while, usually when people are trying to make sublimation do what it is not intended to do, the durability issue will come up. When it does, be honest about it. Don't try to paint a rosier picture than really exists and you will always have a happy customer. Lie or exaggerate and it will hurt you and your business.

GETTING STARTED IN SUBLIMATION 4

"Price is what you pay. Value is what you get." -Warren Buffett

WHAT MAKES A SUBLIMATION PRODUCT VALUABLE?

They say, "value is in the eye of the beholder" and they are right! There are several things that make a sublimated product valuable, but it is rarely the product itself. Chances are, the customer can buy a coffee cup or picture frame somewhere else for far less money and they don't have to wait for you to make it.

The value of most products is perceived. Perceived value can add greatly to what someone will pay for a product. Here is my best illustration: I once had a customer order a coffee cup with her child's baseball picture on it. When it was done, she paid for it and gave it to the child's grandfather who loved it. When she came in the next time, she complained about the $20 price tag, so I offered to buy it back from her. "No way", she said. "He loves that mug". The mug didn't mean much to her but to him, it was priceless. That is perceived value and that's what makes sublimated and personalized products so valuable.

Keepsake items like this photo on glass become something really special to the recipient.

Some talking points:

- A great many sublimated products are made in the USA and of course, the decoration is done in the USA.
- Each product requires time and consideration prior to the artwork being made, let alone the product.
- Each product is made one at a time (usually) with great care and professionalism.
- Each product is totally unique and made to order.
- Personalized products are treasured gifts and are rarely ever discarded.
- Even when the purchaser doesn't assign a lot of value to the product, the recipient does.

GETTING STARTED IN SUBLIMATION 5

"The quality in a service or product is not what you put into it, it's what the customer gets out of it."
-Peter Drucker

WHO YOU BUY FROM DOES MAKES A DIFFERENCE

If you are like most people, you love a bargain – we all do. Most people will spend hours searching the Internet in the hopes of finding the bargain of a lifetime. Unfortunately, we rarely do.

You may choose to do the same when it comes time to buy the equipment for your sublimation business and that's fine. You don't have to buy from Condé. There are other quality distributors you can buy from.

Just know that we want to earn your business and it isn't for the reason you think. You see, we help people every day who buy equipment from other distributors, Amazon, eBay and even their next-door neighbor. You don't have to buy from us to get our service and support – we are delighted to help anyone – anytime.

Offers like this one from Hong Kong promise all this for just $49.95. Really? Think about it.

But, here's the rub. In the sublimation industry, service and support is everything. If you buy from a source with no support, we will try to help you, but understand, we can't fix a junk heat press from China. We may not be able to fix the old heat press you bought from your neighbor. And, yes, there are all kinds of junk on the market you can buy that will never work as promised.

Trying to get used or inferior equipment to work as it should, especially the stuff from China, may not be possible and you will waste hours trying – not to mention the frustration.

Even if you don't buy from Condé, please, please, please, buy only the products recommended in this book. Even if it costs a little more, it will pay for itself in the long run. Companies like George Knight, Sawgrass and others have a proven track record you can depend on. Quality comes at a price; trouble comes cheap with lots of promises.

Remember the old adage, "If it sounds too good to be true, it probably is".

Service and support, along with quality equipment, is the key to your success

"The best marketing strategy ever: CARE." –Gary Vaynerchuk,

WHY WE RECOMMEND SAWGRASS PRODUCTS

People often ask, "Why should I use Sawgrass products? What's wrong with Epson or other brands?" And the answer is, "Nothing is wrong with Epson products". But there is a caveat: Programs such as CreativeStudio and GO Exchange are only available to people with Sawgrass printers. These free programs, along with Sawgrass customer support is only available to those who use Sawgrass printers.

When people see that Epson inks are so much less expensive than Sawgrass inks, their first reaction is to use Epson ink; but there is more to the equation than ink cost.

First, all ink is cheap. Anytime I can take four $77 ink cartridges and turn it into several thousands of dollars profit (and I do it all the time), I don't really care if the ink is $18 or $80. The cost of the ink is insignificant. The question then becomes, "What advantages come with the more expensive ink?". With Sawgrass inks, the advantages include:

1. Their printers are considerably less expensive than other brands.
2. Customer support is available through both Sawgrass and Condé Systems.
3. Color management software is free.
4. CreativeStudio design software is free.
5. Training webinars are free.
6. Membership in the Sawgrass Network which includes Go Expression and Go Express is free. (Go Expression allows you to sell sublimated products without buying any equipment.)
   (Go Express allows you to become a fulfillment center for other people who are selling sublimated products through their own store, website, Etsy, Pinterest or Amazon.)

The new Epson printers do a fine job. Although the printers are more expensive, the ink is far less expensive. In fact, we are very fond of the Epson F570 (24" printer), especially for the more experienced user. The newcomer is usually far better off with the Sawgrass line because of all the support listed above.

CONVERTED PRINTERS

Some people are converting cheap printers so they can use sublimation ink. You can see this on YouTube. This is a terrible idea for many reasons. Not the least of which is the loss of any support (even Condé can't help you with a printer they have never worked with). Besides, Sawgrass printers just aren't that expensive.

Beyond the obvious issues with converting a printer to do what it isn't supposed to do, there is a lot more to consider than how to get the ink into those little cartridges. Printers use both software and firmware to function properly. Only sublimation printers have the correct firmware to control the amount of ink that goes through the nozzles, speed, etc. A converted printer may seem to work, but it may be wasting a ton of ink with every project. How much do you save then?

THE SAWGRASS NETWORK

The Sawgrass Network is one of the advantages of working with Sawgrass. The Network is free to join and offers several helpful tools. These are listed in the pages following and can be found on the Sawgrass website (www.sawgrassink.com):

GO EXPRESSION

START A SUBLIMATION BUSINESS WITHOUT ANY EQUIPMENT

Yes, you read that right. You can start your own sublimation business without buying any equipment. All you need is a computer with an Internet connection. The program is part of the Sawgrass Network and is called "GO Expression".

It works like this:

STEP ONE: Go to the Sawgrass website and click on "The Sawgrass Network". Then select and join "Go Expression".

STEP TWO: Setting up an account is easy. You will need a PayPal account and a credit card to complete the registration.

STEP THREE: Continuing in the Sawgrass website, setup your store on Shopify (Shopify is a service that puts your products in front of people worldwide). This is easy and uses CreativeStudio so your customers can design their own products. All you have to do is forward the job to Sawgrass. They will take it from there. Sales can be online or in person.

STEP FOUR: While you are setting up your own Store on Shopify, you can also set up the ability to sell on Etsy, and Amazon.

STEP FIVE: Using a computer or tablet, you or your customer can design the product using CreativeStudio (see Part Two, Section xx). This is a cloud-based program so you can use it on any device connected to the Internet.

STEP SIX: Once an item is designed, you send the design to Sawgrass through Go Expression. Sawgrass will then forward the design to someone who makes the product for you. Then they will produce the product and ship it directly to you or your customer.

STEP SEVEN: Go to the bank! When the order is complete, Sawgrass will send you 25% of the purchase price through PayPal. They will also pay the person who makes the product and of course, take a percentage for themselves.

This simple program won't make you the kind of profit you would make using your own equipment but it will let you "test the waters" and start to build your business while making a few dollars to boot.

Best of all, this is all free and open to anyone who wants to be part of it. All you have to do is register and start selling.

Go Expression can be accessed on any device that can connect to the Internet.

GO EXCHANGE

READY MADE FULFILLMENT BUSINESS JUST FOR YOU

GO Exchange is the second part to the Sawgrass Network. It is for those who would like to do "fulfillment". Fulfillment is where someone (in this case, Sawgrass) sends you an order to be made to be sold to their customer. It is very much like being a wholesaler of sublimation products.

This is a great way for anyone with equipment and skill to have an instant business. You don't even have to design the products. They come to you already designed through CreativeStudio. All you have to do is print the transfer, make the product, and ship it off to the actual customer.

Here's how to get started:

How You Profit in The Sawgrass Network

A shopper buys a crew sweatshirt for:

$49.98

A seller earns:

25% ($12.50)

A producer earns:

45% ($22.49)

STEP ONE: Go the to Sawgrass website (www.sawgrassink.com) and select "The Sawgrass Network". Then scroll down and click on "GO Exchange". Once there, you can register and set up an account. You will have to indicate what kind of equipment you have and what products you are willing or have the capability to make. You will also set up a PayPal and credit card account (if you haven't already).

STEP TWO: Once approved, Sawgrass will begin sending you orders to fulfill for people using the GO Expression portion of The Sawgrass Network.

STEP THREE: Watch the training course for "GO Exchange" to become more acquainted with the program.

STEP FOUR: Your job is to fulfill the orders from Sawgrass and ship them out to the customer as soon as possible.

STEP FIVE: Once the job is done, Sawgrass will send you a payment equal to 45% of the sale price.

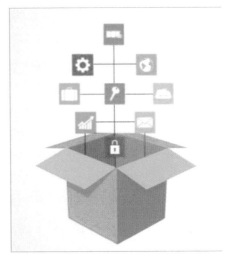

BUSINESS IN A BOX

Using the Sawgrass Network is like getting a Business in a Box for FREE!

The number of products available through this program is limited, but new products will continually be added to the list as time goes on.

Needless to say, you will want to produce a top-quality product and ship it out in a timely manner. Take the time to become proficient in making whatever products you agree to before you actually start GO Exchange. Remember, you do not have to do any design work since the file will come in ready to print through Creative Studio. Sawgrass will monitor the quality of the products to ensure the customer is satisfied and Sawgrass will take care of all the payments. All you have to do is make the product.

The best part of this program is that it is totally free. All you have to do is sign up and own a Sawgrass printer.

GO SERVICES

PERSONALIZED TRAINING & SUPPORT

For those who need the occasional help designing a product, using CreativeStudio or marketing, GO Services offers lots of help. When you go to GO Services (Under "The Sawgrass Network" on the Sawgrass website), you will find a list of people who are willing to help you with various tasks. These folks have very generously offered their phone numbers and email addresses, not to mention their time, to help you figure out a problem or learn a new skill.

This service is free to all Sawgrass users who are registered in The Sawgrass Network.

GO PRODUCTS

THIS IS WORTH ITS WEIGHT IN GOLD

Obviously, you can't make products you can't find, and finding a source for some products can be a real challenge. Now there is help in the form of GO Products, (free to all those registered in The Sawgrass Network, all you need to do is open the Sawgrass website, select "The Sublimation Network" followed by "GO Products" and fill out the bottom of the page. Instantly, the name of a certified supplier should appear.

This can save hours of searching catalogs and websites for some "out of the ordinary" product.

Like all of the Sawgrass Network features, this is new and has limited information. Given a little time, the database should expand quickly.

Dealers in Area

Conde Systems
(Sawgrass & Easy
Subli)

14221 Artesia Blvd
La Mirada, California 90638
US
+1 251 633 5704

Visit Website

PART ONE
SECTION 1

"Those who say it cannot be done, should not interrupt those doing it." -Chinese Proverb

INTRODUCTION TO THE
SUBLIMATION DECORATING PROCESS

What it is...

In the simplest terms, using a computer, we print to a printer with sublimation inks onto a sublimation paper. We then carry that printed paper to a heat press along with a substrate and create a sublimation sandwich and cook it.

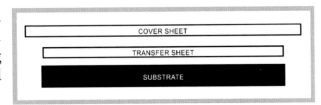

At high temperatures (usually 400° F) the inks on the paper turn into a gas. At the same time, the pores of the substrate open to receive these gases. Wow, is that neat! After a short time, we remove the heat and our substrate cools, closing its pores and trapping the sublimation dyes inside the substrate or its coating.

Section I of this book will explain, in detail, the steps required for sublimation decorating. It will break down these parts:

1) My suggestions for a workable computer
1) How to select the right sublimation printer, inks and papers
2) What you need to know about heat presses
3) How to create and press a sublimation sandwich
4) Some of my favorite process tips & tricks

In Parts II and III, we will fill in the gaps regarding the substrates we can decorate and how to market our products.

Biggest Mistake....

After all these years of learning, I have some simple advice for success with sublimation decorating:

1. Don't piece-meal your system or the process.
2. Follow our instructions and my best practices tips.
3. Document your questions, answers, successes and failures so that you can learn from them.

I love looking at the big picture because that's the best place to plan your sublimation journey. This comes down to such topics as to what you should expect, how long it will take to master sublimation and what do

I need to do it right – the first time. I often see folks try to skip steps or piece meal their equipment. It almost always turns out to be a disaster.

With that said, sit tight and let's get on the road to success!

RECOMMENDED INVENTORY OF EQUIPMENT

Sawgrass SG1000 Printer with By-pass Tray to Accomodate 13" Wide Paper

George Knight DK20s Heat Press

George Knight Heat Press Stand

Accutter 4001 Shear for Cutting Metal

ProSpray

Ink

Several Sizes of Sublimation Paper

24" Butcher Paper and Dispenser for use as cover sheets

Sublimated Color Charts You Can Make Yourself

Software such as CorelDRAW or Creative Studio

A Counter Top Convection Oven for Making Cups, Etc.

KoolPlate for reducing the cooling time for productions orders

Maxi-Press for Rounding Corners and Punching Holes in Metal

Shrink Wrap Film for Making Drinkware, etc.

Heat Gloves

By-Pass Tray allow you to print on paper up to 13" wide

Although not everyone can afford to invest this much money in the very beginning, this is the ideal for most startups. Don't piecemeal or buy cheaper equipment if at all possible. It will just mean you will eventually want to replace it.

"It's not about ideas, it's about making ideas happen." Scott Belsky

COMPUTER

Yes, we still need to print using a computer. Good news, computers are now very powerful and a great value for the money. Let's cover some of the most common questions for success with your computer.

Macintosh or Windows? Which is better?

I suggest you use what you already have, if it's not too old and has enough memory and hard drive space. I am both a Mac and PC person. My first Mac was a Lisa. If you are not already a Mac owner, I lean towards suggesting a PC due to the success of CorelDRAW in the sublimation industry. Corel is our Swiss army knife when it comes to design and it is only available for Windows. Corel is competition for Adobe Illustrator. If you are an Illustrator person, then you can go either way. With that said, I use my Macbook with CorelDRAW by running a special program that allows my Mac to also run Windows at the same time. This is done with programs like VMWare or Double. So bottom line is that you can go either way. Fortunately, the latest versions of CorelDRAW are written for both PCs and MACs.

How much RAM (memory) do I need?

The most important feature of your computer is the amount of memory or RAM that is installed. Memory is where our programs live when running. A short time ago, the minimum amount was 8GB but with newer computers I strongly recommend at least 16GB. In addition, look for a computer that is upgradable to more RAM. Good news, RAM is usually inexpensive and will add years to the useful life of your computer.

Should I buy a Laptop or Desktop computer?

You will get more for your money with a desktop, but I lean towards a laptop for portability. With a laptop, you can consider going sublimation mobile and setting up at events.

How do I protect my computer and data?

Two ways. First connect your printer and computer to a UPS (Uninterruptible Power Source), which is a small battery backup and surge protector. FYI, do not plug your heat press or a laser printer into the UPS as it draws way too much power. I recommend the brand APC (American Power Conversion), as they make it easy to replace the battery every two to three years.

Next, you need three types of backups. First, keep your customer artwork and other data in the cloud through services like Google Drive. Next, backup your drive with Window's File History or Mac's Time capsule to an external USB hard drive. Swap this drive out every month and take that drive off site in case of fire or theft. And last, use a cloud backup service like Carbonite or iDrive.

Dual Monitors

I love having two monitors! Most computers now support two monitors. Really makes it convenient when working on art files and doing emails or surfing.

What Design Software should I use?

This topic will be covered in much greater detail in the next section. Design software is the tool we use to create the designs we print. My first suggestion is to use what you know.

For instance, if you already know & use design software like Silhouette, that is a great place to start. Great programs like CorelDRAW, Illustrator and Photoshop will take time to learn and if you are not familiar with them, this may delay your success in sublimation.

What if you don't have or know any design software?

After years of helping folks come up to speed, my friends at Sawgrass came up with cloud-based designer software called "Creative Studio". This is included at no charge with the purchase of a Virtuoso printer. It is accessed from your web browser with your internet connect to provide Corel like features. Interestingly, with Creative Studio, you can design using your iPad or tablet. You still need your computer to print. See the appendix for a link to try out this virtual software.

I also suggest you create a lifeline with a "starving artist". There are lots of very talented folks available you could work with. Check the Graphics Department or IT Department at your local college or university. Spend your time where it makes sense. Working a design for four hours and then selling an item for a few dollars may not make sense. Outsource! My lifeline artist is Todd Till and he is amazing.

PART ONE
SECTION 3

SOFTWARE
CORELDRAW – THE EVIL BOOGIEMAN &
OTHER VIPEROUS SOFTWARE PROGRAMS

My first rule, when folks ask about what software they should use, is to tell them to start with the software they already know. That way, they can begin immediately. My suggestions are that most PC folks should invest in CorelDRAW and Photoshop/Photoshop Elements. For MAC folks, substitute Adobe Illustrator for CorelDRAW. MAC owners can choose to run CorelDRAW on their MAC by installing programs like Double. The latest version of CorelDRAW is available in both PC and MAC formats.

To hear some people talk, you would think that learning CorelDRAW was something akin to being accosted by the Evil Boogieman. Let me assure you, it isn't like that at all.

CorelDRAW, the software graphics program used by the vast majority of sublimators, isn't nearly as difficult to learn as people make out. Perhaps it is something of a rite of passage that people like to make it sound more difficult to learn than it really is. Whatever the case, if you give it your undivided attention for a couple of hours a day, you will have it under your belt in no time.

Although I tell people CorelDRAW has 350,000 commands in it (I don't really have a clue how many there are, but there are a lot), there are really only about 30 or 35 that you need to know to get started in sublimation and all those are demonstrated on CondéTV. Just type in CorelDRAW.

Some of the things you need to know include: how to use the drawing space, drawing a line, inserting text, drawing shapes (circles, ovals, squares and rectangles), selecting colors, setting the program to RGB colors; how to move and change the size of the various elements, changing fonts and how to put text on an arc. With these, you are pretty well equipped to start designing projects.

The best way to learn CorelDRAW is to challenge yourself with an actual job. After watching some of the videos on CondéTV, create a design in your head, then using CorelDRAW, put that design into the computer. If you run into trouble, go back and check the appropriate learning module in CondéTV. If you are not comfortable working with a mouse, it will probably take longer to learn to control the mouse than to learn CorelDRAW.

CorelDRAW also has an excellent tutorial included. The problem with it is the people at CorelDRAW tend to try and teach more commands than you need to know and that can make it both confusing and frustrating. Still, help is only a mouse click away.

CorelDRAW is, of course, only one of many programs that can be used to produce sublimation. Some people use Photoshop or Photoshop Essentials. Others use Adobe Illustrator. A few even use Word. All will work just fine but CorelDRAW is preferred by most because it is less expensive, easier to learn (my opinion) and contains a couple of tools the other programs do not, such as "Power Clipping", which is an incredibly powerful tool for sublimation.

Advanced sublimators generally use two types of programs with sublimation: A graphics program and a photographic program. A graphics program is a vector based program. That is, it works best with lines and shapes and text. Although you can do a great deal with photographs in these programs, there is also a great deal you can't do, so we use a photographic program to gain those capabilities. These photographic programs are often referred to as bitmap programs. They don't work nearly as well for lines, clipart and text as a graphics program, but they work miracles with bitmaps (photographs).

CorelDRAW and Adobe Illustrator are both graphics programs, just made by different companies. Photoshop and PhotoPaint are both bitmap programs. Again, they are just made by different companies. Some people love one and hate the other and visa versa but truth be known, both are equally good even though some people prefer one over the other. I recommend CorelDRAW because it is cheaper, easier to learn and contains that all powerful Power Clip tool. I prefer PhotoPaint over Photoshop because I think it is easier to learn and it comes free with CorelDRAW, while Photoshop costs $20+ per month to access off the Cloud (there are special deals as low as $10 per month if you search for them). Photoshop and Illustrator cannot be purchased on disk. They must be rented with a monthly fee. Corel products can still be purchased on a disk, although one has to wonder when they will follow Adobe's lead to renting software rather than selling it.

One of the nice things about using CorelDRAW along with PhotoPaint is that although you can do many bitmap functions right in CorelDRAW, when you need to do something more demanding, all you need do is click on "Edit Bitmap". Corel takes you immediately into PhotoPaint and allows you to do whatever you need to do and then when you click "Close", it transfers all your changes directly into CorelDRAW. You don't have to go through all the hassle of saving the file, closing the program and then importing the new file into Corel. For big projects that require a lot of editing, it saves a ton of time and circumvents mistakes that might otherwise force you do a series of edits over again.

So, although many make these programs out to be nearly impossible to learn, they are difficult only when you expect them to be difficult. In reality, they are pretty intuitive, especially CorelDRAW and with a little practice, you can master this program in a reasonably short time. The hardest part is getting started!

ADOBE LIGHTROOM

Lightroom by Adobe is like no other program on the market. Relatively new, this is both a cataloging program for photographs, plus an editing program. A professional photographer and Photoshop expert told me he used Lightroom to do 90% of his photo editing. This is a very powerful program and a challenge to understand. It is available with Photoshop (below) or as a standalone program for about $150. This program is extremely helpful in cataloging photographs. Photographs can be stored anywhere you want on your computer. When you edit the photo in Lightroom, it also leaves the original intact. Alterations are filed separately. I highly recommend this program but with one caveat: Do not buy this program until you are comfortable with CorelDRAW. Cost is about $150.

ON1 RAW

"Raw" is ON1's version of Adobe Lightroom and does about the same thing. It makes altering photos fairly easy, either singly or in groups. Like Lightroom, it offers "non-destructive" editing which is an absolute must have. It means you can alter photos as much as you want but it will always preserve the original so you can go back and start again any time you want. Cost is around $120.

ADOBE PHOTOSHOP ELEMENTS

For years, the value of Elements has been the ability to resize and enlarge the resolution of images. This feature has been taken over and much improved by ON1 RESIZE but that doesn't mean Elements isn't still an important program. Along with most of the photo manipulation features in previous versions of Elements and Photoshop, the most unique one is the ability to clip out highly detailed images such as people, including single strands of hair relatively easily. The feature that does that was originally called, "Knockout" and is now incorporated into this inexpensive photo editing program. There are two versions of this program ranging in price from about $70 to $150.

ADOBE PHOTOSHOP

Adobe Photoshop is a major photo editing program used by many professional photographers, newspapers, magazines, etc. It is, by most people's opinion, harder to learn than PhotoPaint (which interacts with CorelDRAW), but it is very powerful, and the best known of all the programs. If you have extensive experience with Photoshop, you can be sure, it will perform very well for sublimation. If you are not an experienced Photoshop user, I suggest you stay with CorelDRAW and PhotoPaint. Photoshop has moved to become a "Cloud" based program. This means you can no longer purchase a copy of Photoshop. Instead, you pay a monthly fee for the privilege of using it on two computers (other options are available). There is both good and bad in this relatively new way to "buy" software. On the good side, you always have a fully updated version. This means you never have to buy an upgrade. It also means that other programs are usually bundled with Photoshop for free. Currently, Lightroom is bundled with it along with several other programs. They also claim to have a library of 50 million high resolution, royalty free photographs available for your use. Currently, these programs sell for as little as $9.99 per month. The bad thing about this new Cloud software idea is that it costs $9.99 per month whether you use it or not.

CREATIVE STUDIO

Creative Studio is a cloud-based program. A Cloud-based program is one that is not physically loaded onto your computer but is stored remotely. You can access the program from any computer by using your ID and password. This program comes free with the purchase of a GS500, GS1000 or the VJ628 Sawgrass sublimation printer. It is something of a CorelDRAW knockoff but in a good way. The program was designed specifically for sublimation and therefore, contains only the tools typically needed for sublimation. It also includes some clipart and especially some really good school mascots which are hard to come by. Many sublimators could get by using this software and never upgrading to anything else. Still, I encourage that you learn CorelDRAW as you go along. You will find tools and capabilities there that Creative Studios was not designed to provide. Additional information about this product can be found in the Section "Help for the Non-Designer".

ON1 RESIZE/GENUINE FRACTALS

For years, we used a program called Genuine Fractals to increase the resolution of an image and it did a good job. That program has been replaced in a new one called ON1 Resize. Like Genuine Fractals, its greatest contribution to the industry is for people who work with murals but it can also be very helpful when someone brings you an image with very low resolution. The program is almost magical – it can increase the resolution of some images up to 1000 times, so the advertisement says. In a way I will never understand, it does an amazing job of adding pixels to an image using logarithmic formulas. It is weakest when working with web based images of 72 or 94 dpi but with an image of 200-300dpi, it is amazing. The cost of the program is about $70. It runs on both MAC and PCs. The program includes a process called, "Gallery Wrap" that creates extended margins for wrapping a photo around wooden stretcher boards by either extending an image or creating a mirror image of the extended portions. It also includes a tiling feature that is really nice. This is not usually needed for the novice but as your business grows, this will become a "must have".

COREL PHOTOZOOM PRO

This is an inexpensive program for enlarging bitmaps. If you plan on doing murals, you will need a program that can enlarge the resolution of images. According to the hype for this program, which was just released in early 2020, it can enlarge an image by 1000% without loss of clarity. I wouldn't count on that or anything close to it, but it will allow considerable enlargement of bitmaps.

PART ONE
SECTION 4

"Behold the turtle, he makes progress only when he sticks his neck out."
-Bruce Levin

SUBLIMATION INK

This is the magic ingredient. When heated, these dyes (called disperse dyes) convert from a solid to gas and seek a compatible home. See the section on substrates for more info. Over these many years, sublimation inks have become amazingly good at producing brilliant colors with excellent stability. My research has indicated that these dyes were accidently observed in the early 1940's in the UK when they stained an acetate type material. It took a few more years until the invention of polyester (around WWII), that disperse dyes became exciting. At first these dyes were screen printed onto paper and then transferred to polyester. Some folks also printed the dyes onto paper using a printing press. Spring forward many years and the development of a rich assortment of substrates from ceramic mugs to metal has propelled this technology to viral status.

Believe or not I have a set of sublimation markers on my desk. With these, we can completely forget the need for a computer and printer and just paint and draw our transfers! Learning to draw in mirror image is just a bonus. That aside, the most common way to do sublimation is using a computer and printer.

Through the years, we have fitted dozens of printers, mostly Epson, with sublimation ink, sometimes with disastrous results. Placing sublimation ink in a printer not designed for it, is like waking through a mine field. Before you know it, something is going to blow!

Fortunately, in today's world, we have a number of printers that were designed from the ground up just for sublimation inks. Gone are the days of clogged printheads, dead printers and countless head cleanings. Hallelujah! It has been a long road to where we are now.

We have a number of inks available today and it is likely more are on the way, as Epson, Canon and Mutoh enter the desktop printer ink world.

This is the Virtuoso SG-800 with its ink set and paper.

Selecting your printer, usually determines your choice of sublimation ink.

23

INK MINDER

Ink Minders is an invention of Condé Systems. It is no more than a sticker you can place on the front of your printer that tells you two things: One, the printed date is the date the ink was made. You can then write in the date you installed it in the printer.

Sublimation ink should be changed at least once a year. Ink that is over one year old (from time of manufacture), may cause a shift in color. The printer to the right has a magenta cartridge that is much older than the others. The color has not shifted and there have been no clogging issues thus far. Of course, it could be that the operator just forgot to put on a new sticker. Keeping track of ink age has always been a challenge until Condé introduced "Ink Minder" labels. Be sure to use them!

Ink Minders are just little stickers that comes with the ink to remind you of its age.

Here Is the Short List on Sublimation Inks:

Ink colors and sets: Many printers have only four colors with a few having more. More is not necessarily better as most modern four-color printers print with what's called variable dot technology, meaning that the printhead can produce different size dots to improve the "Dithering" or quality of print for light areas. A few printers have odd extra colors for special effects like the fluorescent colors available for the Sawgrass printers. These extra colors are fun and can create exciting stand-out designs. Selecting these colors requires extra software called a RIP (Raster image Processor). In short, a RIP is more powerful print driver. So, as you select your printer, ask what inks are available. Or you can ask what printers support special ink sets. Remember, once you install a certain type of ink, that printer is committed to using only that ink. You cannot switch them back and forth.

Cartridges: Most printers support a one-time use cartridge that contains a bag of ink inside. Once empty the cartridge is replaced. Each color is a separate cartridge and can be replaced individually. Some printers support two sizes of cartridges: standard and high capacity. I recommend beginning with the standard as modern printers are highly efficient with ink usage. Once you have a run rate, you can decide to go to large capacity, and you can mix and match these sizes of carts. Ink use by dates: There should be a date stamped on the cartridge that indicates the expiration date of the ink. My ink minder plate is placed on the front of the printer and helps you keep up with these dates. After inks reach this date, ink performance is not guaranteed, and color shifts are possible. Should you stock extra ink: In general no but order when inks are getting low. Ink storage: I suggest inks be stored at room temperature and not be allowed to freeze or exposed to high temperatures.

Bulk ink: A few larger production printers support refillable cartridges using bottles or bags of ink. This is a great solution for large printers that drink lots of ink from lots of printing. This also provides a nice cost savings. Smaller printers usually do not benefit from this strategy as the bulk ink will expire long before it is used up. Also, most bulk systems are exposed to air and ink oxidation will occur over a long period of time if you are using ink slowly. Also, bulk ink systems are more susceptible to air bubbles which will drive a print head crazy, so follow the proper instructions when refilling. Be extremely careful to pour the correct color of ink into the cartridge. Many mistakes have been made like this. You must monitor your ink levels manually.

Ink Usage/Cost of Printing

Once loaded in the printer, ink can only go two places. Either on paper or in the waste ink container. A good quality ink and printer along with proper usage will minimize the amount of wasted ink.

FAQ on Inks:

Can I sublimate with normal inks (dyes or pigments)?

No, you must use sublimation inks.

Should I save money and use generic sublimation inks?

That's a terrible idea. You will likely encounter inconsistent colors and quality from batch to batch.

Is the "Use by date" important?

Yes, the sublimation dyes weaken over time and result in a color shift. Use my "Ink Minder" to keep up with these dates.

Can I use sublimation ink with any printer?

Not really. Usually inks are matched with an ICC color profile, driver setting and paper for a limited number of printers. You should go with what is proven.

Can I swap back and forth between sublimation inks and normal inks?

Not recommended and usually extremely wasteful, as you must purge old ink out and refill with new ink.

Is my printer warranty void if I use sublimation inks in it?

If the printer is made & sold for use with sublimation inks and you are using the recommended ink, then you have a full warranty. If you are using a normal printer and loading sublimation inks, then most likely you are on your own. Ask your sublimation provider about warranty and support before buying anything.

Will sublimation inks dry up or hurt my printer?

A good sublimation ink will perform very much like normal ink. Some printers are better than others so ask. I do recommend you leave your printer turned on and use it often. If you do not have a reason to print, I suggest you do a nozzle check at least once a week.

How much does a set of inks cost?

Focusing on desktop sublimation printers like the SG500 & SG1000, a set of inks is typically less than $400. These carts contain a whopper amount of ink because of the GelJet technology. One ml of gel ink is the same as three ml for other brand printers.

Lots of people ask about the cost of sublimation inks. Sure, they seem pretty expensive when you buy them, partly because there are 4, 6 or 8 different colors but the emphasis shouldn't be on the cost of the cartridges, it should be on how much money you can make from your investment. Ink cost was a real concern back in the days of the Epson desktop printers because of clogging issues but now that we have gotten past all that, the ink costs are just plain insignificant. Still, to the best of our ability, Condé has run tests to try and determine exactly what it costs to print with sublimation ink. Here are our findings:

Brand of ink: Buying a name brand of ink is absolutely required. Never buy generic or off brand ink as you will have limited support and consistent color is questionable. Also, is the possible savings with a generic ink worth it when it comes to possibly damaging a print head?

Color profiles: Every sublimation ink set must have a professional ICC color profile. Without a profile, your color balance will be off, and this will drive you crazy. Yellow is usually the strongest ink when sublimating so the profile reduces the amount of yellow so that we get a red instead of an orange. More on color matching later.

Bottom line: If you work with a knowledgeable sublimation distributor, then they will put all this together for you so that you will be on the Road to Sublimation Success!

PART ONE
SECTION 5

"Don't worry about people stealing your work. Worry about the day they stop." --Jeffrey Zeldma

SUBLIMATION PAPER

We print our sublimation dyes on to a type of paper we call "release paper". This paper is used to carry the sublimation dyes from the printer to the heat press. Sublimation release paper is not transfer paper. Transfer papers, unlike sublimation release papers are made of special coatings that let go from the backing of the paper to melt into a piece of fabric or substrate. When these coatings release, they carry the ink or toner with them. Release paper on the other hand has no such coating and therefore are quite inexpensive.

Release papers have three properties. First, they must handle the heat of sublimation which is generally about 400° F. Next, they must keep the dots of the sublimation dyes sharp, minimizing dot gain on the paper. And last, the paper must allow the sublimation gas to be released when heated. This is done with a special coating on the paper that prevents the ink from seeping too deep in the paper. There are many different release papers available today and you use the paper that is matched for your printer, ink and substrate. For example, some papers are designed for fabrics while others are best used for hard substrates such as metal or ceramic tiles.

There are many different release papers available today. Choosing the right paper depends on the type of substrate being transferred. Different substrates require different sublimation release papers. Over these many years, we have focused on two types of release papers, one for hard substrates and one for soft substrates. Mousepads, tote-bags, DyeTrans™ Apparel, Vapor® Apparel and fabrics are best transferred using our JetCol® high release transfer paper. For items such as ceramics, plastics, jewelry, metal and porcelain (but not glass), we recommend our DyeTrans™ Multi-Purpose Sublimation Paper. And for glass cutting boards, clocks and coasters we recommend Beaver TexPrint™ or JetCol®.

DyeTrans is our go to paper for either hard or soft substrates. It works well for almost everything. I recommend it for hard substrates although it really works great for both. TexPrint paper leans towards softer substrates providing a slightly greater ink release at a cost of a little more dot gain. I use this for soft substrates such as glass.

Cut-sheet vs Roll: Sublimation paper is provided in two formats: cut sheet and rolls. Desktop printers generally use cut-sheet with larger printers using rolls. Condé offers many unique sizes of paper to address each printer and each job. For a common 16"x20" heat press and printer with 8.5" ability, we cut our sublimation paper to a size of 8.5"x21" to maximize the printer's printing capabilities.

The paper you use should be matched for your printer, ink and substrate. As discussed, some sublimation release papers are designed for fabrics while others are best used for hard substrates such as metal

or ceramic tiles. It goes without saying, that you must choose the right medium for the right application to ensure superb transfer quality. Pre-cut mug paper as mentioned in the printer section is a wonderful cost-effective aid. This simple change to precut paper can help digital decorators at all levels of production eliminate paper waste and drastically reduce the time and effort involved in producing mugs in an oven or traditional mug press. For printers with 13" paper width, we also have over sized sheets of 13 x 21 to max out a George Knight DK20S heat press. If you use a sublimation size paper, you most likely will need to add this size into the driver. This is easy to do. For step by step instructions check out my videos at

Buying precut paper for mugs saves time and money.

www.Condétv.com.

Roll papers come in various widths. Larger floor standing printers usually use roll paper. A large format printer will have a preset width, maximum of about 44 inches. You are generally able to mount a smaller width roll as needed to reduce waste. Roll papers are also available with an optional tack feature which is quite useful for fabric sublimation. Because an extra coating on the paper becomes sticky or tacky, this tack feature holds the fabric down, preventing the paper from moving during the heating process. This eliminates a shadowy ghost-like image from appearing on the fabric. These tacky papers are not appropriate for hard substrates, however.

25" x 250' ROLL

Helpful Hints

Keep your paper consistent! This is critically important. Any variations in the paper manufacturing can and will cause color shifts. That is why we have manufactured the same paper for the last twenty plus years.

Double check you are using the right side of the paper. This may sound pretty obvious, but always make sure to print on the correct side of the paper. This is a common and easy to fix mistake many rookies make. Even after all these years, I sometimes fall victim to this careless mistake. For your wellbeing, note that most sublimation papers have a print side. For the DyeTrans paper it is a brighter white and smooth compared to the other side. For Ricoh Gel printers, the paper is placed in the bottom tray(s) with the print side (bright white side) down. If you are using the bypass tray, then the print side is face up. In the case of the Sawgrass printers, the paper should be loaded with the bright white side face down in the

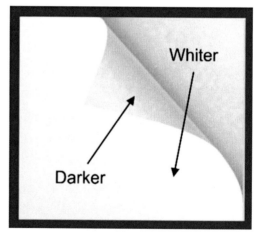

It is often difficult to tell the front from the back on transfer paper that isn't printed on the back. Always print on the whiter side of the paper.

bottom tray(s) and face up in the bypass tray. Always follow your equipment's or supplier's instructions.

Not all sublimation release paper is compatible with the SubliJet HD inks. Some older sublimation papers dry too slow. This will leave "tractor wheel marks" on the paper and will affect your quality.

Keep in mind how much ink is left on your paper after pressing. After you press your substrate, only a small amount of ink should be left on the paper. If you observe a lot of ink, this may indicate that your transfer technique should be reviewed, i.e., time, pressure, temperature adjusted.

Always use your prints within a few days. Prints should always be transferred within a few days to ensure superb image clarity and color vibrancy. While talking about paper, sublimation inks have a shelf life that continues to diminish as time passes. Have all of your ideas and equipment ready so you won't have to be waiting around. so what are you waiting for? Get to pressing!

Frequently Asked Questions:

Why do my colors look wrong after printing?

I receive hundreds of calls from people after they print their first transfer about the colors being "off" upon printing to the sublimation paper. Sublimation inks are heat activated and will look quite strange on the paper after printing. To judge the color, we need to first sublimate to something! Usually this results in an, "Ah Ha!" moment. If this doesn't work, then we might have to explore other options such as color matching.

Can I sublimate the same transfer again?

No. After transferring, there will be a small amount of ink left on the transfer but not enough to successfully use again. Simply throw the old transfer away and start again. Practice makes perfect, and accidents happen! You won't be losing a lot of money and quality will be ensured.

In an emergency, can I use any paper?

The results will most often be problematic. For vivid color and quality always use sublimation paper. If you notice that you are running low, give us a call, and we will be able to help you out.

How should I store paper?

Opened paper should be stored in zip lock bags to prevent it from absorbing moisture from humidity. Some sublimators who have many different sizes will store them in different, labeled Tupperware containers for easier accessibility. Plus, it keeps your workspace organized.

Can I use inkjet T-shirt transfer paper with sublimation ink to decorate cotton shirts?

No. Sublimation dyes require a synthetic fiber it can latch on to. Natural fibers such as cottons and cotton blends will not work.

Can I press two transfers (either at the same time or different times) onto one substrate?

Sometimes folks want to press something bigger than their heat press can fit. Pressing two transfers together would seem to work but usually you get an ugly seam if your image has a background. Another reason would be to press your main section and then come back to press another section that is not connected to the first. That usually works. A good example is the back and front of a shirt.

Can I cut my paper to reduce waste?

Not a good idea. Cutting paper results in paper dust that collects on rollers inside the printer. If you do wish to cut paper, it should be done by a pro. But the biggest issue in cutting paper usually results in a custom paper size. You must "tell" the printer what size paper is being used or bad things happen! You can spray ink inside the printer instead of paper and make a mess. We have lots of custom paper sizes available and you will need to define that paper size in the driver and then select that size paper from the application program you printer from.

How do I know what sublimation paper I should use?

First you match the paper for your printer and ink. Next, ask your supplier which of these papers to use for a particular substrate. Most papers are somewhat universal, but your supplier may recommend a particular paper for some products.

How long can I keep printed transfers before pressing?

I generally recommend that printed transfers be pressed within a few days of printing.

Should I dry my transfers before pressing?

Yes, I recommend you pass the transfer under your hot press without closing for a few seconds before pressing. Moisture is our enemy and you are dumping colored water on the paper, so drying is helpful.

PART ONE
SECTION 6

"What do you need to start a business? Three simple things: Know your product better than anyone. Know your customer and have a burning desire to succeed." -Dave Thomas

SELECTING A DESKTOP SUBLIMATION PRINTER

To do digital sublimation decorating we need the right equipment and of course, stuff to decorate. I think it is usually better for new folks to buy a complete system that includes a heat press and a sublimation printer. When I started into sublimation some 20 plus years ago, our printers were quite temperamental to say the least. Spring forward 20 years and the results are quite impressive. We now have highly reliable, easy to use and cost-effective sublimation printers. This chapter will focus on educating you about desktop sublimation printers. Sort of like the latest iPhone, depending on when you read this, the choices mentioned could have changed. That's of course the nature of our high-tech world.

What makes it a sublimation printer? To a large extent, it's all in the print head! Printers like Canon, HP and Lexmark use a process called "thermal drop on demand," which means the printer uses heat to push or boil the ink out of the print head. Since our inks are heat-activated, this process is not appropriate. Printers like Ricoh, Epson, Brother, Mutoh, Roland, Mimaki and a few others use piezo technology. This technology vibrates the ink out instead of using heat, making it perfect for sublimation.

Typical Ricoh printhead assembly: 2 heads with 2 colors each.

Other than piezo technology, people often ask me what I consider to be a perfect dye-sub printer. My response is simple: a printer that is turnkey for sublimation transfer with features such as fast print speeds, awesome quality, large separate cartridges, vibrant color, a reasonable price, low operating costs and great reliability, along with excellent warranty and support... That's not too much to ask, right?

Some ask about their being able to replace printheads in their sublimation printers. Although this is common with the wide format printers, it is not possible with the desktop models.

As mentioned earlier, it is highly recommended that you purchase a turn-key system and that includes a turn-key sublimation printer. This approach should save you money and greatly reduce your learning curve and all that translates to growing your profits quicker. Why should you spend months studying sublimation technology when you can tap into the experts? That's where folks like me can help save you time and money.

Interestingly, one of the first questions you should answer is, "why do you want to do sublimation?" This will go a long way to helping you decide what to buy, and also set your expectations to what your results will be. We will discuss this all-important question through-out this book.

Epson is the company that I credit with the invention of the piezo print head and many years ago, became the printer of choice for sublimators. About ten years ago, Ricoh, the copier company, introduced their desktop piezo "Green" Gel inkjet printers designed for high volume and diverse office environments. To their credit, Sawgrass jumped onto the Ricoh Geljet platform by creating an excellent sublimation ink named SubliJet-HD. These inks, along with nice large paper trays, large cartridges, and high print volumes, made the Ricoh Geljet printers the go to solution for desktop sublimation.

The new Sawgrass printers (made by Ricoh) provide the ability to expand their paper handling, allowing multiple trays for instant access to multiple paper sizes. Putting all these sources together allows the user to have three different sizes/types of paper available at once. No swapping media types in and out of the printer! You can even program the front panel of the printer to know what size is in each tray so that when you select your paper size at the computer, the printer knows which tray to pull from. Another big innovation with Ricoh printers, is their high viscosity "gel" ink, which gives them the aptly chosen nickname, "Geljet." Their ink is very thick (1 mL=3 mL Epson ink) making it extremely efficient and prevents the need to consider refill or bulk system. Bulk systems use large ink containers which can be exposed to air, oxidizing ink and introducing air bubbles. What makes these (Ricoh & Virtuoso) printers such a force to be reckoned with, however, is that they include a large industrial Piezo printhead for fast, reliable printing.

Jump forward and today, Ricoh has tuned their designs for Sawgrass to create the first "out of the box" desktop printers designed, warrantied and supported for sublimation decorating. As of this writing there are two desktop printers: The SG500 (legal size) and the SG1000 (up to 13"x21" with bypass tray). These are proven road warriors. Epson has introduced wide format sublimation printers from 44" to 63" with the F-series. I suspect that Epson in the future will also provide a family of desktop sublimation printers, but for now, the Sawgrass printers are an excellent turn-key solution.

Sublimation is a scalable technology, meaning that you can start with a small printer and scale up to a ginormous print size. We tend to classify printers into desktop and large format sizes. Although the designation is purely arbitrary, anything under 42" is considered a desktop printer while anything 42" or bigger is considered wide format.

For those needing larger print capabilities, Sawgrass offers the VJ628 which is a full 25" print area.

The newest contribution to the printer segment is the Epson J570 which is a 24" printer that uses Epson sublimation inks rather than the traditional Sawgrass inks. With an actual print width of just under 24" plus the ability to run sheet stock above 8.5" wide, this looks to be a very popular printer.

FAQ on Sublimation Printers

What should I understand when selecting a desktop sublimation printer?

Deciding really comes down to budget and selecting which products you wish to decorate. For most folks, the smaller printer will get the job done. This is because the majority of substrates are smaller than a 8.5"x14" print area. If you wish to decorate shirts, then you really need the larger desktop printer. Also, remember that you need an appropriately sized heat press to complement the printer.

Is the main difference between desktop printers their maximum print size?

Yes. This is true for the Sawgrass desktop printers to be sure. Ink costs, the way they work and even who actually makes them is the same. Only the size and cost are different.

When comparing Epson and Sawgrass printers, there is another difference that is notable. Sawgrass printers use ink cartridges while the Epson printers use bottled ink that you pour into receptacles in the printer. The Epson printers also use a different paper than the Sawgrass printers.

For the desktop, Sawgrass offers three sizes of printers:

The small desktop printer is the Sawgrass SG500: Print size up to 8.5" x 14". This is a four-color printer.

The large desktop printer is the Sawgrass SG1000: Print size up to 11.75"x17" or up to 13"x21" with the optional bypass tray. This is what most serious sublimators choose. This is a four-color printer.

The largest desktop printer from Sawgrass is the VJ628: Print size is up to 25" on roll paper so the length is virtually unlimited. This is a dual CMYK or an eight-color printer.

Epson offers two printers:

The desktop version is the SureColor SC-F170 (F100 outside the USA). This in an entry level printer and limited to letter and legal-size paper. The enticing feature of this printer is that it uses bottled ink which is poured into reservoirs.

The larger version is the SureColor F570. This is a 24" printer that can use either cut sheet or roll paper and bottled ink rather than cartridges.

Sawgrass VJ628

What is the cost of these printers?

Costs will change over time but at the time of this printing, these are the prices:

Sawgrass SG500: $499 with ink.

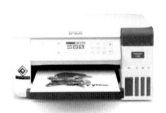

Epson F170

Sawgrass SG1000: $1,595 with ink. Bypass tray: Add $208.

Sawgrass VJ628: Starts at under $5,000 with ink.

Epson F170: (F100 outside the USA) Price TBA, comes with ink.

Epson F570: $2,495 with ink and paper.

Epson Sure Color F570

All printers have an optional warranty program which I highly recommend.

As prices will change over time, I recommend you check with us or your sublimation supplier. Remember, you get what you pay for, so if something looks too good to be true, it probably is. New users should only purchase a complete package that includes ink, paper, ICC profiles, warranty and most important of all is support.

What is the cost of ink & printing?

Only consider sublimation printers with large individual ink carts that can be replaced separately such as the Sawgrass line of printers. Often, wide-format printers will have the option of purchasing a large capacity cart that can be mixed/match with standard capacities. Ask your sublimation provider what the cost of printing is. For the well-established Sawgrass desktop printers, I peg them at about $.01 (one penny) per square inch for full color using standard carts plus the cost of paper (which is inexpensive). For example, a 8"x10" print would cost about $.80 for ink and about $.15 for paper for a total of $.95. These numbers may change so check with us for updates.

Should I go with cartridges or a bulk ink printer?

For desktop printers, I recommend you avoid bulk bottled ink or refillable systems and stick with cartridges from a reliability point of view. Yes, buying bulk ink would seem to save you money but when you look at the big picture, it often turns out to be a challenge due to reliability and ink oxidation when exposed to air. Ink exposed to air will oxide. Large format printers (42" width and larger) often are the best candidates for bulk ink due to amount of ink they use.

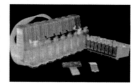

Bulk ink systems like this one should be avoided.

What is the print speed I should expect to see?

Most folks never consider speed until they get their first big order! Yes, speed is quite important on our Road to Sublimation Success as time is money. For our current desktop printers here are some average speeds:

SG500/SG1000: High quality, 8"x11" paper: 29 seconds per page.

VJ628: High quality, 24" wide: 52' per hour.

I see some printers have print quality of 1400dpi or more. What do I need to do sublimation?

High quality sublimation is obtained by printing with 720dpi. Although you can print with higher resolution, the human eye is unlikely to see the difference. With the correct settings, all popular desktop printers will print photo quality output and sharp crisp vector art. Of course, this assumes quality artwork is being used (garbage in – garbage out). If you download internet images and art, they are usually at 72 dpi (dots per inch) and this will produce poor quality on the printers. See Chapter XX on image resolution.

What kind of warranty comes with the printers?

Your sublimation printer needs to be warrantied and supported for sublimation use. No pointing fingers or passing the buck. This really gives you peace of mind. I also recommend you consider the extended warranties that typically add another year to the standard warranty.

What kind of support comes with a sublimation printer?

Sublimation decorating is a unique technology that requires you to do three things well: graphics, print and operate a heat press. *The importance of support cannot be over emphasized.* Condé has well over 1000 videos educating folks around the world how to do sublimation well. These videos combined with our other support elements will greatly increase your success. And having great support is always included with your system purchase.

What do you mean by "Great Color/Accuracy & ICC Color Management Support"?

Obtaining the color and quality you desire isn't always as easy as pressing the "PRINT" button. You may have a great printer and artwork, but without world-class color management you won't get good results. This is an area we have focused on for over twenty years and great ICC color profiles along with application support makes a huge difference. An ICC profile is like a color filter that corrects the color for the sublimation process, but more on that later. What we do is make the complex world of color as simple as a click of the mouse.

Take time to track your printer's usage and problems:

You should always track the usage and any problems you encounter with a sublimation printer. How well did it perform? What issues (if any) were encountered? Having a log like this will make trouble shooting a future problem much easier. Document when the ink cartridges are replaced in relation to the printer's page count so you can keep track of ink costs. Also, documenting error codes and nozzle-check issues will greatly help in solving problems yourself or with the help of technical support.

How long can you expect the printer to last?

Most printers made for sublimation should have a life of at least three years. Some however, last much, much longer.

What about computer/application support?

All desktop sublimation printers should be at home with both Microsoft Windows and Macintosh computers. In addition, they should support all common applications such as Adobe, Corel and Silhouette. In general, we don't care what program you print from but if you need support for that application and it helps if we are familiar with it.

PRINTER LOCATION & ENVIRONMENT

Printer location:

Set your printer up on a sturdy table. A sturdy table that will not allow any shaking when your paper is printing. Any amount of shaking can affect the quality of your print.

Keep your workspace in an open environment. Always allow enough working space for loading paper and clearing jams. The environment should be clean of dust and debris.

Temperature & humidity:

Locate the printer in a normal, comfortable "human" temperature. Temperatures over 90-degree F. can cause the ink to degrade because of the inks' heat-activating properties.

Low humidity, under 30% is not recommend as we are printing with "colored water". Use a humidifier if necessary. Too much humidity may cause Condénsation, and sublimation paper will absorb moisture which can cause the paper to swell, resulting in "cockling" or "waviness," which will, of course, affect the print quality. If you happen to be in a high humidity area, I recommend storing your paper in a Ziploc bag or plastic airtight containers. This will prevent the paper from absorbing moisture as well as keeping your paper organized by size and type.

Power:

Connect your printer and computer to a UPS (Uninterrupted Power Supply). See more in the computer chapter. This is an inexpensive way to protect your electronics.

Keep your printer turned ON. Only turn off your printer if you plan on moving it to another location. Turning the printer on and off only serves to waste ink and put wear & tear on the printer. I know the energy conservationist in you is screaming for you to power off all of your "parasite" electronics, but I want to assure you that almost no power is used by the printer while in idle. Interestingly the Ricoh/Sawgrass printers have an automatic health feature that moves a tiny bit of ink back and forth with minimal waste. You can hear this if you are in a quiet room with the printer. This feature keeps the heads and lines clear and prevents clogging.

Print settings:

Always print to the printer with the proper print settings. Without the correct settings, your color and quality will be affected.

Always "mirror" your output for all substrates except glass & acrylic. And last, as appropriate, select the printer profile in your software.

Make sure you are using sublimation inks. Surprise! Normal ink will not work. It might look good coming out of the printer, but when you send it off to the heat press to be transferred only yellow will show up.

Paper:

Print on the correct side of the sublimation paper. Be careful when loading paper that you have properly loaded the paper (face down in most printers).

Paper size: Verify before printing that the correct size of paper is in the printer, otherwise a paper jam is likely.

Colors on your transfer:

Don't judge the colors on the paper after printing. They will look dull until you activate the ink with 400 degrees of heat and sublimate them.

Printer health:

Make sure you print using a healthy printer. This means performing regular nozzle checks. Also, I recommend at installation time and every six months, check the printer's alignments. There are some great videos at www.Condetv.com that will help.

Print on the correct side of the sublimation paper. This is usually the bright, white side. I know this might sound obvious, but it happens more often than you would think.

Do not be scared to contact your supplier. Your supplier can help you maintain the overall health of your printer. For example, they can teach you how to manually clean a transport belt or a capping station. Your supplier might also be able to provide simple fixes to your printer that might appear "to be on its way out" to get your printer back in good working order. Always contact your supplier before calling Epson or Ricoh.

Recycle empty sublimation cartridges:

We provide a credit for returned empties. That's right, when you change out your ink cartridges, put the old cartridges aside until you have several and send them back to us along with your account number and we will apply the credit toward your next ink purchase. Most, but not all brands of sublimation ink cartridges are accepted. Contact us for more information.

The offer applies to most currently available ink cartridge.

Use your printer!

As in all things in life, using your printer promotes printer health. Imagine a car sitting in a garage for a long period without any use. Over time, Condénsation will form in the fuel tank which will result in the pipes and hoses becoming clogged. These all affect the car's engine. The same goes for your printer. If you don't plan on using your printer often, always do a nozzle check. The average life for a printer used regularly is three years. But you can extend the life of your printer by cleaning the captain station, cleaning the belt, and talking nice to it... well, maybe not so much the last one, but it's always good to treat your printer nice. And hey, whatever works!

Perform a nozzle check:

Each day before I begin working on my own sublimation endeavors, I always perform a nozzle check. This is particularly necessary when you begin to notice visible banding problems. Nozzle checks are a printed test pattern that check the condition of the printer's ink nozzles. If the test pattern is complete, then the printer is ready to

Typical nozzle check for a CMYK printer.

print transfers. An incomplete test pattern represents clogged nozzles and should be followed up with a head-cleaning, followed by another nozzle check. If the head-cleaning fails to produce a complete test pattern, an "auto nozzle check" might be the next step. And if that fails, call your supplier's tech support department for assistance. There is no need to waste ink by performing repeated head-cleanings!

Consider purchasing a backup/spare printer:

Having a backup printer is a great way to get back on track fast when a primary printer fails. If you wait until an emergency occurs, you may not be able to find an exact replacement for your printer as models become obsolete over time, and you might find yourself scrambling to produce a substrate you've produced a thousand times and are no longer able to get the same result. Time is always of the essence! Changing to a different printer will always introduce slight variations in spot colors, and you must always refer back to the ICC profile to figure out what color is right for the right printer.

"I feel that luck is preparation meeting opportunity." - Oprah Winfrey

SETTING UP YOUR PRINTER

Once you have received your sublimation printer, it will need to be set up. The first step is to prepare your printer for use. Our printers will come with a quick start guide to help. In general, you will need to unpack the printer. Save the packaging so you can easily return the printer in the unlikely event it is defective. Once unpacked DO NOT LOAD ANY INK INTO THE PRINTER EXCEPT SUBLIMATION INK. When the inks are loaded and all the strips of packing tape are removed from inside the printer, you can turn it on. Printers will require a few minutes for the ink charging process to occur. During this process the printer is removing inks from the cartridges and filling the ink tubes. No ink is being wasted. After this is complete, load some plain paper in the tray and perform a nozzle check to verify that the printer is healthy. See the quick start guide on how to perform a nozzle check.

The next step is to configure your computer for printing. I recommend you call us or your sublimation supplier and ask the Service Technician to remotely connect to your computer and perform the setup for you. This is by far the fastest and most accurate way to make sure everything is right. To begin the setup, we will need to know what application you intend to print from, as this determines the approach to the all-important subject of color management. In addition, you should decide how your printer will be connected to your computer. Most printers will support USB and Ethernet connects. Almost everyone should go with USB for its ease of installation. If you intend to share the printer with others, consider Ethernet. Ethernet is how your computer usually connects to the internet. Sublimation printers do poorly when connected over Wi-Fi, so it is not supported. Here are the quick steps to the printer installation:

Install the printer driver

Connect the USB or Ethernet cable from the computer to printer

Install the Condé ICC color profile or PowerDriver software

Configure the driver

Configure your print application

I recommend once finished to take screen shots of some of the screens should you need to reinstall at a later time. Remember, you can always call the Condé support team to do it for you.

The next step will be to print our first transfer and then to sublimate it. Load some sublimation paper into the printer. It is very important to print on the correct side of the paper. For the Condé papers, you will need to print on the bright white side which is usually loaded with the bright white side face down. Check out my videos on CondéTV for step by step instructions.

PART ONE
SECTION 8

"As a general rule, every dollar spent on preventative maintenance, you will save five-dollars in subsequent expenses." – Kansas State University

NOZZLE CHECKS

What is a nozzle check? It is our test to the quality of the basic printer operation.

Why do we do them? You should run a nozzle check often to ensure that ink is flowing properly through all the nozzles in the printer's printhead. Should one or more of the nozzles clog, it will leave a band of white in the printed image.

How do we do them? To run a nozzle check, you must find your way to the "Maintenance" portion of the print driver. This is done a bit differently if you are using an ICC Profile or PowerDriver. Follow the one that you normally use:

If you use PowerDriver for the SG500/1000:

Click "Print" as you normally would. Then in about the middle of the screen, there are some tabs. Click on "Utilities" which will bring up the screen on the left. Click on "Nozzle Check" and it will bring up the screen on the right and send the command to the printer.

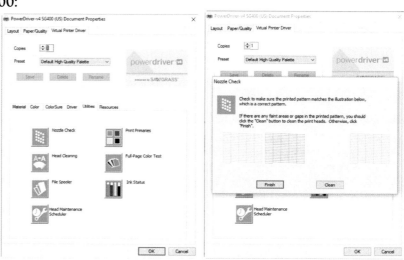

If you use Condé's ICC Profile, follow these steps:

Click on "Print" as you normally would. That will bring up the screen on the left (previous page). Next, click on "Maintenance" and the screen on the right (previous page) will appear. Click on "Nozzle Check" and follow the instructions.

I recommend doing a nozzle check at the beginning of your printing day or whenever you suspect there may be a nozzle check issue. If you see banding on your transfers, that is an appropriate time to perform a nozzle check. I suggest you print the nozzle check on plain paper or, if you find it hard to see (the yellow is very faint), try using sublimation transfer paper and actually transferring it to a piece of Unisub material. Once printed, you should examine the print and look for breaks or missing lines in the test. Not only will this help with

Typical screen where the driver is selected.

visibility, it will also confirm you are printing with sublimation ink.

On Sawgrass printers, the bottom line of the nozzle check will not be complete. See image below.

If the nozzle check is incomplete, run a "Clean Nozzle" and then print the Nozzle Check again. Do this up to three times, as needed. If the Nozzle Check still isn't complete, contact Customer Support.

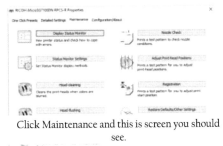

Click Maintenance and this is screen you should see.

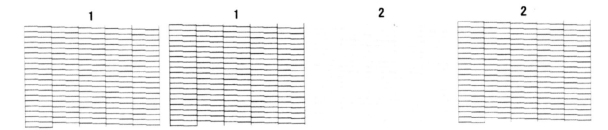

This is an enlarged version of a good nozzle check. Note all the lines are solid. The number above each one is to tell you which head needs cleaning. This keeps you from wasting ink cleaning heads that don't need it.

PART ONE
SECTION 9

"Your most unhappy customers are your greatest source of learning." -Bill Gates

TROUBLE SHOOTING PRINTER BANDING (Horizontal)

Banding is the appearance of vertical or horizontal lines going across the printed transfer. The most common banding is horizontal. That is if the page has exited the printer but before you touch it, you see lines going across the page. See photo. This is usually caused by one or more of 5 reasons:

Simulated image of vertical banding issue.

1. Incomplete nozzle check. Perform a nozzle check to verify all the nozzles are firing. This can be done at the computer or at the front panel of the printer. Use plain paper for this for desktop printers.

2. Incorrect driver settings. We must print with the correct driver settings. The default settings for most printers is high speed/plain paper mode. We require higher quality settings that slow the printer down in order to print with photo quality output. In addition, the settings select the proper color mode of the driver. This selection is in concert with the color management settings of our application (Corel or Photoshop). Contact us for the proper settings.

3. Out of alignment. If the print head is out of alignment, it can produce banding. Check out the videos on Condétv.com and type in "horizontal banding" or call our technical support team. For desktop printers, there are usually a vertical and a horizontal alignment feature in the maintenance menu. I suggest you do both.

4. Computer is sending data too slow. If the computer is not able to keep up with the full print speed of the printer, it will stop and start, causing banding. Areas of concern are: not enough memory or hard drive space, marginal cable, external USB hub and so forth. Call us for trouble shooting. Important: Never print to your printer over a wireless link. This is a sure way to get banding. Other suggestions: change to a different USB cable and port or connect the printer to the computer using the Ethernet port.

5. Printer maintenance. If the printer has some age on it, it may be time for some cleaning. I recommend cleaning the transport belt. For Sawgrass desktop printers, this belt is how the paper is moved through the printer. See our videos on Condétv.com to learn how to clean the belt correctly.

And finally, do a print head cleaning of all heads. I have seen cases where nozzle checks looked complete with banding and after a single cleaning, the banding disappeared. Be sure to verify the nozzle check after cleaning. Never go crazy with head cleanings or flushing as you will not correct any issue and only waste ink.

If you are still unable to resolve banding, we can perform what I call our PRN test. This test sends a pre-printed file directly to the printer without going through much of the over-head of the Mac or PC. We are always happy to help you with this. Just call our technical support department.

TROUBLE SHOOTING PRINTER BANDING (Vertical)

Just as a sublimation printer can develop horizontal banding, it can also develop vertical banding and the causes are sometimes the same but there is one additional cause. Although it requires removing one side and the back of the printer cabinet, it isn't difficult and almost anyone can do it.

Inside the printer, there is a wheel that is belt driven. This wheel rides over the paper to determine the length of the paper and tells the printer where the paper is in relation to the print heads.

The back part of the wheel has a number of tiny black stripes on it. Over time, this wheel can pick up dust and dirt from the air or paper and becomes dirty. To rectify this issue, all you have to do is wipe off the wheel with denatured alcohol and a soft cloth. Unless one of the things listed above is also involved, cleaning the wheel will solve the problem.

For step by step instructions for cleaning this wheel, go to Condétv.com and type in "vertical banding".

Simulated banding. Note the stripe on the left-hand side of the image.

If this doesn't resolve the problem, feel free to call our technical service department.

PART ONE
SECTION 10

"The important thing is not being afraid to take a chance. Remember, the greatest failure is to not try. Once you find something you love to do, be the best at doing it." -Debbi Fields

WIDE-FORMAT PRINTERS

Although wide-format is usually considered to be bigger than 24", there are two relatively new 24" printers that really don't fit into the desktop category. One by Epson and one by Sawgrass. Each uses their own brand of ink and are worth serious consideration by anyone really serious about sublimation. True, they are more expensive but they also produce a lot more output for less cost.

Sawgrass Technologies introduced their VJ628 24" printer around 2017. It is a 8-color multi-configuration printer that allows a full 24" wide print. It uses roll paper to eliminate paper jams and high capacity cartridges. This printer, like all Sawgrass printers is built by Ricoh and is known for their toughness and the fact they almost never clog. The printer uses the Sawgrass PowerDriver software or the Condé ICC profile for excellent color. The starter package comes with a roll of paper, eight ink cartridges of your choice, and the printer. Cost is under $5,000.

Starter package for the VJ628 includes a full set of inks, a roll of paper and the printer. Everything you need to get started.

Because this printer can accommodate 8 ink cartridges, you can choose the combination that works best for your application. Once selected however, it is very difficult and costly to change. The combinations include:

C=Cyan; M=Magenta, Y=Yellow, K=Black with two of each color for longer print times.

CMYK + LM=Light Magenta, LK=Light Black, LLK=Light-Light Black. Gives better color graduations.

CMYK + O=Orange, B=Blue, FLP=fluorescent Pink, FLY=fluorescent Yellow.

CMYK + FLP=fluorescent Pink, FLY=fluorescent Yellow, LC=Light Cyan, LM=Light Magenta.

CMY + Kxf=Archival Black, LC=Light Cyan, LM=Light Magenta, LKxf=Archival Light Black, LLKxf=Archival Light Light Black. Used with archival paper gives longest life expectancy.

Confused? Don't be. Your Condé Representative will help you make a wise choice.

Released in late 2019, the most recent addition to the sublimation world is the Epson SureColor F570 24" printer. This is a 24" printer that uses Epson's brand of sublimation ink and refillable cartridges. Ink comes in bottles with special tops to make cartridge filling easy and clean. This is a 4-color CMYK printer that can use cut sheet or roll paper and has many of the features of the larger wide-format printers including a touch screen that controls every facet of the printer. Epson also provides their own color correction software to ensure accurate color. The cost of this starter package is about $2,500. Ink for this printer is less than $20 per bottle, making it by far the least expensive to use sublimation printer in this size range.

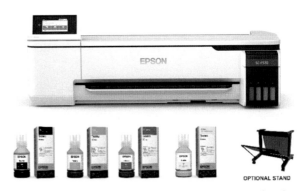

The starter package for the J570 by Epson includes the printer and 2 sets of ink. There is also an optional stand available.

If you hope to print products that are 24" wide, you will need a heat press of comparable size. For a press that can print up to 20"x25", there is the George Knight DK25s. An even larger model is the DK32AP which presses 26"x32" and finally, there is the MaxiPress which is 40"x60". Most of these presses are also available in a pneumatic versions.

The air operated version of the DK25SP is configured as a tabletop press and requires a small compressor.

There are a wide variety of heat presses available depending on your specific application. For assistance as to which will be best for you, contact your Condé Representative.

Above is the DK25s press from George Knight with stand.

OTHER WIDE-FORMAT PRINTERS

Typically, a wide-format printer is considered to be one that is over 42" wide and we recommend the Epson SureColor printers for these sublimation applications. There are three models to consider and each was designed specifically for sublimation. They are the F6200, the F7200 and it's almost identical twin, the 9370. Let's look at each:

The Epson F6200 is a 44" printer. Like all the 42" and above printers, this demands a serious investment but allows prints up to 42" wide at whatever length you need, or you can gang a ton of small jobs for a more economical output. If you desire a matching heat press, you can expect to invest about $14,000 for a MaxiPress by George Knight. It will accommodate a 44"x64" impression.

Included with the F6200 printer is the stand, set of 4 ink refillable cartridges, ink, waste tank and Wasatch SoftRip software. We recommend the Maxi-4464 heat press. Both printer and press are available for about $22,300.

The Epson F6200 is a 44" wide CMYK printer.

The Epson F7200 is a 64" printer that runs in the ballpark of $14,000. Needless to say, this is a serious investment and will likely merit a wide-format heat press to go with it. Most people probably go with the MaxiPress mentioned above, but there are alternatives that go much larger and start around $30,000.

The Epson F7200 and F9370 are identical CMYK 64' printers except the F6370 has two print heads for faster printing.

The Epson F9370 is identical to the Epson F7200 except it has two printheads for much faster printing.

Both the F9370 and the F7200 come with a set of inks, refillable cartridges, a take up spool, stand and Wasatch SoftRip software.

If you think you need to start with one of these larger printers, contact us and let us advise you as you plan out your business needs. Even more important than saving you money, we can save you from making mistakes that can be fatal to any new or existing business.

PART ONE
SECTION 11

"Sublimation without a heat press is like a broken pencil — pointless."
- Sawgrass Technologies

FLAT HEAT PRESSES

Sublimation decorating is a lot like cooking. Put together the right ingredients and cook at the right temperature for the right amount of time and enjoy! The good news is that like cooking, most sublimation substrates have a large sweet spot of success, meaning that cooking is easy. So, we need a heat press to do our cooking.

When you first print your transfer, the image will appear dull and muted. This is because the disperse dyes are not yet activated. Activation requires... heat! Once heat is applied, the dyes look for their next home—a suitable substrate. This is made possible through heat using a heat press. In order for the process to work, both the dyes and the substrate must be in contact with each other and heated at the same time.

There are four variables involved while using the heat press: time, temperature, pressure, and technique. Technique is what's on top and bottom and what additional press accessories are needed.

Different products and different heat presses require different amounts of time, technique, and pressure, but temperature generally stays the same! The standard sublimation temperature is 400 degrees. Our instructions and videos are an excellent start, but you should ultimately document what works for you and please share with us.

Most sublimation substrates are flat and are decorated using a flat press. To help guide you with your heat press selection, I group flat presses into seven characteristics. Don't worry about having to study all this information as I will tell you which heat presses I recommend.

Closure type: Clam-shell and swing away. For sublimation, we greatly prefer swing-away as we are able to achieve even pressure and can easily press thicker substrates like SubliSlate and Unisub MDF plaques. If you have an existing

Clam Shell DK20 Press.

clamp shell press, don't run out and buy a swing away just yet. Chances are we at Condé, can help you do just fine with your old press, just make sure your next press is a swing away.

Pneumatic or manual: A manual heat press requires that the operator open and close the press using a large handle. A pneumatic press is connected to an air compressor and is closed by pressing a switch on the press and which opens automatically after the timer counts down to zero. For most sublimators, I recommend that you purchase a manual heat press as pneumatic presses cannot be programmed for the light pressure that is required for shirts and fabrics. Too much pressure on fabrics results in permanent crease marks on the fabric where the edge of the transfer paper was located. So pneumatic presses would need to be dedicated to hard substrates. Yes, they can be an extreme labor and time savings option.

Air operated heat press.

Swing-a-way type DK20s press.

Heat platen size: This indicates how big a heat surface is available for substrates. Please note that it is not possible to reliably press to the very edge of the heat platen so you will always need about a half of inch of margin on all four sides. For most folks, I recommend the George Knight DK20S swing away digital press as its platen is 16"x20". That corresponds well with common desktop printers that can print 13"x21" transfers. For those with smaller printers, you can press multiple transfers simultaneously.

Top & Bottom heat: Most presses will only have top heat and that will serve you well but folks that are heavy into double sided products such as koozies and FRP bag tags, can benefit from top and bottom heat presses.

Heat output: This topic often goes unnoticed. Imagine your home stove with small and large burners. When both burners are on, they are all at about the same temperature, but you know that you can cook much faster with the large burner as it puts out a lot more heat. So, it is with different heat presses; it's the amount of heat that really counts. So, if possible, buy a heat press that puts out a lot of heat. Usually the thicker the platen and the better the heating element, the greater the heat output. The George Knight DK20S is an excellent example of a BIG burner with its "SuperCoil Microwinding" heater technology. Having a big burner heat press also means that it will maintain temperature when in use and recover much faster. If you go with a smaller portable heat press or no name brand heat press, be aware that substrates with long cook times like ceramic tiles and glass may not be appropriate.

Made in USA: Avoid at all costs buying made in China heat presses. Yes, I know they are cheap, but you really do get what you pay for. Chinese presses are a hit and miss with little or no support and poor warranties. They also have a track record of uneven platen heating and poor temperature regulation. If you already own one, we will do our best to help you use it. So, buy a made in USA heat press. There are only a handful of companies that make presses in the US and by far my favorite is the George Knight company. So, ask when buying a heat press where it's made as a number of US companies promote their presses with USA sounding names, but they are really just poor quality China presses.

Warranty and support: A major benefit to buying USA made presses like a George Knight model, is the excellent support and warranty. Because of this, there are many Knight presses that are quite old. If something goes wrong, the folks at George Knight can diagnose the issue and send out the necessary spare part. In addition, our folks at Condé are experts at supporting these presses.

If all this seems too much to take in, let me make it simple.

In my opinion, this is the all-time sublimation heat press champ from the George Knight company, founded in 1885. It is a 16"x20" swing away that puts out an amazing amount of heat and pressure but provides that ability to also have a light touch for fabrics. For USA clients it is a 110 volt/ 16-amp press and can be ordered in a 220-volt configuration. The platen (the thing that gets hot) is warrantied for life to the original purchaser. This press is a fully digital press with a built-in pressure sensor. The DK20S also features interchangeable bottom platens to allow easier loading and unloading of substrates. See my videos on the DK20S.

We use George Knight presses (Geo Knight) at Condé because they are easy, dependable and reliable. George Knight has been making long-lasting commercial grade equipment since 1885. Their equipment is superb because they use a "SuperCoil-Microwinding" heater technology in their platen that provides heat quickly, disperses heat evenly, and has a faster recovery time.

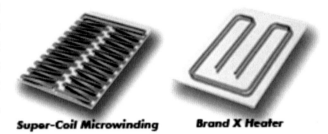

The two types of heating elements used in heat presses. The design on the right is used in all George Knight presses.

At a recent Condé Open House of ours, Aaron Knight from George Knight Press stated, "One of the things Condé loves about [our] presses, is that they are life-time presses. These are made in the USA. They are not disposable, imported presses. We can set a customer up... and they can run their company or business for the next decade or two, or longer! This is very true! We stand behind quality and durability, always. And if you are serious about expanding your business, then you should too! We hear horror stories all the time of people who opted to buy cheaper, disposable presses from other countries just to have them completely fail them a short time later. Just because they are inexpensive, does not make them a good deal. More often than not, they could cost you more money in the long run by having to replace them. Taking shortcuts will only stunt your business's growth. Moving forward is the key! (Are you listening, George Knight? We like what you are doing!)

What about smaller/budget presses?

For clients that have a limited budget or need portability for events & travel, I recommend the George Knight JP14S. This is a light duty press, 14"x12" platen size and is a good choice for those that want to go mobile. It is also a place to start for home businesses. Due to its size it is like cooking on a smaller burner on your stove and you will need to increase your time when pressing.

Larger presses

Usually your press should be matched to your printer. Larger presses that I recommend include the DK25S: This is a 20"x25" manual swing away

FAQ for Flat Heat Presses

Can I use my existing press?

Most likely. You can give us a call to discuss your particular model.

My heat press is broken, should I buy another?

Maybe, but let's talk first, as most made in USA heat presses are easy to repair.

Should I have a spare heat press?

Maybe not at first but once your sublimation business takes off, it's nice to have extra capacity.

Should I buy a stand for my heat press?

I say yes, as it really helps with keeping things in order. Usually not expensive.

Do Heat presses need maintenance?

Yes, see my section on Heat press maintenance. Things like lubrication, cleaning and calibration.

I have a heat press, should I buy a larger one?

Larger heat presses are great for pressing more things at once or if you have or are going to purchase a larger printer.

What accessories for my heat press, do I need?

See section on heat press accessories.

Will I need to add extra power for my heat press?

I recommend a dedicated 20 Amp 110 Volt circuit. Sharing an existing circuit can be an issue. Have a licensed electrician check out your situation.

PART ONE
SECTION 12

"Do one thing every day that scares you." -Anonymous

IT'S HOT!

Heat presses get hot! Are you surprised?

Most of the things we sublimate are made at 400° F which is about the same temperature you would bake bread in an oven. Anyone who has ever baked bread of any kind has probably gotten a burn and it hurts. In fact, contact with anything that is 400° F for less than a second will create a second-degree burn, usually resulting in a blister. Longer contact results in a third degree burn that may have to be treated by a doctor.

Heat presses are no different than an oven. They get hot and sooner or later; you will get burned. Some people brag they have been burned so many times their fingertips don't have any feeling anymore. For others, it's their knuckles. The truth is, I have been doing this for over 25 years and I still have all the feeling in my fingertips, and my knuckles are just fine. If you are constantly getting burned, you are doing something wrong and should change your habits!

The swing-a-way DK20.

Although it is destined to happen sooner or later, getting burned should be a rarity, not common place and here are some tips to keep it that way:

1.   Buy a swing-a-way press. This allows you to move the heating element completely out of the way making it much harder to come in contact with it.

2.   If you do buy a clam-shell press, buy one that opens wide – at least 60° so it is much more difficult to come into contact with the heating element.

3.   Pay attention to what you are doing. Never look away from the press when you are working with it.

The truth is, however, most burns come from handling the product and not from touching the heating element. The product, when it first comes out of the press, is also going to be 400° F and unlike touching the heating element, when grabbing the product, we tend to clamp down on the material, making a burn far more severe. Here are some tips to help keep burns a rarity:

The clamshell DK20.

1.   Buy and use heat gloves. In most cases, I find it cumbersome to wear two gloves, so I handle the product with the gloved hand and keep the other free for other things. In the case of sublimating drinkware in the oven, however, I make an exception and wear two gloves so I can hold the cup in one hand and loosen the bolt and/or the heat wrap with the other.

Holding a hot item up to 500F is no problem with a good heat glove.

2.   Learn to use your fingernails to assist you when working with a hot product. Fingernails have no feeling so I let the nails on my index fingers grow out a little longer than my other fingers to make it easy to move the cover sheet or Teflon sheet around, or to scoot a product close to the edge of the heat press so I can pick it up with my gloved hand. A longer fingernail also helps to remove the protective film on some products prior to pressing. Women who wear acrylic nails should be warned that acrylic melts at about 250° F (you do the math).

Fingernails don't feel pain. Learn to use them to move hot items.

PART ONE
SECTION 13

"Timing, perseverance, and ten years of trying will eventually make you look like an overnight success." -Biz Stone

HEAT PRESS ACCESSORIES

These are just a few of the most common accessories that can be used with your heat press.

KoolPlate™: Properly cooling sublimated products after they are taken out of the heat press is just as important as making them properly in the first place. KoolPlates™ allow the products to cool much faster than normal on a perfectly flat surface. Some products that normally take 7 minutes to cool will cool in less than a minute on a Kool Plate™. This stops the sublimation process and encourages more accurate, consistent colors. Available exclusively from Condé Systems. The newest version of the A6000 Kool Plate™ has a stainless-steel shell with a heat conductive aluminum top for faster cooling along

Having a KoolPlate allows you to better control sublimation, increase productivity and produce a higher quality product. Except for an acrylic baffle on the inside, the new KoolPlate is all metal construction.

with four high-efficiency 12 VDC fans for fast, quiet cooling. The top area is 12"x18".

KoolPlates are available exclusively from Condé Systems. This is a must-have for anyone serious about sublimation. Each one is handmade in the USA.

Each KoolPlate has four high performance, Swiss made whisper fans.

Heat Glove(s): These come in a variety of styles and are available as a single glove or a pair. I find one glove adequate for most things but having a pair is helpful when making cups in an oven. Available from Condé, Amazon.com and some hardware stores. Be sure the gloves are rated at over 450°F.

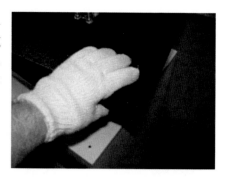

Heat gloves like this one will allow you to handle items up to 500 F.

DyeTrans Pro Spray II: When you open a heat press, air rushes in and can cause the transfer to move. As it lands in a new spot, it will continue to sublimate causing a shadow print or double take. DyeTrans Pro Spray is the industry standard tack spray to keep the transfer from moving. Just spray a small amount on the transfer and then build your sublimation sandwich. I use Pro spray for soft substrates like huggers, fabrics and mouse pads but it is the "go to" solution for many other substrates as well.

Digital Pyrometer or Digital Candy Temperature Thermometer:

Although 'old school', this cooking thermometer can be used to test the temperature of a heat press.

It is imperative that you check the accuracy of your heat press from time to time. The preferred way is with a pyrometer (a digital thermometer with a special probe) but these cost about $85. A less expensive way is to use a digital metal candy thermometer with a metal stem. These are a little difficult to find in stores, but eBay does carry them.

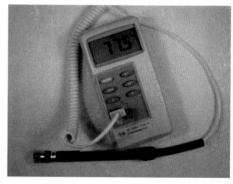

Although this looks like a digital thermometer, it is actually a digital pyrometer and is ideal for checking the temperature of a heat press.

The brown material on this heat press is Teflon.

Two Sheets of Teflon Film: You should *avoid* Teflon sheets like the plague. Although people say sublimation ink won't stick to Teflon, they will! Once that happens, it will get on the next substrate it touches. It also acts as a moisture barrier and will trap moisture under it. You *should* use Teflon for a handful of products however, because they have an adhesive on them that can stick to your heat press when pressure and heat are applied. These include sublimation patches, Rowmark Mates materials and our oven gloves. See the instructions on our website for more details. Remember, don't use Teflon outside of these products.

Use newsprint to cover products while sublimating except for self-adhesive products.

54

Goo Gone: Goo Gone comes in handy for a number of uses. It is great for cleaning a cold heat press, removing residue from using too much Pro Spray or the residue from the protective films on plaques and other products. It is also available in a spray bottle, at your local hardware store or Amazon.com.

Uncoated white butcher paper with dispenser: You must use cover paper on the top and bottom of your sublimation sandwich. By doing this you will trap the sublimation gas and not contaminate your top platen or bottom pad. And if you really screw up and have a meltdown, then clean up on isle 3 is easy! This is a must for working with large items or when you gang a bunch of items on the press at the same time. When sublimating something, a layer of paper should be both under and over the item(s) being sublimated to prevent any stray dye from getting onto the press and then being transferred to the next item. These are available from Sam's Club, office supply stores and art supply stores. A dispenser is not mandatory but sure is helpful when tearing off pieces of butcher paper or newsprint. Some people build their own dispenser from a wooden dowel mounted in a wood frame. Professional models are available where you buy paper.

Uncoated butcher paper makes a great cover sheet for sublimating products.

Ordinary copy paper makes a good cover sheet for sublimating products.

Uncoated cut sheet copy paper: Both 8.5"x11", 8.5"x14" and 11"x17" white copy paper is handy to keep next to your press to use as cover sheets. Since most products made are smaller than copy paper, it makes a fast, inexpensive replacement for butcher paper. Cheap copy paper is often available from online office supply houses like Quill for less than a penny a sheet for letter size. Just be sure you buy uncoated paper.

Heat Tape: Heat tape keeps things from moving during the sublimation process. Read our instructions as some substrates like plaques will be damaged if the tape is placed on the foil edge.

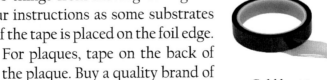

For plaques, tape on the back of the plaque. Buy a quality brand of heat tape, as some tapes can leave *Gold heat tape* a tape residue that can't always be removed. Condé offers a new "gold" heat tape that is proving to be very well received.

Heat tape comes in several colors and a couple of thicknesses. What you use is purely personal preference.

Having a tape dispenser is like having an extra hand.

Heat Tape Dispenser: Although this isn't required, it is certainly helpful. You will need a dispenser with a 3" core to match the heat tape. I recommend one that has a very heavy base. These are available from Condé, Amazon.com and local office supply stores.

Green heat conductive rubber pads: Always read our instructions as many substrates require accessories such as the green rubber pad. This pad is often used with glass and Sublislate to diffuse the heat evenly into a substrate. Some people prefer using a green pad rather than the Nomex pads listed below. These come in 1/8" and 1/16" thicknesses. These pads are expensive so store them carefully by laying them flat or rolling them into a scroll.

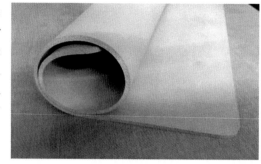

Green heat pad.

Nomex™ pads: These are thick felt pads in white or yellow and are placed under our sublimation sandwich when pressing some products such as glass or ceramic tile. Its purpose is to protect a substrate from too much stress and/or to cradle a substrate (like a tile) so the transfer wraps around the substrate to have a great over the edge transfer. These come in the same sizes as heat presses and in 1/8" or ½" thicknesses which are often used in combination.

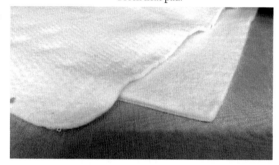

Nomex pads.

Ceramic tiles for example, require heat insulating felt pads to go on the bottom of our sublimation sandwich. For ceramic tiles, we prefer to place the transfer on the bottom, face up on top of our Nomex pad (always use cover paper on top and bottom of our sandwich). Then we place the tile face down. When we close the press, we force the tile into the Nomex pad causing the transfer to conform to the tile and transfer "over the edge" of the tile, making a very attractive product.

Foam Pillows:

This is an important and inexpensive accessory for decorating fabrics. This product is a big roll of grey foam and you will cut a piece of it to go on the bottom of your sublimation sandwich. Using this product is a great way to reduce or eliminate the creases in the fabric caused by the edge of the transfer paper. The edge of the paper has thickness and as we press, this edge causes a very visible "permanent press" crease that will not come out. The solution is to cut a piece of vapor foam that is slightly smaller than the size of the transfer but larger than your image size. The cut

Example of raw foam that can be cut to size. Available from sewing centers or Amazon.com.

Professionally made pillows come in a variety of sizes.

vapor foam is placed on the bottom with a large cover sheet on top. Then place your fabric or shirt and then the printed transfer face down. Using your fingers, align the foam to the transfer and then press with light pressure. The effect of all this is to allow the edge of the transfer paper to float and not hit the hard-bottom pad thus reducing the visible creases. The real trick is to calibrate your pressure. Too much pressure just flattens the foam; not enough pressure and we get a poor transfer due to lack of contact. With presses like the DK20S, you can get to eye level with the side of press and adjust pressure so that we are making appropriate contact. For thin fabrics, you may want to "Ducale" the edge of the transfer by tearing it on each edge. This irregular edge is results in a feathering out of the paper's edge. See our videos for more details.

PART ONE
SECTION 14

"What would you do if you weren't afraid?" Sheryl Sandberg

HAT & SPECIALTY HEAT PRESSES

Trucker hats continue to be very popular with both men and women and sublimation affords one means of decorating them. Hats do, however, require a special press that conforms with the shape of the hat.

There are two ways to approach this product: One is to buy a dedicated hat press. This is the best choice if you plan to do a lot of hats. This press is called a DK7. A production model of the DK7, the DK7T is also available. The DK7T allows the operator to load one hat while the other is being pressed. This is really helpful since caps have to be stretched over the platen and therefore, take more time to change than flat items.

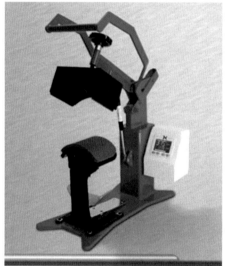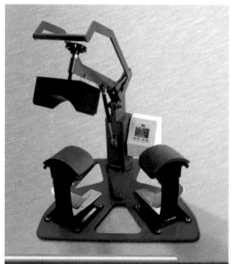

George Knight DK7 and DK7T Cap Presses.

If, however, you expect to do only an occasional hat, an option is the DK16s Digital Combo press by George Knight. This press has interchangeable stages that can accommodate flat objects, hats, plates, and even custom-built platens. One such custom heating element was built to sublimate cue balls – yes, cue balls are sublimatable. This makes the DK16 a good choice for those who do mostly flat stuff but have an occasional hat to make. The base unit has a 14x16" stage that lifts off to accommodate other appliances. Likewise, the heating head is also interchangeable. With the optional attachments, the press will make hats, cups, ceramic plates and all the flat stuff that can be pressed on a 14x16" platen.

George Knight DK16S Digital Combo with its available appliances.

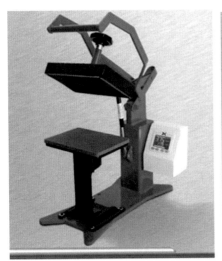 

Clamshell presses for small format products.

Other specialty presses available include a label press, the DK8 and DK8T. These presses have 6x8" platens for making small items such as sublimatable labels but can also be used to make anything that will fit on the platen. The DK8T is basically the same as the DK8 except it has two platens so the operator can be loading one while the other is being pressed, etc. This greatly increases production.

Sleeve presses for pressing the sublimatable sleeves are also available as an attachment. These drop on the pedestal of some of the larger presses such as the SK20s and larger that were made after 1/1/2017. They do not work with the DK16 Digital Combo or presses made prior to January 2017. These come in two widths, 3.5" and 5". They are 20" long.

Elongated platen for pressing sleeves.

PART ONE
SECTION 15

"The new source of power is not money in the hands of a few, but information in the hands of many." -John Naisbitt

DECORATING MUGS

Mugs are perhaps the largest volume hard substrate. Many great sublimation pioneers have paved the way to our success.

Mugs can be decorated in four ways. With a heat press or using an oven, a mug wrap or the newest way, with shrink wrap sleeves.

Mugs are part of the drinkware family and consist of ceramic, plastic and metal products. See my chapter on drinkware. Since this is a very high-volume category, methods were created many years ago for volume production.

Mug Type Heat Presses:

This method is used to produce one mug at a time, but many folks operate several presses at the same time as needed. See photo below. The transfer is attached to the mug along with a cover sheet. The mug is placed in the press and closed. The press should be adjusted to properly contour to the mug to insure good contact. We then press generally at 400 degrees F for about 4 to 5 minutes for a ceramic mug. Times do vary for different types of drinkware and mug presses.

Constant Temperature Mug Presses

For some reason there are generally two types of mug heat presses. Constant and variable temperature presses. The mug press I use is the George Knight DK3 and it is a constant temperature press. You turn it on, and it gets up to the preset temperature (i.e. 400 degrees F) and maintains it within a normal range. It will dip quite a bit once a mug is placed in the press but will quickly recover. This constant temperature press works exactly like a flat press and therefore provides predictable results.

George Knight DK3 is our recommended mug press for standard shaped drinkware.

Variable Temperature Mug Presses:

The other type is what I call variable temperature and I recommend it be avoided. This type of mug press has two temperatures: idle and press. The press stays at idle temperature while it is not in use. Once the handle is closed, the press then starts climbing until it reaches the press temperature. Once reached, the timer then begins to count down. The challenge is that the timer does activate during the journey from idle to press temperature. This really throws a monkey wrench into timing. Your best bet is to increase the idle temperature as high as it can go and then use an external timer started then the handle is closed. The unfortunate thing is, these presses don't look much different from the constant temperature presses so it can be difficult to know which one is which. I recommend you not buy one of these type presses.

Mug Wraps: Wraps have been around for a few years now and are made to work with all the mugs, cups, travel mugs, water bottles, pet bowls and other ceramic items. They consist of a heat resistant rubber pad that is stretched around the object and held in place with some type of clamp. For heat, a dedicated conventional oven or countertop oven works well. The wraps are reusable and can last for years if cared for properly.

Typical mug wrap.

Shrink Wraps: The newest method of decorating cups and other such items is with a shrink wrap bag. With this method, the item is placed in the bag which is heat shrunk around the item using a hair dryer. Once the shrink wrap has been molded to the object, it is placed in an oven or countertop oven for heat. This method works well for edge to edge imprinting as well as handle to handle imprinting plus imprinting on the handle itself. The wraps are not reusable but are very inexpensive and come in a variety of sizes to fit the various types of sublimatable objects available.

Shrink wrap bags.

Conveyor Oven: For large volumes of mugs, I recommend a conveyor type oven. These ovens are loaded at one end and then move into and through the oven and exit at the far end. Hix Corporation makes a family of great conveyor ovens perfect for high volume production of mugs and other like items.

PART ONE
SECTION 16

*"Success seems to be connected with action. Successful people keep moving.
They make mistakes, but they don't quit." -Conrad Hilton*

SHUTTLE PRESSES

A shuttle press can be manual or automatic and some conventional heat presses can be converted to become shuttle presses. We recommend George Knight presses because of their many years of dependable service; the type of heating element they use in all their presses and the customer service they provide.

The purpose of a shuttle press is to speed up production. In the most basic terms, a shuttle press incorporates two platens or stages to one heating platen. This allows you to load one while the other is being pressed. When the first finishes, you can shift the platens, so the second unit is being pressed while the first is unloaded and a new product is loaded and readies for pressing. This greatly increases the productivity when doing large orders.

The commonly used DK14 Combo Press and the DK20s can both be upgraded to become shuttle presses.

The Geo Knight 394 is a 20"x25" press that comes set up

The Geo Knight DK14 upgraded to a shuttle press.

as a shuttle press. This press operates with air pressure (compressor required) to open and close the press. At the end of each cycle, the press automatically opens. This feature eliminates much of the fatigue of using a manual press. It also insures accurate and consistent pressure, even when the thickness of items varies.

For pricing and availability, visit our website at www.Condé.com.

PART ONE
SECTION 17

"To improve is to change; to be perfect is to change often." – Winston Churchill

TOP & BOTTOM HEATING PLATENS

All heat presses come with a top heating platen which closes down onto a stage (platform where the product to be pressed is placed). That's typical.

What isn't typical is adding a bottom heating platen, but this is an add-on that is becoming more and more popular for several reasons.

Of course, not all presses can accommodate a bottom heating element, but most of the Geo Knight presses can. The DK16 (a clamshell press), the DK14 (also called the Digital Combo press), the DK20s and the DK25s are designed to be upgraded if and when it is desired.

The upgrades can be done in a matter of a few minutes by the consumer. Just remove the stock lower platen and slide the heated version in its place. The lower heating element comes with its own control panel and power cord so it can be bypassed when not needed, returning the press to a top heat only press without having to exchange the lower platen.

NOTE: Each heating element draws 15 or more amps of current! Because most electrical circuits are only 20 amps, a separate circuit or special wiring will be required to operate both elements.

Geo Knight offers a variety of bottom platens for their presses.

PART ONE
SECTION 18

"Opportunities don't happen. You create them." -Chris Grosser

WIDE FORMAT HEAT PRESSES

Although some people buy wide-format printers just to maximize their print abilities, if you invest in a wide format printer, chances are, you will want a heat press to go with it.

Most wide-format presses are considered to be 40" or more; there are a few intermediate size presses that don't take up the equivalent of a typical bedroom.

Most wide-format presses require 220-240-volt circuits, so special wiring is required.

The smallest heat press we will consider to be wide format is the George Knight DK25s. This design is identical to the very popular DK20s but has a heat platen 25"x20".

The next size, which is truly wide format, is the George Knight DK32AP. This is a 26"x32" drawer type heat press that is air operated.

Next is the Maxi-Press by George Knight. This press can be set up in several variations, including a shuttle style. This is a 32"x42" press that can be either manual or air operated.

Finally, there is the George Knight 931 Triton. This monster can also be set up as a shuttle style press and is capable of pressing a full 4'x8' panel.

Custom presses can also be designed to specific applications up to 5'x10' or larger.

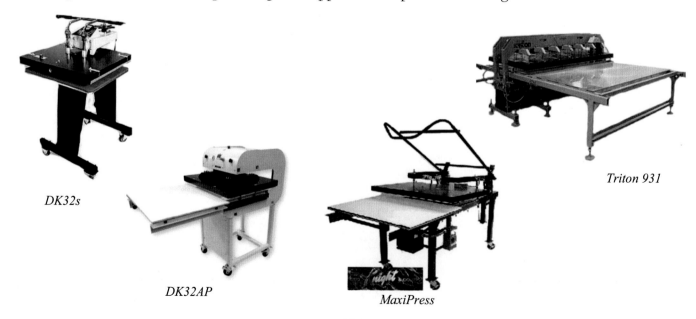

DK32s

DK32AP

MaxiPress

Triton 931

PART ONE
SECTION 19

"If you really want to do something, you'll find a way. If you don't, you'll find an excuse."
-Jim Rohn

ADDITIONAL EQUIPMENT YOU MAY WANT TO SUPPORT

YOUR SUBLIMATION BUSINESS

You know already that you will need a computer, a sublimation printer, sublimation inks and a heat press but what else might make the job easier and faster? Here is a list of items you might consider either now or later:

Product Catalogs: Condé produces a very nice, full-color product catalog (without pricing) that you can buy in small quantities. You can add your company name and contact information to the back and share these with friends, neighbors and other potential customers.

½" Nut Driver with Hollow Shank: This is for loosening or tightening the nut on mug wraps. Available at Sears and other hardware stores.

Oven Thermometer(s): For use when making mugs in an oven. With a dial type thermometer, adjust the temperature to the thermometer and not the dial on the oven since many ovens are off by as much as 50°. Available from Amazon.com or most kitchen or department stores.

\

KoolPlate™: With this device, you will find it so much easier to make products when you can control the cooling time and not have to wait ten-minutes or more before you can stack or package each product. Kook Plates reduce cooling from one-minute to seconds for most products and from fifteen minutes or more to about seven-minutes for a ceramic tile. This is a must for production work.

Mug Wraps: There are a number of mug wraps available for making sublimated cups, steins and pet dishes in a conventional oven. These allow you to make many products and even mix products in a single batch. Process time is approximately 20 minutes. Wraps are available from Condé Systems.

Jigs: UNISUB jigs are for people who make a lot of UNISUB products such as name badges, bag tags and other FRP products. They save a great deal of time when making large orders of a single product. Available from Condé Systems.

Foam: Having a sheet of 1", 1.5" or 2" foam on hand comes in extremely helpful when working with fabric to act as a pillow under the transfer. This helps prevent a distinct box or lines around the edges of the transfer. Even if you use Sublimation Pillows, foam is useful for those odd shaped or odd size transfers. Available at your local hobby or sewing center.

Sublimation Pillows: If you prefer something a bit more professional than a piece of raw foam, Teflon covered pillows are available in a variety of sizes for sublimating fabric. Available from Condé Systems.

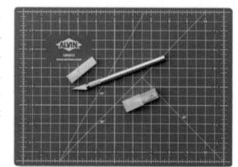

X-Acto Knife and Self-Healing Cutting Pad: There will be times when you need to trim transfers. Although this can be done with scissors, it is much faster and more accurate to use a razor knife, such as an X-Acto brand knife and a special pad that is pre-printed with rulers that actually heals itself after being cut. Some substitute single edged razor blades for the knife which is personal preference. Available from most hobby or sewing centers.

Simple Green: The household cleaner Simple Green is one of the few cleaners that will easily mop up spilled sublimation ink. In spite of all precautions, accidents do happen. Without Simple Green, even a little spilled ink can cause a terrible mess. Available at most grocery stores.

Large Set of Permanent Markers: When you sublimate a piece of FRP, the edges will remain white. When this is not preferred, a permanent marker can be used to "paint" the edges. To ensure the marker doesn't come off on someone's clothes, be sure to wipe it with alcohol after it has dried. This leaves a finished edge on the FRP. Available from any art supply store or Amazon.com.

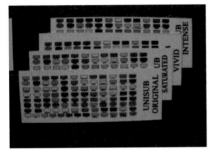

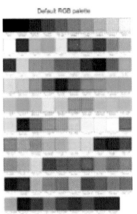

Homemade Color Charts: It is imperative that you have a set of color charts to allow you to select the right color the first time. These are available on the Condé website for download. You will have to print your own actual chart on whatever substrates you plan to make; metal, FRP, fabric, etc. Changing substrates will have an effect on color, so make one for Unisub products, one for every color of fabric you plan to use and one for all the other products you need to color match, such as tile, wood, acrylic, etc.

Pantone™ PMS Color Chart: This is not necessary for most sublimators but for those who work with companies that require stringent color matching, this chart will make life a lot easier. There are a lot of charts available and they are expensive so choose carefully. There are also devices that digitally check and compare colors available from the Pantone™ website. There is also an app for your phone that uses your camera to capture a color and compare it to a built-in chart. Some are free, others cost a couple of bucks. Go to you App Store for the app. Go to Amazon.com or www.Pantone.com for the charts.

Metal Shear: There is no safe way to cut metal without a shear.

Accucutter 2001 metal shear.

These devices start under $400 and go to $4,000 but fortunately, most sublimators can do fine with a $400 model. These may be ordered directly from the manufacturer at www.accucutter.com. There is a complete review of the Accucutter 4001 in the September issue of Engravers Journal. It will help you understand the value of investing $1,000 in a metal shear.

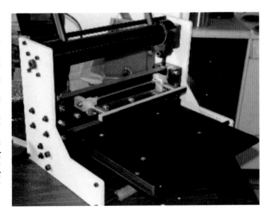

Accucutter 4001 metal shear.

Tesa Tape 4970: This gold carrier PVC tape has an acrylic adhesive that is great for attaching findings to name badges or binding pieces of MDF, FRP, metal or other hard substrates together or in place. It is water resistant and good for temps around 158°. For even more demanding jobs that might require higher temperature capabilities, Tesa Tape 4965 is a clear acrylic tape that is weatherproof and can handle up to 300°F. These are available in a variety of widths and are available from Amazon.com.

Curved Photo Panels: The Chromaluxe™ Photo panels are really great, but they do require either a wall hanger or an easel to hold them – unless your curl them so they can stand by themselves. This makes a great impression and is super easy to do. It does require an additional piece of equipment, however. That is a metal roller device from

Accucutter. Just feed the metal panel into the roller while turning the crank and out comes a perfectly bent, self-standing photo panel. Want more bend? Just adjust the roller or feed it through again. To learn more, go to www.accucutter.com.

Rolling device for light metals.

Corner Punches: If you have a shear, you will want a corner punch. Several are available depending on how often you will use it; you can get a light duty punch, a heavy-duty punch or an automatic punch (perfect for those will without a lot of strength in their hands or upper body).

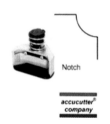

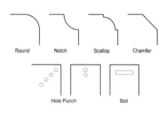

Light Duty Punch   Heavy Duty Punch   Actual Punch Insert   Shapes Available

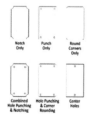

3-in-1 MaxiPress: The 3-in-1 MaxiPress is a good introductory device for punching holes and rounding corners. Available from Main Trophy Supply, it costs about $375.

PART ONE
SECTION 20

"...for the laborer is worthy of his hire...." Luke 10:7

THE BIGGEST MISTAKE PEOPLE MAKE

Perhaps the most damaging of all the mistakes people make in sublimation is underpricing their products. It not only hurts you but the industry as a whole. This pricing problem may occur because dealers know the initial cost of the products we use causing them to price projects with an almost knee-jerk reaction that says, "if I double or triple my money, I'm making a heck of a profit" and that may or may not be true.

Consider the elements of making a product:

1. Meeting with a client takes time. What is your time worth? Before you say, "it's just my time", remember, your time has to be justified by the hour just as if you were an employee working for someone else. Time is money and, in many cases, the most costly element of all.
2. We have to design the product. Again, this takes time. In some cases, people spend an hour designing a $15 coffee mug. This is not an exaggeration. Time yourself when you design your next project and see how long it really takes. You may be shocked at what you learn.
3. It takes time to press the product. There's time again, and even if the product takes only a minute or two to make, it will take much longer to get the press ready, make the transfer, position it on the product, manipulate the press and cool and package the finished product(s).
4. Then there is the time delivering the product. Just as it took time to sell the product, it takes time to deliver it to the customer, writing up the sales slip and taking care of the payment. Earnestly, the amount of time "shooting the breeze" with a customer at this point can cost you more than the product could ever produce.
5. But we are hardly done counting up the cost yet. There is the cost of the product itself and the shipping. In most cases, when ordering product, you should order some extra in case something goes wrong and it will – about 5% of the time (but that percentage goes way up for single products). Once the press is set up and your mind is focused on making a particular product, it is easy to turn them out as fast as the press will allow, but when you are just making one of something, there are lots of opportunities for something to go wrong – distractions, a setting that is incorrect or just a forgotten step. All result in the same thing – a ruined product that goes on the "Wall of Shame" rather than in the customer's hand.
6. A price that is doubled means one mistake and you might break even on the cost of the product, but you sacrifice all the other costs. That takes the failure percentage from 5% to 50%!
7. There's more. What about the cost of operating your shop? The electricity, gas, upkeep, equipment costs, maintenance costs, taxes and rent? These and more all have to be figured into the final cost, and truth is, most business owners don't have a clue how much this is per hour, day or even year.

8. Notice I list the cost of ink and paper last. That is because in comparison to all the other costs, this expense is insignificant. Although dealers often fret over what it costs to make a transfer, it amounts to mere pennies per square inch while labor can cost dollars per square inch!

Pricing sublimation products is unique in the industry. Unlike other products in the engraving world where the manufacturer suggests a retail price of at least three times the cost plus engraving, sublimators are left to their own resources to try and figure out what is reasonable and even when we know all the numbers referenced above, it still isn't easy.

Sometimes products just shouldn't be sold because they bring with them too much risk, while the fate of

SKU	PRODUCT DESCRIPTION	WHOLESALE PRICE FOR ONE ITEM	QUANTITY SOLD	WHOLESALE COST FOR PRODUC	ESTIMATED SHIPPING COSTS 15X1	PRODUC T & SHIPPIN G PER PIECE	TOTAL FOR PRODUC T & SHIPPIN	SUGGESTED RETAIL PRICE RANGE SINGLE UNIT SALES	SUGGESTED RETAIL PRICE RANGE FOR QUANTITY SALES	WHAT YOU WANT TO CHARGE	RETAIL PRICE FOR JOB	GROSS PROFIT	50X MARKUP	200X MARKUP JKEY STON	300X MARKUP EACH	400X MARKUP EACH	500X MARKUP EACH	600X MARKUP EACH
U4171	Unisub Aluminum Ornament, Oval Single	$2.52	1	$0.00	$0.25	$2.77	$0.00	$5.95-$9.95	$5.95-$7.95	$0.00	$0.00	$0.00	$4.15	$5.54	$8.52	$11.83	$13.86	$16.63
U4172	Unisub Aluminum Ornament, Hexagon Single	$2.52	1	$0.00	$0.25	$2.77	$0.00	$5.95-$9.95	$5.95-$7.95	$0.00	$0.00	$0.00	$4.15	$5.54	$8.52	$11.83	$13.86	$16.63
U4173	Unisub Aluminum Ornament, Horizontal Single	$2.52	1	$0.00	$0.25	$2.77	$0.00	$5.95-$9.95	$5.95-$7.95	$0.00	$0.00	$0.00	$4.15	$5.54	$8.52	$11.83	$13.86	$16.63
U4174	Unisub Aluminum Ornament, Vertical Single	$2.52	1	$0.00	$0.25	$2.77	$0.00	$5.95-$9.95	$5.95-$7.95	$0.00	$0.00	$0.00	$4.15	$5.54	$8.52	$11.83	$13.86	$16.63
U4175	Unisub Aluminum Ornament, Taper Single	$2.52	1	$0.00	$0.25	$2.77	$0.00	$5.95-$9.95	$5.95-$7.95	$0.00	$0.00	$0.00	$4.15	$5.54	$8.52	$11.83	$13.86	$16.63
U4193	Unisub Aluminum Ornament, Prayer Single	$2.52	1	$0.00	$0.25	$2.77	$0.00	$5.95-$9.95	$5.95-$7.95	$0.00	$0.00	$0.00	$4.15	$5.54	$8.52	$11.83	$13.86	$16.63
U4194	Unisub Aluminum Ornament, Berlin Single	$2.52	1	$0.00	$0.25	$2.77	$0.00	$5.95-$9.95	$5.95-$7.95	$0.00	$0.00	$0.00	$4.15	$5.54	$8.52	$11.83	$13.86	$16.63
U4198	Unisub Aluminum Ornament, Gingerbread Single	$2.52	1	$0.00	$0.25	$2.77	$0.00	$5.95-$9.95	$5.95-$7.95	$0.00	$0.00	$0.00	$4.15	$5.54	$8.52	$11.83	$13.86	$16.63
U4351	Unisub Aluminum Ornament, Star Single	$2.52	1	$0.00	$0.25	$2.77	$0.00	$5.95-$9.95	$5.95-$7.95	$0.00	$0.00	$0.00	$4.15	$5.54	$8.52	$11.83	$13.86	$16.63
U4352	Unisub Aluminum Ornament, Heart Single	$2.52	1	$0.00	$0.25	$2.77	$0.00	$5.95-$9.95	$5.95-$7.95	$0.00	$0.00	$0.00	$4.15	$5.54	$8.52	$11.83	$13.86	$16.63
U4353	Unisub Aluminum Ornament, Bell Single	$2.52	1	$0.00	$0.25	$2.77	$0.00	$5.95-$9.95	$5.95-$7.95	$0.00	$0.00	$0.00	$4.15	$5.54	$8.52	$11.83	$13.86	$16.63
U4354	Unisub Aluminum Ornament, Tree Single	$2.52	1	$0.00	$0.25	$2.77	$0.00	$5.95-$9.95	$5.95-$7.95	$0.00	$0.00	$0.00	$4.15	$5.54	$8.52	$11.83	$13.86	$16.63
U4355	Unisub Aluminum Ornament, Ball Single	$2.52	1	$0.00	$0.25	$2.77	$0.00	$5.95-$9.95	$5.95-$7.95	$0.00	$0.00	$0.00	$4.15	$5.54	$8.52	$11.83	$13.86	$16.63
U4485	Unisub Aluminum Ornament, Ghost Single	$2.52	1	$0.00	$0.25	$2.77	$0.00	$5.95-$9.95	$5.95-$7.95	$0.00	$0.00	$0.00	$4.15	$5.54	$8.52	$11.83	$13.86	$16.63
U4486	Unisub Aluminum Ornament, Pumpkin Single	$2.52	1	$0.00	$0.25	$2.77	$0.00	$5.95-$9.95	$5.95-$7.95	$0.00	$0.00	$0.00	$4.15	$5.54	$8.52	$11.83	$13.86	$16.63
U4487	Unisub Aluminum Ornament, T-Shirt Single	$2.52	1	$0.00	$0.25	$2.77	$0.00	$5.95-$9.95	$5.95-$7.95	$0.00	$0.00	$0.00	$4.15	$5.54	$8.52	$11.83	$13.86	$16.63
U4492	Unisub Aluminum Ornament, Football Single	$2.52	1	$0.00	$0.25	$2.77	$0.00	$5.95-$9.95	$5.95-$7.95	$0.00	$0.00	$0.00	$4.15	$5.54	$8.52	$11.83	$13.86	$16.63
U4495	Unisub Aluminum Ornament, Helmet Single	$2.52	1	$0.00	$0.25	$2.77	$0.00	$5.95-$9.95	$5.95-$7.95	$0.00	$0.00	$0.00	$4.15	$5.54	$8.52	$11.83	$13.86	$16.63
U4447	Unisub Aluminum Ornament, Candy Cane Single	$2.52	1	$0.00	$0.25	$2.77	$0.00	$5.95-$9.95	$5.95-$7.95	$0.00	$0.00	$0.00	$4.15	$5.54	$8.52	$11.83	$13.86	$16.63
U4448	Unisub Aluminum Ornament, Stocking Single	$2.52	1	$0.00	$0.25	$2.77	$0.00	$5.95-$9.95	$5.95-$7.95	$0.00	$0.00	$0.00	$4.15	$5.54	$8.52	$11.83	$13.86	$16.63
U4449	Unisub Aluminum Ornament, Paw Print Single	$2.52	1	$0.00	$0.25	$2.77	$0.00	$5.95-$9.95	$5.95-$7.95	$0.00	$0.00	$0.00	$4.15	$5.54	$8.52	$11.83	$13.86	$16.63
U5922	Unisub Aluminum Ornament, Round Single	$2.52	1	$0.00	$0.25	$2.77	$0.00	$5.95-$9.95	$5.95-$7.95	$0.00	$0.00	$0.00	$4.15	$5.54	$8.52	$11.83	$13.86	$16.63
U5923	Unisub Aluminum Ornament, Oval Single	$2.52	1	$0.00	$0.25	$2.77	$0.00	$5.95-$9.95	$5.95-$7.95	$0.00	$0.00	$0.00	$4.15	$5.54	$8.52	$11.83	$13.86	$16.63
										$0.00								
	Unisub FRP Ornaments									$0.00								
U5589	Unisub FRP Ornament, Round Single	$2.52	1	$0.00	$0.25	$2.77	$0.00	$5.95-$9.95	$5.95-$7.95	$0.00	$0.00	$0.00	$4.15	$5.54	$8.52	$11.83	$13.86	$16.63
U5598	Unisub FRP Ornament, Tree Single	$2.52	1	$0.00	$0.25	$2.77	$0.00	$5.95-$9.95	$5.95-$7.95	$0.00	$0.00	$0.00	$4.15	$5.54	$8.52	$11.83	$13.86	$16.63
U5575	Unisub FRP Ornament, Star Single	$2.52	1	$0.00	$0.25	$2.77	$0.00	$5.95-$9.95	$5.95-$7.95	$0.00	$0.00	$0.00	$4.15	$5.54	$8.52	$11.83	$13.86	$16.63
										$0.00								
	Glass Ornaments									$0.00								
GL801	Glass Ornament, Round	$2.52	1	$0.00	$0.25	$2.77	$0.00	$5.95-$9.95	$5.95-$7.95	$0.00	$0.00	$0.00	$4.15	$5.54	$8.52	$11.83	$13.86	$16.63
GL802	Glass Ornament, Oval, Vertical	$2.52	1	$0.00	$0.25	$2.77	$0.00	$5.95-$9.95	$5.95-$7.95	$0.00	$0.00	$0.00	$4.15	$5.54	$8.52	$11.83	$13.86	$16.63
GL803	Glass Ornament, Oval, Horizontal	$2.52	1	$0.00	$0.25	$2.77	$0.00	$5.95-$9.95	$5.95-$7.95	$0.00	$0.00	$0.00	$4.15	$5.54	$8.52	$11.83	$13.86	$16.63
GL804	Glass Ornament, Hexagon	$2.52	1	$0.00	$0.25	$2.77	$0.00	$5.95-$9.95	$5.95-$7.95	$0.00	$0.00	$0.00	$4.15	$5.54	$8.52	$11.83	$13.86	$16.63
										$0.00								
	Brickone Ornaments									$0.00								
204	Hard Ball Ornament (laurel incl.)	$2.52	1	$0.00	$0.25	$2.77	$0.00	$5.95-$9.95	$5.95-$7.95	$0.00	$0.00	$0.00	$4.15	$5.54	$8.52	$11.83	$13.86	$16.63
205	Poinsettia Ornament (laurel incl.)	$2.52	1	$0.00	$0.25	$2.77	$0.00	$5.95-$9.95	$5.95-$7.95	$0.00	$0.00	$0.00	$4.15	$5.54	$8.52	$11.83	$13.86	$16.63
DS805u	Extra Inserts	$2.52	1	$0.00	$0.25	$2.77	$0.00			$0.00	$0.00		$4.15	$5.54	$8.52	$11.83	$13.86	$16.63
										$0.00								
	Porcelain Ornaments									$0.00								
K181P-2	Porcelain Ornament, Star Shape	$2.52	1	$0.00	$0.25	$2.77	$0.00	$5.95-$9.95	$5.95-$7.95	$0.00	$0.00	$0.00	$4.15	$5.54	$8.52	$11.83	$13.86	$16.63
K182P-2	Porcelain Ornament, Scallop Shape	$2.52	1	$0.00	$0.25	$2.77	$0.00	$5.95-$9.95	$5.95-$7.95	$0.00	$0.00	$0.00	$4.15	$5.54	$8.52	$11.83	$13.86	$16.63
K183P-2	Porcelain Ornament, Snowflake Shape	$2.52	1	$0.00	$0.25	$2.77	$0.00	$5.95-$9.95	$5.95-$7.95	$0.00	$0.00	$0.00	$4.15	$5.54	$8.52	$11.83	$13.86	$16.63
K184P-2	Porcelain Ornament, Wreath Shape	$2.52	1	$0.00	$0.25	$2.77	$0.00	$5.95-$9.95	$5.95-$7.95	$0.00	$0.00	$0.00	$4.15	$5.54	$8.52	$11.83	$13.86	$16.63
K228P-2	Porcelain Ornament, Star Shape	$2.52	1	$0.00	$0.25	$2.77	$0.00	$5.95-$9.95	$5.95-$7.95	$0.00	$0.00	$0.00	$4.15	$5.54	$8.52	$11.83	$13.86	$16.63
K226P-2	Porcelain Ornament, Round Shape	$2.52	1	$0.00	$0.25	$2.77	$0.00	$5.95-$9.95	$5.95-$7.95	$0.00	$0.00	$0.00	$4.15	$5.54	$8.52	$11.83	$13.86	$16.63
K585P-2	Porcelain Ornament, Heart Shape	$2.52	1	$0.00	$0.25	$2.77	$0.00	$5.95-$9.95	$5.95-$7.95	$0.00	$0.00	$0.00	$4.15	$5.54	$8.52	$11.83	$13.86	$16.63
										$0.00								
	Holiday Stockings									$0.00								
HS18	Holiday Stocking, 17"	$2.52	1	$0.00	$0.25	$2.77	$0.00	$5.95-$9.95	$5.95-$7.95	$0.00	$0.00	$0.00	$4.15	$5.54	$8.52	$11.83	$13.86	$16.63
HS19	Holiday Stocking, 24"	$2.52	1	$0.00	$0.25	$2.77	$0.00	$5.95-$9.95	$5.95-$7.95	$0.00	$0.00	$0.00	$4.15	$5.54	$8.52	$11.83	$13.86	$16.63
HS20	Holiday Stocking, 17", Red Liner	$2.52	1	$0.00	$0.25	$2.77	$0.00	$5.95-$9.95	$5.95-$7.95	$0.00	$0.00	$0.00	$4.15	$5.54	$8.52	$11.83	$13.86	$16.63
HS21	Holiday Stocking, 17", Green Lizard	$2.52	1	$0.00	$0.25	$2.77	$0.00	$5.95-$9.95	$5.95-$7.95	$0.00	$0.00	$0.00	$4.15	$5.54	$8.52	$11.83	$13.86	$16.63
HS22	Holiday Stocking, 17", Poly Dawk	$2.52	1	$0.00	$0.25	$2.77	$0.00	$5.95-$9.95	$5.95-$7.95	$0.00	$0.00	$0.00	$4.15	$5.54	$8.52	$11.83	$13.86	$16.63
HS23	Holiday Stocking, 17", Gaming Cloth	$2.52	1	$0.00	$0.25	$2.77	$0.00	$5.95-$9.95	$5.95-$7.95	$0.00	$0.00	$0.00	$4.15	$5.54	$8.52	$11.83	$13.86	$16.63
	TOTALS FOR THIS PAGE ONLY:	$0.00		$0.00							$0.00	$0.00						
	GRAND TOTAL FOR ALL PAGES	$0.00		$0.00							$0.00	$0.00						

Page 1 of the Pricing Spreadsheet from Condé.

others must be determined by perceived value vs. how difficult they are to make or what a particular market might be. Still others hold a potential for 600% markups and more but are too often delegated to a mere shadow of what they should be just because dealers don't understand the real costs involved, nor choose to take advantage of these huge profit makers when they have the chance.

Until recently, sublimators have been left to their own resources in this matter. Condé offers a resource to help dealers determine a framework of prices. These are not intended to be "set prices" but do provide dealers with information about what others might be charging for a product or service so they can determine what works for them, their locality, and their customers. The spread sheet is available free from the Condé website.

Once downloaded, you can do anything you wish with it, change it, edit it, etc. no problem. If this doesn't meet your needs, let us know and we will give it another try.

PART ONE
SECTION 21

"Some people dream of success while others wake up and work." -Unknown

HELP FOR THE NON-DESIGNER

Are you good at Graphic Design? Probably not. Although a few sublimation companies have added professionally trained graphic designers to their staff, most of us neither have the money to hire a designer nor the ability to do much in the way of graphic design ourselves.

Yet, the sublimation world demands a lot of design work. Most of it you will learn by experimentation. It isn't all that difficult to design basic products or put a picture and a few words on a gift item. Occasionally, however, you will be called upon to design something that goes far beyond your skill or training. What then?

I consider myself a mechanic, not a designer. I could never come up with some of the beautiful designs I see coming from true designers. Yet I can copy just about anything I see, so that's what I do. I collect copies of the designs I really like and when I need to produce something, I borrow from my collection. Of course, I never cross the line into stealing copyrighted material, but the vast majority of graphic design is not licensed or copyrighted in any way. To those, I say, "Imitation is the greatest form of flattery".

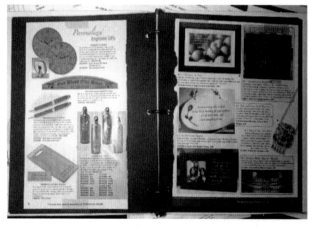

These ideas come from everywhere. Many come from mail order catalogs. Others from magazines or print ads. When I find something I like, I cut it out or photocopy it and place in a 3-ring binder for later reference. These designs pop up at the oddest places like a wall sign in a hotel or other business. I tend to find quite a few in tourist traps or antique stores – they are all around us – and although most designs are pretty blah, occasionally, there is a golden nugget. When that happens, I take a picture of it with my cell phone and file it away on my computer. I may never use it but then again, it might be just the ticket for some demanding client.

Sample of an "Idea Book". A 3-ring binder works fine. Just clip or photograph the ideas you run across and stick them

Another source for ideas is the Condé Systems website. There, they offer thousands of design elements you can purchase for very little (www.Condédesign.com) money. You can also pull up almost any product they sell and see what other people have done with it. Again, a treasure trove of ideas you can copy.

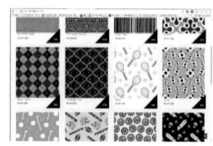

Hundreds of backgrounds available.

There used to be several CDs you could purchase called "Designs4U" made by the UNISUB people. These were an effort to help non-designers like me have a library of readymade designs at my fingertips. Although these are no longer being sold, Condé Systems has obtained permission to put these on their website and allow you to download them and use them royalty free. These are especially helpful when you are building your showroom. Rather than spend hundreds of hours coming up with mediocre designs for plaques, cups, etc., you can pick out designs from the Designs4U library, apply it to the product of your choice and build a showroom full of sublimated products in a fraction of the time it would take otherwise.

One of the original Designs 4 U packages.

Although expensive, there are many design and clipart packages you can purchase that work with sublimation. If you are a CorelDRAW user, you already have a collection of clipart. Granted, so far as sublimation is concerned, it seems like the clipart in the CorelDRAW packages has become less and less usable. Look around for old CorelDRAW clipart disks ranging from version 4 to 7 especially. These, in my opinion, have the best clipart and are often for sale on eBay for just a few dollars. All you care about is the Clipart disk and the Photo disk. The others are pretty much useless to you.

If you would like to learn more about designing, I recommend reading The Non-Designer's Design & Type Books by Robin Williams. It covers a wide range of topics but especially the use of typefaces in design, which is where I see many newcomers making mistakes. Of course, there are hundreds of books covering everything from color to type to hand lettering available from Amazon.com. Just type in "Graphic Design" to be overwhelmed.

Another source of education is YouTube. The "Beginners Guide to Graphic Design" offers 46 short videos about Graphic Design. Don't waste your time with all of them. Pick out the ones that involve topics you want to know more about.

PART ONE
SECTION 22

"Satisfied customers who spread word of mouth are the most valuable assets you have." -Andy Sernovitz

CREATIVESTUDIO

CreativeStudio is a Cloud based software program created by Sawgrass. The base version comes free with the purchase of any of the Sawgrass printers although you must go onto their website (www.sawgrassink.com) to register and obtain a password to access the program. With that, you can access the program along with your creations from any computer or notebook with an Internet connection.

The program was completely rewritten and released in late January 2020 and they continue to make modifications and upgrades on it.

This software works much like CorelDRAW or Illustrator but has been greatly simplified to eliminate all the features that do not apply to sublimation. It also includes the ability to actually create specific products that are pre-loaded into the program. This eliminates most of the sizing and engineering aspects to apply text or clipart to a product. The only thing you would normally have to import and manipulate are the photographs.

If you are not already familiar with a software program like CorelDRAW or Illustrator, I suggest you consider CreativeStudio to get started. As your business grows, you will likely need more sophisticated artwork capabilities that only Corel or Illustrator can afford, but in the beginning, CreativeStudio is a very powerful and relatively simple program to use.

There is a second level to Creative Studio that you might want to consider. This upgraded version costs $19.95 per month ($199.95 if paid annually). With the membership, you gain access to hundreds of readymade, royalty free designs and several additional features.

The working page in CreativeStudio.

74

PART ONE
SECTION 23

"If you do what you always did, you will get what you always got." -Anonymous

CONDÉ CLIENT GALLERY

One of my favorite features of our website is the Condé client gallery. This area is used by our clients to share photos of finished products. It is exciting for me to see the tremendous creativity of our clients, and in general, the amazing flexibility of sublimation decorating technology.

I suggest you visit this often to see what folks are doing and I strongly recommend you contribute your creations to this area. We run a weekly contest to highlight some of the amazing contributions.

After someone contributes, we then place these images on the product page below the product they represent. So, if you are looking for mug ideas, for example, just navigate to the product page and click on "Gallery".

PART ONE
SECTION 24

Customer satisfaction is worthless. Customer loyalty is priceless." -Jeffrey Gitomer

CONDÉ DESIGN

Finding backgrounds and patterns suitable for making products can be a very time-consuming process. Even when you find something you like; it will likely be copyrighted and not legal to use.

Free clipart sites offer some of these but searching them out can be frustrating and even if you find something, downloading it can bring all kinds of software programs you don't want, not to mention viruses and a lifetime of pop-ups.

To help remedy this, Condé created "CondéDesign". This is a website inside the Condé.com website where you can quickly search for thousands of backgrounds and elements you can use royalty free. You just can't pass them on to anyone else in electronic form.

Thousands of designs available for download.

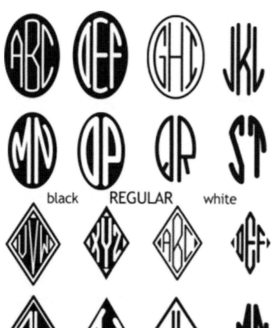

The Monogram Font is a must.

Some of the artwork is pre-shaped to fit cell phone covers or mugs but most are just backgrounds that cover most every sport, occasion, and holiday you can think of. Most can be disassembled in CorelDraw and the colors changed or elements moved or deleted.

Most images are $2.99 each. Some include multiple images and may run as much as $7.99. The best deal is the Monogram Font which you can download for $25.00. If you have ever tried to find a Monogram font to purchase, you have probably seen prices as high as $1,000! This one is a must-have.

PART ONE SECTION 25

*"Being able to touch so many people through my businesses,
and make money while doing it, is a huge blessing." -Magic Johnson*

DESIGNS 4 U

In the early days of inkjet sublimation, the UNISUB people produced a series of CDs with pre-sized artwork on them. Some was clipart and some professionally made bitmaps. Each disk carried a theme and included a photo manual of all the layouts which could be printed so customers could select what they wanted. All you had to do was call up the design and send it to the printer. Of course, there were places where you could insert text or modify the various elements to your customer's liking.

These CDs have long been discontinued but through a special arrangement with the folks at UNISUB, we have made the designs available to you for download from our website. These are available to anyone who purchases this book and can be found at www.thesublimationbook.com/resources. Although worth several hundred dollars when sold on disks, these layouts are free, curtesy of UNISUB and Condé Systems.

Here's how it works: Each "disk" has a base menu of about a dozen categories. Open any one of them and you will find a list of ready to print artwork you can open in CorelDRAW. In total, there are hundreds of designs and dozens of amazing photographs – all yours to use. The only restriction is you can't sell or distribute the images electronically. These are for *your* use only.

The "Base" or "Main Menu"

The "Sub-Menu:" lists the individual layouts.

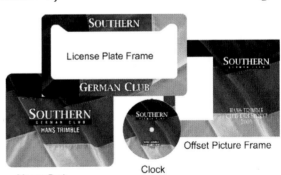

Four sample layouts from Designs 4 U.

PART ONE
SECTION 26

"All progress takes place outside the comfort zone." -Michael John Bobak

INTRODUCTION TO SUBLIMATION COLOR & COLOR MATCHING

Newcomers to the sublimation industry are often bewildered by the way we refer to color. Color is, of course, the heart of sublimation and it can be very tricky to get it right.

Over the years, those who have gone before you have figured out what works and what doesn't, and if you will spend a few minutes learning the do's and don'ts, you will find color to be an easy obstacle to master. The rules are few, but they are stringent. Breaking a rule almost always means throwing a product in the trash and starting over.

Understanding a little bit about "why" we do the things the way we do can help us keep the rules in mind and accept the reasons behind them, and in this chapter, I will try to explain, in a rudimentary way, what the rules are and the reasons for them.

Just some of the color pallet options available in CorelDraw.

The only color pallet we use with sublimation is RGB.

Color can be created, managed or manipulated in many different ways. In CorelDRAW alone, there are dozens of possible color formulas we can choose from. Newcomers are often enticed into using the Pantone™ color pallets. It just makes sense. If you want to match a Pantone™ color chart, you use a Pantone™ color pallet. Right? Wrong! It won't work. What you might end up with is a base color with thousands of tiny red dots in it. You might wind up with anything – who knows? What you won't wind up with is a usable color or a sellable product.

For our discussion, there are only two ways to mix colors. These are referred to as RGB and CMYK color pallets. When you first open CorelDRAW, the default color pallet on the right side of the screen is CMYK. The first thing you should do is change that to RGB. To do so, go to "Window › Color Pallet ›RGB". While you are there, unclick the CMYK so it won't confuse you later.

Just so you will know, the RGB pallet represents Red, Green and Blue while the CMYK pallet represents Cyan, Magenta, Yellow and Black.

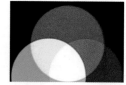

When color is created with light, it is done using three colors - RGB.

The primary difference between the two is that by using the RGB primary colors, we can obtain any one of millions of colors using light. This is why you so often see stage lighting in a theatre use a row of Red, Green and Blue lights over the Arch of the stage. You will notice there are no white lights. This is because they don't need them. When they turn on all the red, green and blue lights at the same time, they get a pure white light. When they begin to alter the intensity of any one of those colors, they begin to get shades of various colors. By combining two or more of the colors, they can get even more colors.

This is how your computer monitor works. In the screen of modern monitors, there are clusters of red, green and blue LEDs (or LEDs that can change to any one or combination of colors). By changing or combining these at different intensities, the monitor can reproduce millions of colors and shades of colors. When your eye sees these tiny clusters of three colors, the brain automatically combines them into a single speck of light. You can see this better illustrated by looking at a color LED billboard where the LEDs are large enough you can actually see them with the naked eye.

The sumation of this (what you need to know) is that all colored light is created using these three primary colors and any device that uses light, uses these same three colors.

CMYK colors on the other hand have to do with creating color using ink or paint. A few printers use only CMY (cyan, magenta and yellow), but for sublimation purposes, they all use CMYK.

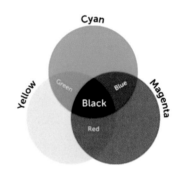

When color is applied through a printer, it is usually done using four colors - CMYK.

If we tried to mix RGB ink colors, we would only come up with a mess of unusable dark colors. Using CMYK colors, however, with ink or pigments of some kind, render a full pallet of colors on paper just like RGB does with light.

Now, here's the problem: How do we translate what you see on the computer screen to what you want to see on the finished product since the screen uses RGB and the printer uses CMYK? The simple answer is that we use some kind of a RIP (Raster Image Processor) to do the translation for us. These RIPs are sometimes sophisticated pieces of software written for specific applications such as those needed for wide-format printing but most often, for desktop printers we use a print driver. These drivers, usually created by the printer manufacturers, take what is sent from the computer and puts it in a language the printer can understand, namely, CMYK.

So, one would wonder, if we want to end up with CMYK, why don't we just start with that in the computer and keep things simple? Good question. but it won't work, and it won't keep things simple; it actually makes them much more complicated. Here's why: The communication that comes from any Windows computer to any printer comes out of the computer as RGB. Perhaps this is because in the early days of color monitors, no one thought there would ever be any color printers, but whatever the reason, that is the way it was years ago and that's the way it is today.

That being the case, if you create your artwork in CMYK, the computer has to translate that to RGB to send it out to the printer. The printer has to then convert it back to CMYK. That's three conversions from the program to the printer. If, however, you create your artwork in RGB, the computer doesn't have to do anything with it except send it out to the printer. The print driver then converts it to CMYK and prints it. One conversion, not three. See the reason? There is only one conversion, not three.

Over the years, Condé Systems and Sawgrass have both learned to develop some excellent print drivers. Sawgrass calls theirs PowerDriver. Condé just uses the stock print driver that comes with the Ricoh printers and adds what is called an ICC (International Color Consortium) profile to it that is customized to sublimation inks. Why not just use the print driver that comes with the printers? Another good question. The answer is that the print driver that comes with the printers is adjusted using an ICC profile made to match the ink colors in the manufacturer's standard inks, not sublimation inks. The colors of sublimation inks are different than those of standard inks and must be adjusted for with their own ICC profile. That's what Condé does with their profile and that's what Sawgrass does with PowerDriver.

A typical PowerDriver screen used for sublimation.

So, what have you really learned about sublimation color so far? Use the RGB pallet – always – without exception!

Now that we have that understood, let's go one step further and talk about how to get exactly the color you want – first time, every time.

One of the things you will quickly learn when you start actually making stuff is that what you see on the screen isn't what you see on the transfer paper and it isn't what you see on the finished product.

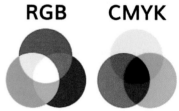

We don't care what the colors on the transfer paper looks like. That means nothing to us. Pay no attention to it. You can look at the transfer paper to be sure all the nozzles in your printer are working (blank lines indicate a non-functioning nozzle), but it doesn't tell us anything about colors.

When using light (monitor), red, green and blue are used. When using ink (printer), cyan, magenta, yellow and black are used.

The problem comes with the finished product. When the colors are wrong on the product, you have a problem but there is usually an easy fix.

When working with artwork, there are two types of art: Vector art and bitmaps, sometimes called raster.

Bitmaps are easy to understand. They are photographs or various kinds of artwork that has been converted to a bitmap. You can know a bitmap by the fact you can't ungroup it or take it apart. It is a single element. These elements should print pretty close to the right colors right off the bat. The print driver you use for sublimation likes bitmaps and it does a good job interrupting them. Changing the colors within a bitmap can be done but it requires special software such as PhotoPaint or PhotoShop and is fairly involved. We'll save that for another time.

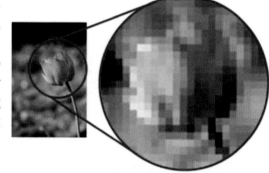

Bitmaps pixelate when enlarged. A vector image retains its quality when enlarged. Image by WordPress.

Vector art on the other hand, is art you (or someone) has created in CorelDRAW or another graphics program that is made up of lines, shapes, text and other elements that you can control by selecting them, grouping or ungrouping them, moving them around, etc. This also means you can add or change the colors used easily and that is where the rub is. For instance, if you want a bright red, you naturally select the bright red from the pallet on the right-hand side of your screen. Unfortunately, what looks like bright red on the screen but may or may not look like bright red on the finished product. What went wrong?

Remember all the talk we did about RGB conversions to CMYK? Well, that's part of it. The other part is the fact that any color produced by light is going to look different when produced with ink. They may be close, but they will be different.

There is a simple solution to this, however. On the Condé website, there are color charts you can download for free and print on the various substrates you work with. Once this is done, you can know with confidence that anytime you call up a color on your color chart and insert it into a vector drawing, that is the color that will result on the finished product. Some color charts are short and fit on one page while others are very extensive. There are also ways to create your own color chart in Corel.

If you need to match a color? Go to the color chart for that substrate, find the color and insert it in your drawing. It is both simple yet one of the hardest things for some sublimators to accept. They always want to guess at the color, but you cannot guess at sublimated colors from a computer screen.

What about monitors that can be adjusted to match a printer? There are such animals and I have experimented with them. Some use "magic eyes" to view your monitor's output, some use software but here is the thing: no matter how accurate you get your monitor, changing one thing such as brightness, changes everything. For me, it just wasn't worth the trouble; especially when such a simple solution as color charts works so well.

So, what have we learned?

One: Only use the RGB color pallet in CorelDRAW.

Two: Always use a sublimated color chart to select or match colors.

COLOR MATCHING

Some people work for hours trying to match a spot color. It isn't that hard. Infact, if you use this method is a piece of cake.

How do you match a school color? What about a pantone color? This is perhaps the most common question we are asked. Most folks try to match the color by comparing it with what is on the monitor. Some even invest in fancy matching devices that attach to the monitor or buy expensive monitors that claim to be accurate. That's crazy. Just walk into any big box store and look at the flat screen TV's. No two look alike. So matching colors with your monitor just does not work.

Here is the solution:

From the graphics program you design (like CorelDRAW), print and transfer a color chart that paints color swatches. (We can help you create your own color chart or provide one for you.) Once you have the file, sublimate it onto whatever kind of substrate you want to work with and then find the color you need and note its position on the color chart (Page 2, row 4 and column 7 for instance). Reopen the color chart in your graphics program and go to that location and select that color. You then design with that color in your artwork. That's it! There is a variety of color charts already made and waiting for you to download them from www.Condé.com – everything from simple charts with fifty or so colors to a complete chart that has 27 pages of colors!

27 Page color chart.

PART ONE
SECTION 27

"If opportunity doesn't knock, build a door."   *-Milton Berle*

VECTOR VS. RASTER GRAPHICS

There are two types of "graphics" we work with: Vector and Raster. It is important you understand the difference and how to work with each.

Vector graphics are usually line drawings. They may be very complex and may even be filled with color but basically, they are a group of lines that you can manipulate in CorelDRAW or some other graphics program.

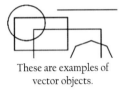

When taken into CorelDRAW, you can move the lines around, shorten them, change the arc of them, change the color and so on. You have total control over the drawing.

These are examples of vector objects.

The great advantage of a vector drawing is that it can be enlarged or reduced at will with no restriction. Whether it is one-inch square or one hundred feet square makes no difference to the art. It will remain just as sharp and crisp at one extreme as the other. It also requires far less memory than a raster image of the same size. Most vector images can be measured in kilobytes while a raster image might easily be measured in megabytes or even terabytes for very large murals. Needless to say, it takes a lot of computing power to handle large raster images than it does a vector image.

A raster graphic is also referred to as a bitmap. A bitmap can look like almost anything, even a line drawing, but when imported into CorelDRAW, you cannot manipulate the individual elements of the image – everything is locked together and cannot be unlocked. When you look closely at a raster image, you will see it is not made up of lines (even if it looks like a line drawing) but of individual pixels referred to as "dots". On a computer screen, pixels are always square; when printed on paper, they are round. The combination of many dots or pixels, make up an image. Each dot is some variation of dark or light or of some color which is referred to as "shades". By combining hundreds or thousands or tens of thousands of these dots, we begin to see a picture appear on the computer screen.

Although this looks like a bitmap, it is actually a line (vector) drawing.

This is a high-resolution bitmap.

Obviously, this type of image is an illusion. Unlike a true photograph where the image is captured on a piece of film, a digital image is just a series of dots or pixels that trick our brain into thinking we see a picture.

It is important to understand the difference because the manner in which we work with these two types of images is drastically different. Vector drawings give us total control and can be changed in any way we want using CorelDRAW or Adobe Illustrator. These drawings can even be turned into a raster (bitmap) image but doing so, will eliminate our ability to make changes as we could before. Bitmap (raster) images cannot not however, be changes into vector images. Once a bitmap, always a bitmap.

This is an example of a low-resolution bitmap.

Bitmap images are manipulated in either special photographic software such as PhotoPaint, PhotoShop, PhotoShop Essentials (a simpler version of PhotoShop), Lightroom or ON1. You have probably heard the phrase, "Photo-shopping an image". This is where that comes from. It is common for people in the art departments of magazines to "PhotoShop" an image by removing flaws, wrinkles, etc. Those who are really good at it can change a person's body type, face or expression. For our purposes, these programs are used more for removing flaws such as power lines or scratches in the original image.

To do this, many specialized "tools" are used including brushes and magic wands and fills which are all found in any of the bitmap modification programs such as those listed above.

Learning one of these programs takes considerably more time than it takes to master CorelDRAW so many in our industry only learn the bare bones of the program – just enough to get along – and that's fine. You can always learn something new when you need it and since there are literally thousands of commands in these programs with more being added daily, it only makes sense to learn as you go.

One of the keys to understanding bitmap images is to understand "resolution". Resolution is simply the number of pixels or dots per inch in an image. Vector art has no resolution since it can be expanded or reduced without limits, but bitmaps will "fall apart" if they are enlarged too much. We will cover this in greater detail later in the book.

"I don't look to jump over seven-foot bars – I look for one-foot bars that I can step over."
-Warren Buffett

CREATE A SUBLIMATION JOURNAL

Mr. Buffett is saying (see quote above), to take small steps that you can accomplish rather than try to do the impossible. The same is true with sublimation. That's what the "Sublimation Journal" is all about.

When you run into a problem, either with your printer, color management or a substrate, and call for help, it is important that you can give an accurate account of what you have done to get you to this point. What temperatures have you tried, what pressures, what times? Did you print the item face up or face down? Did you use Teflon sheets or butcher paper as a cover? How old are your inks?

Usually, when something goes wrong and you can't figure it out on your own, it is because two or more things are working in concert with each other. If you can tell the technician the facts of what you have been doing, chances are, they can get you back on the right road in a matter of minutes. If you have to guess or try to remember what you tried and didn't try, then the technician also has to guess as to what the problem might be.

Recording what you do with each job; time, temperature, pressure, etc., will help paint a clear picture of what is going on for the technician and will usually make a diagnosis obvious to someone with a lot more experience.

Just jot down the facts in a notebook each time you do a job. If the job came out alright, as it usually will, this is quick and easy. When things don't work out the way they should, take detailed notes of everything you do, from computer to finished product. Ultimately, this will save you a ton of time and trouble (and money). Plus, as you gain experience, it will help you diagnose your own problems and fix them without depending on someone else.

PART ONE
SECTION 29

*"Success does not consist of never making blunders,
but in never making the same one a second time."*   *-Josh Billings*

CREATE YOUR WALL OF SHAME

What on earth is a Wall of Shame? And why would anyone want one?
It's simple to make, just find a small area around your heat press where you can hang your blunders. It is a great way to spark your memory, so you don't make the same mistake again.

We all make mistakes especially when learning new things. I think the trick is to minimize repeating the same mistake over and over again. Trish Lambert taught me this trick: When you make a mistake like transferring something upside down, post your mistake prominently near your heat press (for mistakes made at the press) or computer (for mistakes made at the computer) to remind you not to repeat your mistake.

That wall of products in the background of all the CondéTV videos is made up of their mistakes. It is their Wall of Shame!

Many of us too often hide our mistakes and really don't learn from them. We must understand what went wrong and how to prevent it from happening again. So, after a mistake, I document my mistake in my sublimation journal (See Part One, Section 32) and then try to understand how to prevent it from happening in the future. If we push our mistakes out of mind quickly, I think we are doomed to repeat them or even worse, to give up.

So, the tip here is simple, learn from our mistakes. If you do not understand what went wrong, pick up the phone and call us. In almost all cases, you will not have been the first person to make that mistake! And once understood, post your mistake to your Wall of Shame.

Even the best of us blow it from time to time.

A square plaque looks the same no matter how you print it but if you print it upside down, it won't be easy to hang!

86

PART TWO
SECTION 1

INTRODUCTION TO PART II – THE PRODUCTS

As we continue our journey into the world of sublimation, we come to place where we have to stop talking and start doing. This section is all about the products we make and how we make them.

Unlike the days when I started in sublimation; when we had no more than a dozen products to decorate and sell (and those didn't work very well), we now have a thousand or more different products and hundreds of variations of some of those.

When I started, we had a shirt. It didn't sublimate very well because it was 20% cotton (sublimation doesn't like cotton) and we had a cup and a cup press, but we had no way of making full-color transfers. The only way we could get two colors on a cup was to cook them twice and that never worked out well.

Now, after generations of printers, inks and lots of mistakes, we have a system that is as close to foolproof as one can get with beautiful full-color images that dazzle the eye for only pennies.

In the early days, the equipment was crude and super expensive ($14,000 in 1990 money) and capabilities were limited, but people wanted color – any kind of color – and they were willing to pay dearly for it. Today, they still want color but today's audience expects quality as well, and if you will take some time to practice a little, and partner up with a good supplier (like Condé), who will support you and help you when things go wrong, you can be assured of success.

Sublimation is a wonderful science and a fantastic business to be in. I have products I actually make a 95% profit on some orders that can reach into the thousands of dollars on a regular basis. You may not find that kind of success, especially at first, but you can easily clear 50% and even 66% profit on most of the products you sell.

Turn the page and let's learn how...

PART TWO
SECTION 2

"The golden rule for every businessman is this: Put yourself in your customer's place."
-Orison Swett Marden

BUILDING A SUBLIMATION SANDWICH

Once you have printed your sublimation transfer, it's time to decorate your substrate. I call this next step "building our sublimation sandwich" because we need to stack things in a particular order to be successful.

One interesting note first: After all these years and countless pressing, there is often more than one way to do things. So, don't freak out if you are told or read a different set of instructions for a given substrate, because we are tuning and updating our instructions and videos every day in an effort to provide you with the best techniques. Often our instructions will change due to changes in the substrate or its coating.

Where can you find our instructions? If you go to our website (www.Condé.com) and find the product in question, there will be a few tabs under the product. These tabs are very important and contain our templates, video and written instructions. Feel free to watch our videos but use our written instructions for actual details, as videos generally don't contain exact details.

Also, this is a great time to begin your sublimation diary. A diary is perhaps to best way to stay on the road to sublimation success! I document my successes, failures and questions. It is also an excellent learning tool to share with an employee that you are training.

STEP ONE: Secure the Transfer to the Substrate:

There are six steps that are important when pressing a product:

1. Build the sublimation sandwich
2. Check the time, temperature and amount of pressure being used
3. Place it in the heat press and close the press
4. Open the heat press when time is up
5. Remove the substrate
6. Cool the substrate

Once the transfer and the substrate are positioned together, we must be careful that there is no movement. If it moves during the first step then we could sublimate on the wrong spot. If it moves when opening the heat press then we will see a shadow transfer. Once we open the heat press, we must remove the transfer by lifting instead of sliding either the substrate or transfer. If they slide, this will cause a shadow image as there is still active sublimation occurring.

For those who are familiar with t-shirt transfer paper, you know that after pressing you peel the transfer off the shirt. The paper is stuck to the shirt and effort is required to peel. This is not the case with sublimation. There is nothing sticky about the paper. This is why we must anchor the transfer paper to the substrate.

There are three ways to secure the transfer to the substrate. The best method will depend on the substrate.

Method 1: Heat Tape

Using heat tape, secure the transfer to the substrate in more than one place. Heat tape often is the best choice for hard substrates like Unisub Plaques. See our instructions and videos for detailed instructions. For instance, with Unisub plaques, we must never place our tape on the edge of the plaque as this will destroy the foil edge. Instead, we place our tape on back of the plaque.

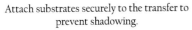

After pressing is complete, we need to separate the two. I prefer to do this while the substrate is still hot. We must separate the two without sliding the transfer or substrate as this will cause a shadow image to form as there is still some sublimation ink active. Instead, we must lift the transfer away from the substrate quickly. Using a "heat glove", available online or at many hardware stores, can make this a lot easier. Be sure to get one (or two) that are really flexible and easy to get on and off. Most gloves are good for up to 450° to 500° F.

Heat tape comes in red, green and clear. I recommend the clear.

Attach substrates securely to the transfer to prevent shadowing.

Method 2: Pro Spray

For soft substrates like shirts and mouse pads, heat tape turns out to be a poor solution for many reasons. I recommend putting a _light_ mist of DyeTrans Pro Spray on the printed side of the transfer. Pro Spray is a tack spray that if done correctly will not interfere with the sublimation process. This method is required for pressing double sided materials such as bag tags, as heat tape can leave a mark on the substrate. Because the nozzles on these cans like to clog, I recommend you always keep an extra can around – just in case.

It's a good idea to use Pro Spray over a trash can or empty box.

Because you are likely to get some over-spray when applying Pro Spray, we suggest you always spray it over a trash can or empty box so the adhesive doesn't get on your floors or work area.

Method 3: The Paper Weight Method

I do not recommend this method to newbies. For experienced folks, we can often use tricks such as gravity to hold things together. For example, when pressing name badges, we can place our transfer face up with the name badge face down. Since the name badge has some weight, it will act as a paper weight during the transfer. So, if we are careful not to bump the press during closing and opening, we can use this method. Doing it this way also saves considerable setup and removal time since no heat tape is handled. This method works best for substrates that can go on the top of the transfer.

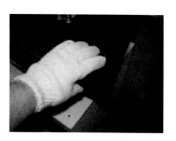

Always use a heat glove when working with glass, tile or other materials that hold heat for a long time.

In the case of glass cutting boards and ceramic tiles (where the transfer is on the bottom and the product on top), the weight of the product will work quite well holding the transfer in place. Just don't be too anxious to pick up the tile or glass product after opening the press. Give it a few minutes to cool and then pick it straight up leaving the transfer embedded in the pad below. Moving the tile sideways or twisting it as you pick it up, may cause ghosting. Remember these products hold heat for a long time and the sublimation process can continue long after you open the press.

The secret to this method is being able to open and close the press in stealth mode. That is, without moving the transfer or the product. It isn't hard, just go slow. Easy does it!

Cooking the Sublimation Sandwich

Our final step in the sublimation process is to cook our sublimation sandwich. This is the step that causes the ink on the paper to turn into a gas and permeate into the pores of our substrate.

There are four variables in this process. They are time, temperature, pressure and technique. This process is quite similar to cooking food and is easy to master.

1. Temperature: Most sublimation decorating is done at 400 degrees F. You should refer to our instructions for our recommendation.
2. Time: Just like cooking, time is required to complete the sublimation process. Time is dependent on a few variables:
3. The substrate we are decorating. The size of the substrate or the number we are pressing. Sort of like a bigger pot takes longer than a smaller one.
4. The heat output of our press. Do we have a big burner or a small burner?
5. Pressure: We work with three general amounts of pressure. These usually aren't critical so long as you are in the ballpark. They are light, medium and heavy. Here's how you judge them:

Light: This is usually reserved for fabric. Too much pressure with fabric can cause a permanent crease in the material. To adjust this level of pressure, you should be able to open and close the press with almost no effort. If you are using a sublimation pillow, try to compress the pillow about 50%. Too much pressure and the pillow won't be able to do its job. If you have a pneumatic press, it will be 15-20 psi.

Medium: This is considerably more pressure than the light. Most people can open and close the press with one hand and some effort to obtain medium pressure. If you have a pneumatic press, it should be about 40 psi.

Heavy: Obtaining heavy pressure usually requires using both hands and considerable effort to open and close the press. Usually when using heavy pressure, there is either a rubber pad or Nomex pads so the substrate is cushioned by the various pads. This is usually reserved for glass and ceramic products.

Technique: Technique can be everything. The way you open and close the press can mean the difference between perfection and disaster. Always open and close the press as gently as possible. When opening the press, lift up until the press just sits slightly above the substrate, then open it completely. Opening too fast may cause the transfer and substrate to move, which causes ghosting. Go slow and easy, especially when opening the press.

New folks will read our instructions and assume that this is the gospel. Well, they're not. It's a great starting point. Your actual equipment will vary some so just like cooking, your stove and microwave require you to tune your instructions based on experience; hence the need to document what happens when you sublimate – even if everything works as it should.

Time and pressure are the two most common variables since almost everything is made with 400° F of heat.

When you know the time is right: Our instructions will give you a starting point of how long to press. One tip is to print a solid black transfer and press each new substrate. Black is the last color to sublimate, so if you get a deep rich black that is consistent across the face of the substrate, then you are dialed in! If you press too long, usually the black will have a brownish tone. Just like cooking, if you have a larger amount of food, you will need to increase your cooking time. If you have unusually large or multiple pieces being pressed at once, you will need to increase the press time. Metal, FRP and other thin products usually don't require an increase in time, but thicker items (plaques, tiles glass, etc.) certainly do.

When you know the pressure is right: If you remove a product after the appointed time and there are areas that are washed out or not sublimated, it is probably too little pressure. If the transfer isn't pressed tightly against the substrate, the dyes won't transfer. Increase the pressure and try again.

Are you sure the temperature is right? The only way to be sure the temperature reading on your thermometer is correct is to test it. It isn't uncommon for the temperature readout and the actual temperature to be different. There are two ways to accurately confirm the temperature is correct.

PART TWO
SECTION 3

"If you don't ask, the answer will always be NO!". -unknown

PRODUCTION JIGS

As your sublimation business grows, hopefully you will be faced with volume orders of products such as dog tags, luggage tags, pet tags, coasters and so forth. To help speed up production, you will likely want to check out the various product jigs that allow for easier bulk sublimation.

Some jigs like this one are specific for a single product or at least a specific size product.

These jigs are particularly helpful for double sided metal objects such as pet tags as the jig allows sublimation to both sides at the same time. Instructions for using these jigs are available on CondéTV.

There are currently 27 jigs available. Check our website for a complete listing.

Jigs that allow for two-sided printing can also be used for single-sided printing.

Some jigs come apart to accommodate two-sided printing such as this pet tag jig.

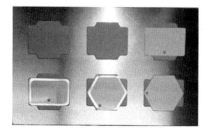

Some jigs are cut to accommodate several products like this one that can hold multiple Unisub ornaments.

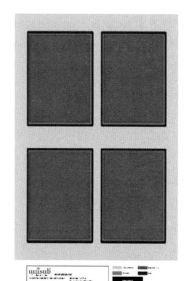

Each jig comes with a downloadable template like this one that can be imported into Corel or other programs to make alignment a snap.

PART TWO
SECTION 4

"Be undeniably good. No marketing effort or social media buzzword can be a substitute for that."
-Anthony Volodkin

USING TEMPLATES

So, what is a template anyway and why do I need them? Good question. Templates are patterns you can use to create your products without having to guess at how big they are or without concern about their odd shapes.

Templates are available for most all products and you can find them in multiple places but the easiest source is the Condé website (www.Condé.com). Select the product you want to decorate, and you will find several tabs below the product description. One of those will be "Template". The templates are available in several formats including CorelDRAW (CDR), Portable Document Format (PDF), PhotoShop (PSD), and Adobe Illustrator (AI).

All you have to do is download the template you want into the graphics program you are using.

Not all the templates you run across will be made the same. The two most common designs are shown below, but first, you must learn to unzip the files as most, if not all, templates will come to you as a zip file. If you don't have Unzip already, you might want to purchase it or find a free version like www.unzipper.com. As you can see in the illustration, this Condé file came in with four different formats at the same time. You only need to unzip the one you want.

Condé templates will come in as a single line template. The line assumes you want to use a full-bleed background and if you PowerClip your background, photo, etc. into the outline provided, you will have an easy to manage full-bleed product. Just remember not to resize the template or it won't work at all. For safety, I always delete the outline(s) just before I print the layout.

Some templates, like those from UNISUB, look a bit different as they come in with two or three different color outlines. These also come in as a zip file so they will have to be unzipped.

With this type of template, you have several choices. First, if you are going to leave the product white and only add text or images inside the product, you can use the inner most pattern (magenta) and even go all the way up to the edge with text or art since the template automatically insures you have a reasonable border around your design – that's the purpose for the green line. It is a safety zone and you would not want to trespass into that with a design.

If you want to do a full-bleed background you must work with the blue outside border. It will give you enough image outside the product to insure everything is covered without wasting a lot of ink or making it difficult to position the product.

You may occasionally need to make your own template and that is easy as well. Just take the product you are going to imprint and lay it on a sheet of copy paper. With a fine point pen, trace an outline of the product onto the paper. Next, place the paper in your scanner and scan it into your graphics program. Be sure to import it at a 1:1 ratio and then double check it before creating your design. Next, using your drawing tools, create a vector line (that you can actually use), around the scan and delete the scanned image. You can also use CorelTRACE. TRACE doesn't always create an accurate enough image for my taste. Don't forget to delete the traced image before printing it.

PART TWO
SECTION 5

"Success is not final; failure is not fatal; It is the courage to continue that counts."
-Winston Churchill

A GUIDE TO "BASE MATERIALS"

The majority of substrates are made from tried-and-true base materials such as ceramic, slate, glass, aluminum and polyester fabric. Specific products and product families are created by making/cutting the base materials into the appropriate size and shape. Digital decorators can also fabricate their own products from these materials with the right tools and know-how. Some base materials are inherently sublimatable such as polyester fabric and plastics. Ceramic, slate, glass and aluminum, however, need a special coating to accept the transferred image—not just any mug or piece of glass will sublimate!

Substrate is just a fancy word for the thing or object we decorate using the sublimation process. There are now thousands of different products to decorate. Our website: www.dyetrans.com is a good source to see what is available. New products are added to the list almost every day.

Substrates must have three characteristics that allow them to be part of our list.

They must handle the heat of sublimation decorating without self-destruction. This means they must be made of materials that don't melt or deform when heated to 400 degrees F.

They must be white or light colored. Sublimation dyes are relatively transparent and rely on the white to reflect the light through the dyes. If the substrate is black or dark colored, very little light is reflected through the dyes, producing a poor appearance. If the substrate is light colored, only light waves of the color of the substrate are reflected, causing the sublimation to lose some of its color. See my colored shirts video for a visual of this.

The substrate must be made of or coated with an oil loving molecule such as polyester. See my section on how sublimation works (Part One, Section One).

With all that said, folks like me and many others, try to break the apparent laws of physics on a daily basis. For example, the Siser transfer material will allow you to sublimate to it and then heat apply it to almost any fabric, including 100% cotton. This opens the door for you to offer a much wider variety of shirts with a much wider price range.

The excitement for me is how sublimation is growing because of all the things we now have and the many new items we will have!

To bring this point home, I love to tell the following fictional story in my classes. Now remember that I am an Electrical Engineer. The story goes something like this:

Imagine you are a reporter back in the days of Thomas Edison and had the opportunity to visit him at his lab in Menlo Park with our fellow journalism professionals. Each of you is trying to get a scoop on what Tom is working on. At this point Mr. Edison has just rolled out the electric light. So you start the questions by expressing the excitement of his new bulb but then ask: I know you have a lot of excitement of your new electrical inventions, but what's the next exciting thing you are working on after electricity?

Tom would look at you in disbelief and say: We have barely touched the surface of what we can accomplish with the power of electricity. I cannot possible see or imagine the amazing new uses that we will see for electricity in the future! Think of computers, space craft, satellites, smart phones and so much more! Well, that's how I think of sublimation and its future. It is such a low cost easy decorating method to produce high value photo quality products in minutes!

Now let's explore base substrates. These are the building blocks for our products.

The majority of substrates are made from tried-and-true base materials such as ceramic, slate, glass, aluminum and polyester fabric.

Specific products and product families are created by making/cutting the base materials into the appropriate size and shape. Digital decorators can also fabricate their own products from these materials with the right tools and know-how. Some base materials are inherently sublimatable such as polyester fabric and some plastics. Ceramic, slate, glass and aluminum, however, need a special coating to accept the transferred image—not just any mug or piece of glass will sublimate!

Each of those products is made from a base sublimation substrate. This is an important concept because it allows you to better understand the possibilities and to move beyond existing products to create new, unique ones. For example, our DyeFlex material which is used to make lots of products like our Lace Face, could be fabricated into a key tag or business card.

Most base substrates, like metal, Unisub FRP or Unisub hardboard come in large sheets that can be fabricated into smaller pieces using a laser, shear or overhead router. This means that you have three choices:

> 1. Buy existing fabricated products like an FRP name badge,
>
> 2. Using sheet stock, fabricate your own products.
>
> 3. Get us to custom cut products for you.

This is really exciting because it puts you in the driver's seat with growing your business with existing or custom products.

HERE ARE THE BASE SUBSTRATES

Fiberglass Reinforced Plastic (FRP)

An extremely popular material, FRP (Fiberglass Reinforced Plastic) is a thick, lightweight, and a strong polymer material made popular by the folks at Unisub. This white sheet material, available single- or double-sided, is cut into a large variety of products such as name badges, bag tags, coasters, door hangers, key chains, holiday ornaments, and more.

Hardboard (High Density Fiberboard often referred to as Masonite)

Hardboard is an engineered wood product that, for sublimation purposes, has a white coating applied to one or both sides to create a variety of products, including coasters, clocks, message boards and clipboards .

Medium Density Fiberboard (MDF).

Also an engineered wood product, MDF is thicker than hardboard and typically has a pre-finished edge that makes imaged photo panels, picture frames, award plaques and indoor signage look great.

Aluminum.

Aluminum is an extremely popular base material that is coated in large sheets or directly from the coil of

metal. It is available in white, clear (silver), or gold flat sheet stock and is cut into a large variety of shapes and sizes with a router or guillotine cutter. Aluminum can also be punched, bent and even wrapped! Popular brand name coatings include Dynasub, Unisub and ChromaLuxe. Products include water bottles and a ginormous number of cut products such as photo panels, name badges, bag tags, license plates, holiday ornaments, dog tags, bookmarks, interior signage, and iPhone/device cover inserts.

Ceramic Products.

Ceramic products are made from clay that's usually fired with a glass coating in a kiln. Once fired, a sublimation coating is applied and then cured at a much lower temperature than a kiln. Examples include decorative tiles, holiday ornaments, decorative plates, mugs and steins.

Slate.

Slate produces elegant photo gifts but has become quite popular the last few years as a plaque product. Made of metamorphic rock, it is cut to shape, sanded, the edges individually fractured, and a white sublimation coating applied to the image area. Available in a large variety of sizes and shapes, no two pieces are exactly the same.

Glass.

COLORLYTE

Glass is usually coated with a white and a clear layer on the back side and viewed from the uncoated front side. Since sublimation dyes are relatively transparent, the white coating on the glass is used to reflect light from the viewing side. One product, glass floor tiles can be sublimated and installed with the coated/imaged side down, thus protecting the image from abrasion and wearing away due to foot traffic. Examples include decorative floor tiles, cutting boards, photo panels, award plaques and drinkware. A new coating has been developed for Solapix glass products that produces outstanding results without the additional white layer.

Steel.

Steel, similar to aluminum but not as popular, is used for light-switch plates, travel mugs, water bottles and cut products such as magnetic dry erase boards.

Plastics.

Many different products from poker chips to plastic mugs. Plastic-like materials include our poker chips, DyeFlex and FRP (fiberglass reinforced plastic).

Mousepad/Neoprene Material.

Created by adhering inherently sublimatable polyester fabric to a rubber-type base, this material can be easily cut and/or formed into mousepads, coasters, counter mats, drink huggers, game boards, or exercise mats. It is available in a variety of thicknesses including 1/16", 1/8", ¼", ½" and 1".

Fabrics.

For sublimation dyes to work, the chosen fabric must be synthetic. Of all the available synthetic fabrics, polyester is by far superior. Close cousins (e.g., nylon) can be used, but the results won't match those of polyester. Further, 100% polyester fabric is a must—blended fabric such as 50% cotton/50% polyester will produce a faded or burned-out look that is generally unacceptable. The great news is that there are many different types of polyester material used to make T-shirts, bandanas, pennants, flags, holiday stockings, tote bags, hair ribbons, and more! Polyester shirts are now the rage as they have become more cotton-like and are sometimes treated with moisture trans- port packages that keep your skin cooler and drier than cotton.

Wood.

Wood is new to the list. UNISUB has introduced a line of sublimatable wood items include name badges, bag tags, etc. They have also introduced wood floor tiles. These 12x12" or 12x18" tiles can be sublimated and then interlocked together to create floor logos or whatever other graphics a customer might want.

Unisub Wood photo panel and bag tags.

Acrylic.

Acrylic has always been a challenge for sublimators because of its low melting temperature but Condé has developed a line of acrylic products that work great and look great. Coasters and ornaments are especially popular.

Ornament (LEFT) and coasters (RIGHT & CENTER).

DyeFlex Plastic.

Since the beginning of my sublimation journey, digital decorators have asked for a thin sublimatable plastic similar to a credit card. This new product is quite thin and can be laser cut for applications such as device cover inserts. It can also be cut with scissors, X-Acto knife or shear. It has a slight matte finish and renders amazing color and clarity.

Available in 12x24" sheets.

PART TWO
SECTION 6

"Statistics suggest that when customers complain, business owners and managers ought to get excited about it. The complaining customer represents a huge opportunity for more business." -Zig Ziglar

DECORATING HARD SUBSTRATES

There really aren't many affordable ways to decorate hard substrates in full color. There is laser engraving and rotary engraving, of course, and they can do splash or spot color by adding a colored background or a self-adhesive film but when it comes to full color, the choices are very limited.

UV LED Printers: In recent years, the rage has been focused on UV flattop printers. These range in size from paper size to 24"x36" and then huge $100,000 - $500,000 printers that can be as large as 4'x8'. Even the small desktop printers are expensive. The smallest on the market starts about $12,000 and the more common 11"x24" printers start about $60,000 and quickly go up into the high hundred-thousand-dollar range.

Direct Color Systems UV LED Printer.

One of the biggest pieces of misinformation is that an image printed whose ink is cured with UV light, will produce a UV safe image. Although a couple of manufactures boost of a UV stable ink, most are not. In fact, the more popular inks do far worse outdoors than sublimation!

These printers actually use an Epson print system to do the work along with a manufactured gantry system to move the substrate back and forth under the printheads.

Resolution is excellent when adjusted properly but, in my opinion, is not as good as sublimation.

UV LED printers are fairly fast. Print speeds vary depending on the manufacturer, but none compare to the ability to print a 16"x20" panel in about two minutes which is what it takes for sublimation.

One ability most UV printers have is that they can print white. This can be used as an undercoat to print color on dark colors, including black and clear acrylic. Multiple layers can be built up to produce a 3D effect suitable for making ADA interior signage.

George Knight DK20s Heat Press.

Sublimation: Sublimation or digital imprinting, can produce high resolution full-color images on any substrate that has been specially coated to accept the sublimation dyes. The actual image rests under the top layer of coating and depending on the coating, is almost indestructible. Even a knife has trouble scratching the UNISUB coating making it ideal for making signs, key chains, tags and labels.

Sublimation itself is not UV stable. This means that over a relatively short period of time, it will fade when left in direct sunlight. The coating most commonly used to make sublimation blanks, however, has special UV inhibitor molecules in it to lengthen the time it can withstand UV to 12-18 months. This is far superior to just about everything except vinyl. This allows things like license plates to withstand exterior application for an acceptable period of time.

To give you an idea how common sublimation is, note the next hotel room you stay in. The carpet, bed linen and drapes will probably all match. The reason? They were all sublimated. Your car interior and most of your clothes were all sublimated. Through a process called "dipping", odd shaped items such as rifle stocks

Ceramic mugs are one of the most common sublimated products.

are sublimated. I even saw a motorcycle "printed" in this way. If it is a synthetic fabric, it probably started out white and was sublimated. Swimsuits are all sublimated. Even glass floor tiles are sublimated to look like marble or stone. Sublimation is everywhere.

One of the great values of sublimation is that the initial investment is so low. A printer, heat press, some paper and ink and you're in business. Total cost can be under $2,000 for a first-class system. No other business opportunity I know of comes anywhere close to matching that entry price. Most start about $10,000 and quickly go up.

The hard substrates most commonly imprinted with sublimation or UV include: Metal, wood, plastic, glass, ceramic and porcelain. With sublimation, all these are possible although they do have to be specially coated. In the world of metal, aluminum and brass are the alternatives and they come in many sizes and grades. Wood is usually in the form of MDF board which is used for plaques, signs, clocks and other products. It also comes in the form of hardboard which is used for coasters, clipboards and signs. Plastic is in two forms: FRP used in key chains, bag tags and a host of other small items and DyeFlex which is used for guitar picks and the backs to most phone covers. Glass is used for cutting boards and tiles while ceramic is used for cups, mugs, and tiles. Porcelain is used for Christmas ornaments and tiles. Rubber, which is covered with fabric, is used for mousepads.

One of the things you can do with metal is create a huge variety of plaques and other awards.

PART TWO
SECTION 7

"Nothing is impossible. Even the word says, 'I'm possible'." -Audrey Hepburn

WORKING WITH METAL

Metal is a mainstay in the sublimation industry. Almost any type of metal can be coated for sublimation, but economics has limited the metals used to include aluminum, brass and steel. Aluminum is by far the most common material and comes in white, silver, gold and bronze colors. Steel is used mostly for magnetic boards and comes in white and silver. Brass is offered in both bright and satin and is commonly used for luggage tags and the like, but sheet stock can be purchased and used for making plaques and signs.

To work with sheet metal, you will need a sheer which is covered in the section, "Additional Equipment to Consider for Your Shop".

You might also want a tool to round or notch the corners of metal or to roll it to form self-standing photo panels. These tools are also covered in the "Additional Equipment..." section.

Metal is measured in tenths of an inch. Most metals are .020" thick while some, ChromaLuxe for instance, is often .040" or .050". It will be rare for you to come across anything less than .015" since thinner metal is difficult to work with because it wrinkles and dents so easily. Rarely will you see anything over .050" thick because it is so difficult to sheer.

Note that most sheers on the market cannot cut more than about .025" aluminum and even thinner steel. If you desire to work with the thicker metals such as ChromaLuxe, you will either need to buy it pre-cut or invest in a sheer capable of cutting .050" or heavier (such as the Accucutter 4001). These are all covered in the section "Additional Equipment to Consider for Your Shop".

"Success does not consist of never making mistakes but of never making the same one a second time. -George Bernard Shaw

SUBLIMATABLE ALUMINUM

Aluminum coated for sublimation decorating is one of the most popular substrates due to the fact that it has so many uses. In addition to flat sheets, aluminum finds its way into drinkware like water bottles and travel mugs.

As the years have gone by, this product category has grown to offer many great options. Various types or brands of aluminum are best used for specific applications. If you are in doubt, contact your Condé representative for help.

Here are the differences:

1. Thickness
2. Color
3. Finish
4. Single or double sided
5. Type of coating

Perhaps the most important part of aluminum is the quality of the coating. This, of course, is where the sublimation dyes will be after sublimation. The quality of the coating determines its durability and appearance. For our discussion I will break down these coatings into five categories.

Unacceptable quality: This is usually cheap Chinese metal that looks terrible after sublimation. It's really aluminum that has a coating that is not designed for sublimation. Indicators that it is trashy metal include transfer sticking to metal after transfer, Poor image quality, poor color density, watermarks, visible stripes. Avoid this one.

Plaque grade. DynaSub is a popular brand of metal that gets the job done for graphics and text in a presentation fashion for use on a plaque, trophy plates and gift items. It is cost effective but has limited

scratch resistance. Usually purchased in 12"x24" sheets for use with a metal shear. Single sided, glossy finish in white, silver or gold with a thickness of .020". It is important to use minimal pressure when pressing, as normal pressure produces what looks like "water marks" in the coating that cannot be removed. See our video at www.Condétv.com regarding how to use minimal pressure.

DynaSub is used with all kinds of products.

'Clear' means natural aluminum (silver).

Excellent all-around use. Unisub owns this category. Deep rich colors with superior scratch resistance. Available in sizes up to 4'x8'. Available in white and clear (silver). This metal has some UV protection built into it but not as much as the ChromaLuxe (below). It is ideal for plaques and other high-end photo and gift products.

Top of the Line. Chromaluxe metal is the ultimate in photo and art reproduction. This coating is super thick providing a breathtaking color depth that is 3D like. See diagram below. Available in white or clear (silver) in several finishes. This is the "go to" metal for the ultimate in color fidelity. I recommend you get a sample to evaluate.

When pressing metal, it is recommended that the metal be face down and the transfer image face up. Cover with a sheet of newsprint or butcher paper. Do not use Teflon as a cover sheet. Both sides can be pressed at the same time with two-sided metal. There is no need to increase the time for .020" metal. You should increase time when pressing .045" metal.

Chromaluxe EXT: UV stability has been an issue since inkjet sublimation first came on the scene in 1997. There have been many false claims, both intentional and non-intentional. Today however, we do have some metals that are proving to stand up to the claims. For example, Unisub now promises 2 years exterior for photographs and 3 years for text on their Chromaluxe EXT metal. Available in a variety of sizes, it is available in both Clear Gloss (Silver) and White.

Printed on white ChromaLuxe metal.

"Best startup generally come from somebody needing to scratch an itch." -Michael Arrington

JEWELRY

A product line that has become very popular in recent days is jewelry and Condé offers a variety to choose from. These include silver aluminum with a Florentine border which is light and intended for school jewelry or the younger crowd. It is inexpensive, come in several shapes and sizes and can be used to make a necklace, charm bracelet or earrings.

Silver aluminum with Florentine edge

Silver plated metal bezel type charms for necklaces

Another UNISUB product is their Bezel pendants. These are silver plated and designed so a metal insert can be placed in the bezel with a touch of double-faced tape. These too come in several shapes and are easy to make.

Natural Shell Pendants

The third and newest product line is made using natural shell. This makes a truly unique necklace and sublimates with beautiful color. These make great gifts for any age but especially for adults. A thick conductive rubber pad is required for making these.

Dog tags make another great product that qualifies as jewelry. Made by UNISUB, these come in both white and silver, one-sided and two-sided. They are inexpensive and require nothing special to make them. There is

also a jig available for making large quantities. There is also a version called Iron Clad that is specially coated so it will withstand situations where other tags might scratch.

.

Last but not least are Cuff Bracelets. These aluminum strips can be used for a wide variety of applications, including recognizing military, schools, sports teams, church groups and just average people love these for a variety of reasons. There isn't a product on the market that is easier to make and you can make a dozen or more at a time.

Cuff bracelets come as a die-cut, flat piece of metal. After you sublimate one or both sides (both sides can be done at the same time), you will need a special tool to bend the bracelets into shape. The tool is under $10 so no big deal.

Examples of Cuff Bracelets both before and after shaping them.

Since these are made from UNISUB metal, they are highly scratch resistant so they will look good for a long, long time.

Bending device for cuff bracelets.

Here are some ideas to consider for cuff bracelets, dog tags and jewelry:

Church related: What would Jesus do? prayers, picture of the church or denominational symbol, or advertise an upcoming event.

Military: Gold Star parents, remembering those serving in the military, missing in action.

Schools: School mascot, player number for both player and family members, graduation year, picture of girlfriend or boyfriend, band instrument, etc.

Sports Team: Picture of football, baseball, etc., along with player number or school mascot.

"I Love" Bracelets: Use the "I Love xxx" with anything from a pet to a sport, church, hobby or location.

Pets: Use a picture of a pet or pets.

Monograms: A survey showed that up to half of the people who bought sublimated products wanted just their monogram on some kind of background. A special monogram font is available from Condé for a nominal fee.

Family: Especially great for family reunions, create a design around a family name.

ID Bracelet: A nice design and a person's name is always a winner. Don't forget that customer will want one in a variety of colors to go with their outfits.

Medical ID Dog Tag or Bracelet: Far more information can be included on these than conventional Medical ID jewelry.

CHROMALUXE™
PHOTO PANELS & MURALS

Chromaluxe is the newest coated product line from UNISUB. Although it can be used for any type of sublimation, it is intended for museum quality photography. It was developed with professional photographers in mind and produced a very high-quality image.

The product line that carries this coating is varied but the metal items are much thicker than conventional metal (.045" vs. .020"). These make excellent wall hangings or murals.

These thicker pieces come pre-cut in a variety of shapes and sizes. All you have to do is sublimate them and apply a hanger on the back to have a finished product ready to hang. These products can also be displayed on a shelf.

For the best results, there are some extra steps needed for this metal. Rather than covering it with paper when pressing, Polypoplin fabric is recommended as it absorbs moisture better than paper. The pressing time is also different. While most metal products press for 1 minute, these products press for 1 minute and 45 seconds with heavy pressure.

Unusually long panels are available.

Self-standing designs are available.

A variety of pre-cut shapes are available.

HEAT PLATEN
POLYPOPLON FABRIC
TRANSFER SHEET
CHROMALUXE PRODUCT FACE UP
PROTECTIVE PAPER
BOTTOM TABLE

Stacking order for ChromaLuxe products.

SUBLIMATABLE BRASS

Sublimatable brass isn't terribly popular because of its cost and the fact gold aluminum usually satisfies the customer asking for gold metal. Some companies do make luggage tags and other products from gold brass but again, the gold aluminum is far less expensive and is satisfactory for most applications.

Gold brass is available in sheet form, however, and comes in both bright and satin finishes. There is also a brass product with a white surface. This is usually used in combination with a laser engraver since it would serve no purpose otherwise.

Satin Brass by DynaSub

Imprinting brass is no different than sublimating other metals. Keep in mind that the gold color is going to show through the sublimation dyes, changing the color of the dyes to some degree. To identify a specific color on gold, it will be necessary to imprint a color chart on the gold brass and then selecting the desired color from that test sample.

Bright Brass by DynaSub

TINS

Tins like these can be sublimated easily and used to hold gifts such as candy, socks, a puzzle or many other items.

They are easy to make because they are made with an indention in the metal lid where a second piece of metal can be attached with double-faced tape. Since sheet metal is one of the easiest things to imprint, these are a dream to make.

There are two sizes: 5"x7.75" rectangle (2" deep) and 5.875" round (2" deep).

To print the inserts, place face down in the press for 1 minute at 400° F. Use a sheet of protective paper below the transfer and above the metal. Don't forget to remove the protective film prior to imprinting.

PROTECTIVE PAPER
METAL FACE DOWN
TRANSFER FACE UP
PROTECTIVE PAPER

Stacking order for metal.

PART TWO
SECTION 8

"Success is walking from failure to failure with no loss of enthusiasm." -- Winston Churchill

FIBERGLASS REINFORCED PLASTIC

FRP (fiberglass reinforced plastic) is a mainstay in the sublimation industry. Countless products have been made from it. A few are shown below. Christmas ornaments, room signs, name badges in all shapes and sizes, coasters, door hangers, key chains, bag tags and of course, sheet stock.

It is just what it says, sheets of ordinary fiberglass (which will sublimate in its natural state), that has been sanded smooth and coated with the white UNISUB coating. Many of the products are double-sided and both sides can be sublimated at the same time even with an ordinary heat press: although I prefer to do one side at a time because of alignment issues.

To sublimate this product, it should be placed in the press face up for 1 minute at 400° F and medium pressure. Multiple pieces can be imprinted at the same time, although they should be spaced at least 1" apart to insure good contact with the heating element.

Many of the products can be printed using jigs made by UNISUB to increase production. See the section "Production Jigs" (Part 2, Section 3) for more information.

To print both sides at the same time, align the transfers and tape them in place or use Pro-Spray. Place in the press and cover with a protective sheet of paper on both top and bottom and press for two-minutes at 400° F with medium pressure.

The finished surface is extremely hard and durable. It is waterproof and almost indestructible except when placed in sunlight for a prolonged period of time or in some cases a short period (like on the dashboard of a car in summer).

Findings for the backs of name badges should either use foam tape or an adhesive. Welding, like that used on other types of name badges will not work with fiberglass.

Typical pin type finding.

Individual pin backs are also available.

Magnets have become very popular.

E6000 is a popular adhesive that works with FRP.

Use a permanent marker to "paint" the edges of FRP products.

The edges of FRP are sometimes objectionable because they typically don't sublimate leaving them white with streaks of color on them. To cure this, try using permanent markers to "paint" the edges with black or an appropriate color after sublimating.

Here are a few sample products made with Fiberglass Reinforced Plastic:

PART TWO
SECTION 9

"Don't be afraid to give up the good to go for the great." -John D. Rockefeller

WORKING WITH WOOD PRODUCTS

Wood products in their raw form do not sublimate, but when they are coated with a Polyester resin, they sublimate great.

When we talk about wood, there are a couple of sub-categories included. These are common materials you see every day around the house. Wood, in its natural state, does not sublimate well. What makes them sublimate, is the special coating applied to the surface.

Real Wood: The next section talks about the products made with real wood, usually something like maple with a light color. UNISUB offers a number of these that include key chains, bag tags and name badges.

MDF: Next is MDF board or Medium Density Fiberboard. This is actually thin sheets of paper that are pressed together to form a product that most people would probably think was actual wood. The material holds up very well, can be worked like real wood and is heavier than most wood products of the same design. The only drawback to MDF board is moisture. These boards are sealed with a specific amount of moisture. Should one be submerged in water or placed in the rain, it will destroy the board. UNISUB uses this material to make plaques, picture frames and home décor items.

Hardboard: Often called "Masonite", this is also a paper product that is usually made to be 1/8" or ¼" thick. It is dark brown in its natural state and is known for its ability to remain flat under normal circumstances. UNISUB uses this material to make clipboards, clocks, serving trays and similar items.

Working with REAL wood is a bit different than working with other materials that might resemble wood, such as hardboard (Masonite) or MDF board (used for plaques).

The makeup of these other materials is actually very thin sheets of "paper" adhered together with an adhesive and pressure. So long as they don't get wet, they are extremely durable and easy to work with. Wood, however, is a natural product. It was once alive, and sometimes acts like it still is!

Like the other materials, wood has to be specially coated in order to be sublimatable. Unlike the other materials, wood is coated with a clear Polyester based coating that allows the color and grain of the wood to show through.

To sublimate real wood (usually Maple or Alder), use the same procedure as Hardboard. One minute with medium pressure, face up and covered with a sheet of protective paper – never use Teflon film. Teflon will hold moisture which is a bad word when working with wood. That's the good news.

The bad news is that wood can absorb and then release considerable moisture and moisture can create some interesting problems. It can cause migration of the sublimation dyes, but most often, it will cause a slight warping of the wood. The only solution to this issue is to use a press with both an upper and lower heating element to generate consistent heat throughout the piece.

In most instances however, the warp is very minor and not a serious issue. The rule of thumb is, "the larger the piece, the more warping issue you may encounter".

Wood products come mostly from UNISUB although there are also some wood sign panels available that look like several pieces of wood nailed together to create an antique look.

HARDBOARD

Hardboard (also called Masonite) is one of the most common of all sublimatable materials. Although not sublimatable in its natural state, its smooth surface allows for easy coating by manufacturers, usually in white. It comes in many thicknesses but the sublimatable versions are usually 1/8" or ¼" thick. Edges are smoothed but left natural.

Hardboard is used to make a wide variety of products as shown to the right. They include everything from coasters to clocks.

Imprinting hardboard is simple and straight forward. It should always be sublimated face up for 1 minute with medium pressure. Multiple pieces can be sublimated at one time. Two-sided hardboard must be sublimated separately on each side unless a top and bottom heating element is used.

Hardboard that has been prepared for sublimation can be purchased from Condé Systems and cut with an ordinary table saw, although a safety saw is preferred.

Some hardboard products may come with a protective film applied to one side. This must be removed prior to sublimating.

This material may also be laser cut to a desired shape or engraved and then paint filled.

| PROTECTIVE PAPER |
| HARDBOARD FACE UP |
| PROTECTIVE PAPER |

Stacking order for MDF

TILES

PHOTO PANELS

CLIPBOARDS

SHOUTBOX

GAMES

TROPHIES

WALL HANGINGS

PHOTOS

COASTERS

HANGERS

SERVING TRAYS

DEVICE STANDS

As consumers in a world of Netflix, e-books, and video streaming, we are always looking for the newest, most stylish and convenient way to use and view our electronics. With new Image Stands product line, we can offer you and your customers a product that provides exactly that.

They not only serve as a stand for electronics, but they also have an indention which provides a perfect site for a charging cord. The collapsible, 2-piece design makes them very easy to store when not in use, but as attractive as this product is, you will never want to put it away! With Unisub hardboard, ImageStands' imprintable glossy white surface, and black back and edges, it is exceptionally easy to present your customers with a professional and impressive looking personalized product. It is available in three different sizes, small, medium, and large, with the option of a flat or Benelux-shaped top. We also very recently started carrying the small landscape style stand with a flat top, which is ideal for watching movies and videos on smartphones. Arched holes on the bottom of the main piece and kickstand help to keep the entire stand stable. The small and medium sizes are suggested for smaller electronics like smartphones, while the large size is more suited for tablets, iPads, and e-readers. They can also be used to hold cookbooks or display merchandise in a store, the possibilities are endless.

Customers can use ImageStands for their desks at work, on nightstands for overnight charging, and for merchandise display at their place of business. So, the kids can watch a movie without the risk of breaking something, parents can use these stands to hold phones, iPads, or tablets for hands-free viewing. They can also be great time savers. Instead of stopping what you're doing and picking your phone up every time it vibrates, you can set it up on your desk; so a glance is all you need to see if it is of any importance or if it is just another email telling you about this week's sales at your local grocery store. Every smartphone or tablet user can benefit from this product. Even customers that are not very tech-savvy can use it as a stand for books, artwork, a photograph, or basically anything they wish. This product is a fabulous gift for all ages and is great for birthdays, weddings, housewarming parties, or even as party favors. Need a gift for your co-worker? A matching personalized phone stand and sticky-note holder would be absolutely perfect!

Popular designs for ImageStands include floral patterns, monograms, family names, quotes, and sports themes. Customers love anything personalized, so designing a stand with their favorite sports team and their name or initials, for example, would be something they will enjoy and be interested in purchasing. We also have several designs available for purchase on our artwork download page www.Condédesign.com. For inspiration, visit our Client Image Galleries on our website, www.Condé.com. So you can see the many ways our customers have really made this product their own. A large collection of videos are available at www.Condétv.com with step-by-step instructions on how to get the best results with this product.

Marketing this item is exceptionally easy due to the fact that most people over the age of 5 have either a cellphone, iPad, or tablet of some sort, which means they all have a use for this product. The versatility and collapsible design make it not only a neat accessory, but also a convenient way to prop, charge, and view your devices, which can benefit people of all ages! You might want to market this item to boutiques because they typically sell or offer monogrammed and personalized clothing and accessories. Boutiques' clientele is primarily female and we know women are all about the accessories and their cell phones; so this is the perfect product!

One of the new image stands is this docking station that can house and charge phones, watch, tablet or Apple Airpods.

PART TWO
SECTION 10

"Ideas are easy, implementation is hard." -Guy Kawasaki

WORKING WITH GLASS PRODUCTS

Glass: One might think that glass would go against all the principles of sublimation – it is hard, non-absorbent, brittle and usually not as flat as you might think. Yet, glass is a great substrate for sublimation – remember, it is the coating that does all the work, not the substrate. Glass tiles are available in a variety of sizes and can even be used for floor tile! Yes, I've been told that several Las Vegas hotels have glass floors made to look like marble. Glass, when sublimated on the underneath side and adhered with a white adhesive, can produce any kind of floor you want – wood, marble, gravel or even give direction or display photographs. Of course, unlike the typical glass tile, floor tiles are an inch or more thick. Currently, we offer two types of glass tiles, clear and textured. Most sublimation tiles are non-tempered. This makes it possible to cut, drill and shape a tile. Tempered glass can't be cut except by glass professionals.

This cutting board is made with ColorLyte tempered glass from Conde.

Glass Photo Panels are printed on the back making the face

Glass photo panels have become very popular. The durable surface and the brilliant colors produced make it a highly desirable product. A variety of sizes are available and all glass products are made in the same way, although the press time may vary with the size of the piece.

Likewise, glass tiles (Right) make great gift items or can be used for murals.

Glass panels are also offered that are self-standing. These make exceptional gifts or awards. This one has a gold rod behind it to give support. Larger panels have two rods.

As you can see, images sublimated onto glass can be viewed from both sides.

INSTRUCTIONS FOR MAKING GLASS PRODUCTS

Do NOT mirror or reverse image when printing transfer.

1. Place 1/2" Nomex Felt Pad or 1/8" Heat Conductive Green Rubber on Bottom Table. When using 1/8" Green Pad add 1 additional minute press time.

2. Cover the 1/2" Nomex Felt Pad or 1/8" Heat Conductive Green Rubber with a sheet of protective paper.

3. Use Heat Tape or Pro Spray to attach your transfer to the white side of the Cutting Board.

4. Place the Cutting Board with imaging side face down, textured side up, on top of 1/2" Nomex Felt Pad or 1/8" Heat Conductive Green Rubber and protective paper, on bottom table.

5. Cover it all with a piece of protective paper and press according to time, temperature, and pressure above. When using 1/8" Green Pad add 1 additional minute press time.

6. Check for complete transfer upon opening press. If incomplete, close press and continue pressing for 30 seconds to 1 minute, or until Cutting Board is fully imaged.

7. Cool Cutting Board face up, add feet only after board is cool.

PART TWO
SECTION 11

"Incremental progress leads to long-lasting results." — *Frank Sonnenberg*

WORKING WITH ACRYLIC

Acrylic is an exciting new material for sublimation. For decades, people tried to make acrylic work with sublimation and had very limited success. The problem is that sublimation requires about 400° F to transfer the dyes properly into the sublimation coating. Acrylic begins to melt about 225° F.

COLORLYTE

Bent photo panels are self-standing and viewable from both sides.

Although these facts haven't changed, we have learned to lighten the pressure when pressing acrylic and moving it to a flat surface to cool.

Acrylic doesn't print in its natural state, so it has to be coated. Currently, Condé Systems is the only one coating the product in a serious way; so they are about the only place you will find the blanks. Coasters, Christmas ornaments and photo panels make up the acrylic offerings. Photo panels are especially interesting in that they can be curved by using a special jig. This is just taking advantage of the fact that the acrylic does soften when heated to 400° F for a full minute.

This is a great product to wholesale to frame shops and photographers.

Acrylic ornaments come in several shapes.

Jig for bending hot acrylic.

PART TWO
SECTION 12

"Every day that we spent not improving our products (business) was a wasted day."
-Joel Spolsky

PHONE COVERS

This is perhaps the most dynamic and exciting category for sublimation decorating. From our smart phone to tablets to laptops, all of these devices can be personalized.

In the smart phone world, Apple and Samsung are the two main leaders, so we have concentrated on the devices they offer.

Refer to our web site for the current offering as new models come out at an ever-quickening pace!

These are similar to mugs in the design department because just about any design will look great. Some popular designs for these include photographs, monograms, patterns, names, sports teams, and quotes. We carry most sizes for iPhone and Samsung galaxy cell phones. This product is not only an attractive accessory but is also necessary to protect your devices from drops and falls.

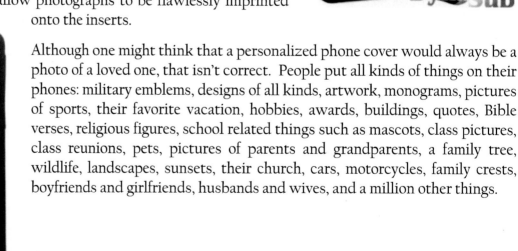

Device covers are a way to exhibit your personality and style in a way that is visible to everyone. We typically have our phones with us constantly throughout the day and when you are looking at something all day you want it to be attractive. The crystal-clear images provided by sublimation technology allow photographs to be flawlessly imprinted onto the inserts.

Although one might think that a personalized phone cover would always be a photo of a loved one, that isn't correct. People put all kinds of things on their phones: military emblems, designs of all kinds, artwork, monograms, pictures of sports, their favorite vacation, hobbies, awards, buildings, quotes, Bible verses, religious figures, school related things such as mascots, class pictures, class reunions, pets, pictures of parents and grandparents, a family tree, wildlife, landscapes, sunsets, their church, cars, motorcycles, family crests, boyfriends and girlfriends, husbands and wives, and a million other things.

RING STANDS

A new product from Condé is the Ring Stand. This little device can be attached to the back of most phones and used to make the phone stand up on its own.

Just sublimate the metal plate and insert it in the device. Once attached to the phone, the ring can be turned to cause the phone to stand up horizontally or you can slide your finger through the ring for an extra secure grip. Perfect as a personalized gift. Design a case to match with it as optimum bundling. Ring is not suitable for notebook style cases. Each includes an extra insert.

MAKES YOUR PHONE STAND ON ITS OWN

PART TWO
SECTION 13

"Chase the vision, not the money, the money will end up following you." -Tony Hsieh

CERAMIC AND NATURAL TILES

Ceramic and other natural Tiles have a high value and beauty unlike any other substrate. Ceramic is fired clay and is made into a sublimation product by applying a polymer coating on the outer surface. We also coat other natural materials such as Porcelain (a denser version of ceramic), stone and marble. Tiles come in many sizes and sometimes shapes. Here are the basic properties:

Sizes: Depending on which brand and type of tile, there are a great many sizes to choose from. One thing you need to know before you design your first tile for anything, is that when a tile is called 4x4", it isn't necessarily 4x4". I've seen 4x4" tiles that actually ranged from 3 7/8" to 4.25". The same is true with all sizes of tiles. Most 12x12" tiles are actually 11.8 something inches. For someone installing a typical bathroom with these, that makes no difference but if you are planning a mural, it can make a huge difference. Always check the actual size of a tile before you do anything else. As for approximate size, there are sheets of 1x1" tiles, 2x2", 4x4", 6x6", 8x8", 10x10" and 12x12" tiles. Tiles also come as rectangles in 6x8", 8x10" and also in a few round sizes.

A mural on a school wall. Note how the wall is also ceramic tile.

With or without lugs (spacers): The lugs or spacers molded into the edges of the tile insure precise spacing between tiles when they are being installed. If you use tiles with these spacers, you will almost have to grout the space between them (more about that later). If you use tiles without spacers, the tiles can be bumped up against each other so there is virtually no gap between them. This eliminates the hassle of grouting them and saves a lot of time.

Spacing lug.

Thickness: Ceramic and other natural tiles vary in thickness due to the way the tiles are made and fired in a kiln. These variations are part of the beauty of a tiled wall and generally is given no attention. It does however, limit mixing tiles from different companies and can mean the face of a tile might not be perfectly flat – in fact, very few tiles are flat which adds to the importance of following our instructions when pressing them. Tiles are generally about ¼" ~ ½" thick. Most glass tiles are about 3/16". Actual thickness is always going to vary from tile to tile so spec sheets are an approximation.

Coating Finish (Glossy, Satin or Matte): Tiles come in at least three levels of shine: High gloss, Satin or Matte. As a rule of thumb, the glossier the finish, the softer the coating and the more easily it can scratch. Although most people think they want a high gloss tile, you will find that those same people love the satin or matte tiles once they see them. High gloss murals, for example, are so reflective that if your customer puts sport lights on them, the reflection will hide the image with reflection. A satin or matte mural is not only more durable, but also looks better under spot lights because it doesn't reflect as much glare. When choosing a tile, you are actually choosing a coating. For years, the options were very limited but now, there are several companies that coat tile and do a very good job of it. Of course we think the IronClad™ tile, which Condé actually coats themselves, is top of the line.

Shape (Rectangle and Square): Ceramic tiles can be used in many different applications and therefore, is offered in various shapes. At Condé, we offer all the common sizes and shapes.

Type of material (ceramic, porcelain, stone): Yes, there are at least four different types of tiles but they all have one factor in common and for us sublimators, that is the most important thing of all – the coating. When selecting a tile, be it marble or ceramic, pay attention to the coating most of all. Truth is, we can coat just about anything, including slate, but what makes the tile a winner is your selecting the right coating for the job.

Ceramic tile is a tile with a fired face on a clay back. The face is like glass and is extremely hard. The back of the tile is also fired (obviously) but it is softer allowing the face of the tile to provide the strength of the tile.

Porcelain tile is different from ceramic tile in that the entire piece is like glass. If you break a piece of porcelain tile, you will see the glass-like surface goes all the way through the material. This is why it is used for Christmas ornaments; it looks the same on both sides. Of course, what determines if it is sublimatable on both sides is whether or not it has been coated on both sides.

Stone: Currently, Condé offers two types of stone for sublimation. One is tumbled stone which is used the same as other tiles. It is actually made from sandstone which is then coated. This material is highly absorbent, so it isn't the best choice for bathrooms and backsplashes, although it is sometimes used and then sealed. The other is Condé 's sandstone coaster. This material is highly absorbent so it is perfect to use as coasters. It is made of natural stone so the base color varies from a light off-white to a beige. This means it is best suited for vector or spot color sublimation.

Tiles tend to be used for two purposes: decorative and functional. Here are some examples of decorative:

Tiles in a stand or with an attached easel on the back for display.

Tile in a wooden or iron trivet. A group of tiles (Mural) mounted inside a wooden

picture frame.

Examples of functional uses include:

>   Kitchen back splashes
>
>   Bathroom wall installations
>
>   Interior entrance/foyer murals

Tiles are for interior applications. Although the coatings have gotten much better over the years, they are still not recommended for exterior use. Direct sunlight will cause tiles, like most other things, to fade.

Although all tiles may look alike, they aren't. At some point, you will be tempted to buy tiles coated in China. I have tested these tiles and although some may work okay, many do not. The savings you might gain in a lower cost, will quickly evaporate as you have to throw tile after tile in the trash.

Framed ceramic mural in a church.

A last word about the IronClad™ brand of tiles: This is Condé brand of natural tiles and we are very proud of them. The tiles are both made and coated in USA. They are also, we think, offer the hardest coating on the best quality tile in the country. Check them out. Call your Condé representative, and they will be happy to send you a sample to try for yourself!

Building a sandwich to press these products should look like this:

You will need a Nomex Felt pad and a Green Heat Conductive Rubber sheet to ensure a good transfer of your image.

For additional instructions, check out CondéTV.

PART TWO
SECTION 14

"Ideas are commodity. Execution of them is not." -Michael Dell

SubliSlate

Metamorphic rock with a white sublimation coating. That's what Sublislate is. As you might expect, it is quite heavy. Some dealers joke about having to have a railroad spike to hang it on the wall and that's almost true, but it is usually is placed in an easel (which comes with it) and displayed on a table or shelf.

It makes a real impact compared to traditional plaques. The weight and brilliance really jump out when being presented. Just the uniqueness and weight communicate that this award is different – special.

The newest addition to the Sublislate family is a slate coaster. Sure to become a conversation piece in any home or office.

Surprisingly, this material is very easy to sublimate. Unlike glass and ceramic, it can be sublimated face up just like a plaque. You will need a thin green conductive rubber pad to compensate for any variation in the flatness of the material which will be demonstrated in my CondéTV videos.

Pricing: One of the things you will notice about Sublislate is it is very inexpensive. For this reason and the perceived value, we have already talked about, it should be easy to get a 600% markup (or more) on these products.

We offer a variety of shapes and sizes of SubliSlate products for sublimation.

PART TWO
SECTION 15

"It's not that we need new ideas, but we need to stop having old ideas." -Edwin Land

CHRISTMAS ORNAMENTS

When it comes to the use of a variety of substrates, I think Christmas Ornaments may be the champ. An awesomely popular product category, Christmas ornaments come in many different shapes and sizes, as well as base materials.

From glass to porcelain, you can see the beauty. Recently, ornaments have expanded to grow larger and to handle additional themes such as Halloween.

I recommend selling ornaments as a Fund-Raising item for schools and organizations.

Glass: The weight of glass makes it a great gift item. It just screams of value. Most glass ornaments are imprinted on the back side so the image shows through (this means you don't mirror the image when printing your transfer). The result is not only an image that shows through the glass but even the back side looks nice as well.

Porcelain: Porcelain is an excellent material for ornaments. It's smooth, high gloss finish produces a high-quality image that can be sublimated. Most ornaments are coated on both sides but not all, so take note of what you are buying. You will want to use a rubber pad and Nomex

FRP: Fiberglass reinforced plastic ornaments are cut into various shapes and sublimatable on both sides. These are incredibly durable.

Metal: UNISUB offers a number of two-sided metal ornaments cut into a variety of shapes: Star, round, horizontal and vertical rectangle, hexagon, oval, tapered, square, stocking, tree and more coming out all the time.

Ornaments for Other Occasions: Ornaments are now being made or can be used for occasions other than Christmas. Halloween is a popular application. Ornaments can be used for other things as well. Consider a heart ornament for the birth of a child with "First Christmas" on it. Ornaments can also be used with a suction cup and hung on a window or tied to a birthday present. They make great wedding favors too.

PART TWO
SECTION 16

*"The new source of power is not money in the hands of a few,
but information in the hands of many."* -John Naisbitt

WORKING WITH DRINKWARE

Mugs are perhaps the largest volume hard substrate. Many great sublimation pioneers have paved the way to our success.

Mugs can be decorated in two ways. With a heat press or using an oven and mug wrap.

Mugs are part of the drinkware family and consist of ceramic, plastic and metal products. See my chapter on drinkware. Since this is a very high-volume category, methods were created many years ago for volume production.

Mug Type Heat Presses:

This method is used to produce one mug at a time, but many folks operate several presses at the same time as needed. See photo below. The transfer is attached to the mug along with a cover sheet. The mug is placed in the press and closed. The press should be adjusted to properly contour to the mug to insure good contact. We then press generally for 400 degrees F for about 4 to 5 minutes for a ceramic mug. Times do vary for different types of drinkware and mug presses.

Constant Temperature Mug Presses

For some reason there are generally two types of mug heat presses: Constant and variable temperature presses. The mug press I use is the George Knight DK3 and it is a constant temperature press. You turn it on, and it gets up to the preset temperature (i.e. 400 degrees F) and maintains it within a normal range. It will dip quite a bit once a mug is placed in the press but will quickly recover. This constant temperature press works exactly like a flat press and therefore provides predictable results.

George Knight DK3 is our recommended mug press for standard shaped drinkware.

Variable Temperature Mug Presses

I would recommend you avoid the other type. This type of mug press has two temperatures: idle and press. The idle temperature is the where the press stays while it is not in use. Once the handle is closed, the press then starts climbing until it reaches the press temperature. Once reached, the timer then begins to count down. The challenge is that the timer does activate during the journey from idle to press temperature. This really throws a monkey wrench into timing. Your best bet is to increase the idle temperature as high as it can go and then using an external timer that you will start once the handle is closed. The unfortunate thing is these presses don't look much different from the constant temperature press, so it can be difficult to know which one is which.

Fixed Ovens

Most sublimators should invest in a small countertop convection oven to take care of odd and oversized items such as dog bowls and large steins. The transfer is applied to the substrate along with a cover sheet and then a "wrap" is applied around the item. It is then loaded into the already heated oven and baked for the appropriate time. Depending on the size of the oven, multiple items can be loaded at the same time making a large oven a great way to do volume products such as mugs. Note that you should NOT use the oven for cooking food. For product of mugs, I recommend purchasing three sets of wraps: one set for mugs that are about to be placed in the oven; One set for mugs in the oven; and the last set for mugs that were just removed from the oven. Typical cycle time for a ceramic mug is about 15 minutes at 400 degrees F.

Before buying an oven, call Conde for their recommendation. They have tested many to find what works best.

One excellent oven Condé has tested is the Wolfgang pressure oven. These are available from Amazon.com and many kitchen stores. These start about $175 and go up to almost $400 depending on features and size. Remember, all you need is the ability to hold a constant temperature of 400° F and enough room for a few mugs or other objects you might want to imprint. You should leave a couple of inches around each product for air circulation to ensure even heating. See our instructions or call for oven recommendations.

Conveyor Oven

For large volumes of mugs, I recommend a conveyor type oven. These ovens are loaded at one end and then move into and through the oven and exit at the far end. Hix Corporation makes a family of great conveyor ovens, perfect for high volume production of mugs and other like items.

Mug Wraps:

The second way to make mugs and other types of drinkware, plus pet dishes, is using a wrap. A wrap is basically rubber pad with a fastening device on each end. When the wrap is pulled tight around the cup, glass, mug or bowl, the two ends are joined. This makes a tight blanket around the shape of the object. The object with its own wrap is then placed in an oven for about 15 minutes at 400 F. Each shape must have a custom wrap to fit it and multiple wraps are used at the same time so multiple items can be sublimated at the same time. Although a standard oven in a cook stove can be used, the oven used for sublimation should not be used for food preparation.

A basic mug wrap.

Once the object has "cooked" for about 15-20 minutes, using a heat glove, remove it and allow it to cool with the wrap still in place. Having a second set of wraps greatly increases production. After about five minutes, you should be able to handle the object with your bare hands and you can then remove the wrap without fear of any ghosting. Set the object aside and allow it to completely cool before packaging.

You will need a 7/16" nut driver to lock and unlock the wrap from the cup.

Mugs, shot glasses and other items that have a funnel shape have to be made with wraps because it would be nearly impossible to create a mug press for the odd shape and a different press would have to be made for each size and shape you wanted to make. Wraps on the other hand, are inexpensive to make and can be easily shaped to fit these non-cylindrical shapes. As you can see in the picture, the wrap has an arc to it that molds to the shape of the glass.

Wraps come in a variety of shapes and sizes. When making tapered products, the wrap must have a taper to match the items.

Another product that is recommended for a wrap are the PolySub mugs. These are the only unbreakable plastic cups that can be sublimated and although they can be made in a mug type heat press like the DK-3, it is highly recommended they be made with a wrap in an oven. These cups, which get soft and can deform when heated, require a special insert to give them strength to resist changing shape. The inserts are inexpensive and should last a lifetime.

PolySub is a non-breakable plastic-like mug that is sublimatable.

Shrink Wrap

The newest development in this saga is to shrink wrap the cup, mug, dog dish or other item with a special film sold by Condé Systems. The process is accomplished using a heat gun or common hair dryer and takes only a few seconds. First, apply the transfer as you normally would then just drop the item into the plastic bag (made of shrink wrap) and hit it with the heat gun. Once secure, you can place it in your oven for about 15-20 minutes.

SubliShrink applied to a water bottle.

With this method, you can not only sublimate most ceramic items or metal drinkware, you can also sublimate edge to edge and even the handles on many items. It is cheap, easy and consistent. The product is called "SubliShrink" and comes in several sizes.

A tapered cup printed edge to edge and all the way around. What would be a sublimator's nightmare before SubliShrink, is now commonplace.

HOW TO USE SHRINK WRAP

Apply the transfer as usual.

You can also apply a transfer to the handle.

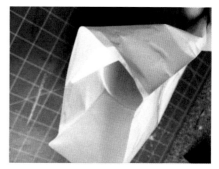

The sleeve is open on both ends. Insert the cup in the middle.

Use a heat gun to shrink the wrap so it is smooth.

15-20 minutes in the oven. A conventional over is fine or a countertop convection oven. Oven should be dedicated to sublimation and not used for food.

Finished product.

PART TWO
SECTION 17

"Whether you think you can or whether you think you can't, you're right! -Henry Ford

WORKING WITH FABRIC

There are a number of ways to professionally decorate fabric. I specify "professionally" because there are things like puffy paint and iron on transfers intended for the craft market and although they are certainly decoration, it doesn't compare with what we do.

Decoration methods are many and I will touch on each. Perhaps you already do one or more of these or are considering adding one to what you do already. As you will see, for the most part, these complement each other rather than compete with one another, so even if you don't do them yourself, you can buddy up with someone who does and sell each other's work.

Embroidery: Embroidery is a wonderful way to do small decorations on garments, but it doesn't do nearly as well for large images. Embroidery is done with specialized machines with one, two or more sewing heads. It is slow by comparison and limited to the colors of thread at hand. It requires specialized software both to run the machines and to convert the design from clipart or text to something the sewing machine can understand. This conversion process, often called digitizing, if often sent out to professionals because it is so complex. New software is attacking this problem but many do still send it out of shop. Embroidery wear and washes very well, does not fade. Embroidery usually requires a backup cloth on the back side of the garment to help hold the threads secure. This can be a problem with large designs. Cost for actually running the machines is very low but the entry cost is high beginning at $5,000 and quickly jumping up to $100,000 for a good multi-head machine, all the adapters needed and a good selection of threads.

Embroidery looks and feels great but for a large design, it takes a long time to create and is expensive.

Screen Printing: This one has probably been around the longest and uses a synthetic silk screen stretched over a wood or metal frame. The screen is somehow exposed so it allows ink to flow through portions of the screen and not others. Most modern screen printers use a light method of exposure that removes a coating that has been applied to the screen prior to exposure but there are also other methods.

Once a screen is produced, it is placed over the garment and ink is then dragged over the entire screen with a rubber squeegee forcing ink through the openings in the screen and onto the fabric. This can be repeated to add additional colors and often is repeated up to produce what appears to be a full-color image. Unlike true full-color printing, this method can only have a limited number of select colors.

The process, though simple, requires a considerable amount of space as each shirt must dry for several hours before being stacked. Larger shops use a dryer (basically an oven that open on each side) and pass the shirts through the oven to speed up their drying time. Again, this requires considerable real estate. It is also a messy process since screens must be washed out with high-pressure hoses after use. Start-ups often take them to a car wash to wash them out (screens must be cleaned after use). To do this in-house, a deep sink with high-pressure hose is needed, plus a place for the screens to dry. Screen then must be stored for future use. Again, this requires considerable space. Equipment for doing this process ranges from a couple of thousand dollars for a multi-color system to a breath-taking amount for a fully automatic system.

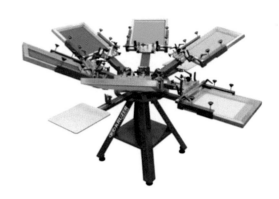

For multicolor screen printing a machine like this one is often used.

The end result is usually one, two or three colors on fabric, usually cotton. Cost for shirts for screen printing is much less than sublimation since these inks don't care what the product is made of. Screen printed images lay on top of the fabric and are not absorbed like sublimation, so they tend to eventually crack and peel over time. Washing and drying excecrbate this process.

Screen printed shirts are usually used to fill large orders (about 100 shirts are required to justify the cost of making a screen and the labor required for setup and cleanup). They are usually sold far too cheap, sometimes as low as a few dollars each. The people who buy these shirts usually don't care how long the image holds up since they are commonly used for a single event that might last only a day or two.

Finally, this process carries a lot of odors with it and is not suitable for use in locations where odor is going to be a problem. Most inks and solvents used in today's screen printing are water based and deemed not harmful, this is in contrast to a decade or two ago when all kinds of dangerous chemicals were common and are sometimes still used today.

Heat Transfer: Heat transfer imprints are very common and very popular in today's decoration market. There are a number ways to make these and we will look at a couple of them here. All are applied with a heat press. At stomething between 200°-250° F, the garment is placed in the press with the transfer on top of the garment and pressed for around 20 seconds with medium to heavy pressure. The difference between methods is in how the image is created.

There are two types of heat transfers overall: Cold peel and hot peel. They are what they sound like. A hot peel transfer must be removed immediately after pressing or it will never come off. A cold peel can be removed any time after it has cooled down. This is clearly the preferred method but isn't always an option.

Heat transfers can be made in-house but are usually sent out to be made with special inks on a small duplicating press. For this reason, there is usually a minimum order of 100 or so pieces and all have to be the same. No personalization.

Like screen printing, heat transfers lay on the surface of the fabric and do not penetrate the material. They wear well but like screen printing, most will eventually crack and peel after multiple washings.

These transfers are also sold as stock images which can be stored and used "on demand". Shop owners will stock copies of images that are most likely to be used in his or her area. This can amount to considerable inventory which may or may not sell.

ALL heat transfers change the "hand" of the fabric. Hand is the term used to describe how stiff the image is as it lays on top of the fabric. Screen printing for instance, usually produces a heavy hand meaning it is very stiff. DTG on the other hand has a light hand. It still changes the feel of the fabric but only by a little. Sublimation does not change the hand at all because it is absorbed by the fabric and doesn't lay on the surface like a heat transfer.

Laser Produced Heat Transfers: A long wished for dream of the heat transfer market is the ability to product "one up" full-color heat transfers in-house. That dream has come true in that Condé now offers two laser

This image was applied with a laser produced heat transfer. Note there is no sheen around the image, and it did not require any weeding.

printers capable of making professional full-color heat transfers both in color and even include white ink (toner). The process is done with an OKI (some other printers will also work) either with or without white toner capability. The printers, currently the OKI 711 and 920, offer the ability to actually print white on black shirts! Because this system is toner based and not liquid ink, there are no issues with agitation or clogging print heads. These do not use special toners. Settings in the printers are critical and they do require a special paper. Some papers produce only color images while others include white. Some papers can print full-color bitmaps (photographs), others are for vector art (text and clipart) only. The cost is reasonably low and varies depending on the paper selected. The difference in the printers is that the 711 prints 8.5x11" only and the 920 prints both 8.5"x11" and 11"x17". This process requires two steps and if done on a production basis is best done with two heat presses that will be set at different temperatures. One transfers the printed image to a transfer sheet. The other moves the image on the transfer sheet to the shirt.

If this method is of interest to you, contact your Condé representative. They will be happy to help you make wise choices. Although this process, like all true heat transfers, rests on the surface of the shirt, it has excellent bonding and doesn't seem to crack or peel like most other transfers. It prints on most fabrics but is aimed at 100% cotton like the Hanes Beefy Tee and adds about $1 or less to the cost of the shirt. Printers cost between $2,500 and $15,000.

Direct to Garment or DTG: DTG is basically an inkjet printer mounted on a gantry that passes over a shirt and prints directly to the garment. These have been around for about a decade now and are quite popular. They use a special ink jet ink that adheres to the surface of the shirt. After printing the shirt, it must be placed in a heat press for about 20 seconds to "set" the ink. This process has a high entry price (up to $18,000 or more with white ink capability) and because it is ink and therefore translucent, if it is used on dark fabrics, it may require several layers of white ink to build a base for colored inks. These multiple layers of white can be very expensive if the areas are large. This process can print full-color photographs and holds up very well to washing and drying.

This is an example of a 'Direct to Garment' printer. There are a number of brands, but all use ink-jet technology and white ink capability is usually optional.

Rhinestoning: Rhinestoning has been around for decades but only recently has it been brought to a place where it can be done on a more professional scale and done in-house. There are a number of companies who provide methods for doing this with the largest being Digital Art Solutions. Computerized systems allow for the creation of the design to be done in CorelDRAW and then "printed" on a vinyl cutter that cuts the pattern out of a special self-adhesive film which is then attached to the garment and sprinkled with Rhinestones, then placed in a heat press for about 20 seconds at about 220°F. The process can be repeated to produce multi-colored designs. Although one might be suspect of how well the stones remain attached to the fabric, they actually adhere very well and will withstand washing and drying multiple times.

Rhinestoning is usually done with a vinyl cutter and heat press.

This process can also be done using a laser engraver if you happen to have one but a vinyl cutter is less expensive and allows for much larger patterns or ganging patterns to reduce labor costs.

UV Printers: Until recently, UV printers could not print to fabric because the inks were not flexible, but no more. Although not the easiest thing to do, inks are now available for at least one UV printer that are flexible. There are three problems built into this process: One, the printers start at about $12,000 and quickly go up to $18,000 for one big enough to print a 10"x24" image. Two, folding a shirt so it will pass through a printer requires a jig and a fair amount of luck to get it aligned properly. Third, the printers that can use flexible ink are limited to a 10" width unless you are willing to spend up to $72,000 for a wide-format printer. These printers will print on cotton and include white ink. Unless you can print a lot of products over a six-month period, ink can become very expensive.

UV Printing onto fabric requires flexible ink and a special jig to hold the shirt. Imprint size is limited.

Sublimation: Sublimation is different from all the methods listed above. It is unique in that you can make the transfers in-house for just pennies. It is a one-step process that allows full-color printing including photographs, line art and text on white to medium color garments, provided they are 100% Polyester or microfiber. The transfer is printed onto a special transfer paper using special sublimation inks from a specially selected list of printers (currently the Sawgrass Virtuoso line made by Ricoh). There are currently two models, the 400 and the 800. These printers are virtually the same except for size. The 400 allows for paper up to 8.5x14" while the 800 (when fitted with an optional adapter), allows for 13'x21" sheet fed paper. Sublimation will not wash out of a garment, so washings is no problem. Because this method dyes the fabric rather than sitting on top of it, it does not change the hand and will never crack or peel. Once the transfer is printed, it is placed on the garment and pressed for about 35 seconds at 400°F. Once pressed and allowed to cool for about 10-20 seconds, the transfer can be removed (it doesn't stick) and the shirt is finished. Polyester shirts cost more than cotton. but they don't shrink, and the microfiber shirts are appreciated for their wicking capability. If this method is of interest to you, contact your Condé representative. They will be happy to help you make wise choices.

Fabric is one material that can be frustrating to do, especially if you try to take shortcuts by skipping a step.

In the most basic terms, the pictures below illustrate how it's done.

Step One is to prepare the transfer. Tearing the edges helps prevent hard lines on the finished product.

Step Four is to quickly press the shirt to remove moisture.

Step Two is to lint roll the entire surface before applying heat.

Step Five is to apply the transfer and press for about 35 sections using enough pressure to compress the foam about 50%.

Step Three is to insert a piece of foam or a pillow between layers of the shirt.

Step Six: Open press GENTLY and allow shirt & transfer to cool for about 10 seconds before removing transfer.

Some things to know:

Ever see a shirt with a physical indentation around the image? Chances are, that is sublimation and that indentation can be difficult to avoid but it can be done using one of two tricks (or both).

Preparation of the Transfer:

Trick One: Use a "sublimation pillow" between the fabric and the stage of the heat press. This provides a soft platform for the transfer paper to sink into and greatly reduces the chance of creating an indentation in the fabric.

When using a pillow, close the press with enough pressure to compress the pillow about 50%. Using too much pressure will defeat the purpose of the pillow.

If you don't have a pillow, you can use ordinary foam from a sewing supply store like JoAnn Fabrics. I recommend 1 ½" – 2" thick foam. If you want to actually make your own pillows, loosely sew two sheets of Teflon film over the top and bottom of the foam. You will find the need for several sizes. The Teflon film will prevent the foam from absorbing stray ink. Condé sells pre-made pillows. Just do a search for "Teflon Pillow".

Commercial Teflon pillow

Trick Two: One of the reasons fabric shows indentations is because the transfer paper has sharp, straight edges. These actually draw attention to themselves. We have found that if you tear (don't cut), tear the paper around the image, the uneven edges of the paper tend to eliminate the unsightly indentations. You don't have to get close to the image or worry about tracing the image, just tear the paper somewhere outside the print area.

Needless to say, if you use both of these techniques, you are very unlikely to see an indentation in your fabric.

The reason fabric does this is simple. Polyester fabric (which is typically required for sublimation), permanently creases at about 220° F. Since we sublimate at 400° F, we are well past the stage where fabric is going to crease.

Placing a shirt in the press:

Although many people will tell you to "split" the shirt and put one layer on top of the stage of the heat press and the other underneath, that usually isn't necessary, especially if you use a pillow and place it between the front and back of the shirt. For those who prefer to split the shirt or if you aren't using a pillow, splitting the shirt is fine.

Always place a sheet of clean butcher paper or newsprint over the stage of the heat press. DO NOT use Teflon film.

Build your sublimation sandwich on the press as shown in the illustration and cover with a second sheet of clean newsprint or butcher paper. These sheets will catch any stray dye and keep it off your shirt and your press. Although people often say this is what the Teflon sheets are for, they WILL hold ink and the next time you use them, they will deposit the ink on the shirt.

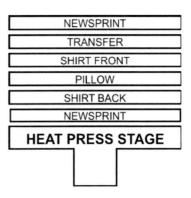

Stacking order for most fabric products.

Close the press over the sublimation sandwich untill the pillow or foam is compressed about 50% and press for the alloted time (usually 35-45 seconds). Then GENTLY open the press, taking care that the sublimation sandwich doesn't move. Allow the entire package to rest for 10 seconds before you proceed. Then begin unpacking the sandwich. Because fabric cools very quickly, it isn't necessary to do anything special with the finished shirt.

If you want to print multiple images:

It is certainly possible to print as many images on a shirt as you want. Simply repeat the same process as above to print the back of the shirt. You can also print on the sleeves using the same process. Be sure to ALWAYS use clean newsprint and cover sheets each time you do an impression.

Print and sew:

Some people print the entire shirt, including the sleeves. This is called "print and sew" and is accomplished by using a bolt of fabric, imprinting it and then cutting out the shirt pattern. This would normally require a wide format printer, heatpress and of course, the ability to sew the shirt. If you desire to investigate this further, call a Condé representative. They will be happy to assist you.

For the latest instructions and temperature settings, check out the Condé website.

WORKING WITH COLORED FABRICS

Can you sublimate colored shirts? Of course you can! There are, however, a couple of caveats:

You can only sublimate shirts that are light colors to about medium colors. No dark colors and no black. (There are ways to print black shirts, but not with sublimation).

When sublimating a colored shirt, you can expect to see your colors change from what is on your computer. This is because all sublimation dyes, except black, are translucent. That means the background color shows through. This can present a number of problems which we will discuss below.

The first problem is that the shirt color will change the colors being sublimated. Because the dyes are translucent, that is, you can see through them, the substrate color will show through. If you remember your high school physics lessons, you know that anytime one color mixes with another color, be it liquid or dry, it will create a new color. Yellow and blue make green, etc. There is a way to print dark and black shirts, but it isn't sublimation. If you are interested, contact your Condé representative and ask about laser printers that print with white toner or Siser transfer sheets.

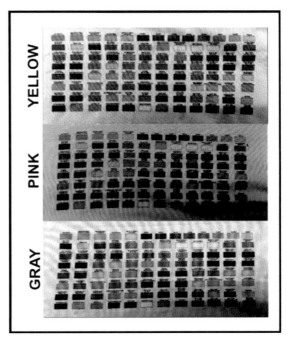

Because sublimation inks are translucent, the background color always shows through. This often changes the colors of the ink.

Lighter color shirts actually print pretty well without doing anything. Cream colors, light browns, blues and greens do affect the final colors but usually not enough to be too concerned unless your customer wants specific colors and then you will have to go the extra mile.

Going the extra mile to insure the end result involves some extra work on your part. Here's what you do: Using a color chart (available from the Condé website), sublimate it on the same color shirt you will be sublimating for your customer and look at the results. Those are the colors you are going to end up with.

Select the colors you want from the chart you printed on the shirt for use in your graphic – no matter how bad they look on the screen, and you will get the colors you expect in the finished product.

When working with bitmaps or photographs, there really isn't much you can do but surprisingly, these look pretty good on colored shirts anyway; in fact, most graphics do. It is really only when you get to colors like red and a medium green or blue that things become questionable. For these, just do a test print and see what

139

the finished product is really going to look like. For this, I keep several of each color shirt (usually shirts I messed up), to print test images on.

Can you sublimate colored shirts? Absolutely. Will your customers love them? Absolutely. You just need to help the customer know what to expect – that being, a slight shift in colors.

One more note: One of the most popular colors is safety yellow and it is just that. In West Virginia, we would say, "It will suck your eyeballs out". It is very bright and will dramatically change ink colors. For this reason, most people only print black on this particular shirt.

WORKING WITH SOCKS

Socks are fun, and we offer just about every kind of sock you can think of. Some have a black toe and heel, and some don't. Some are crew type and some tank type. Some are high on the leg and some barely come above your shoe. Some require a jig to make but most don't require anything extra, just the cardboard that comes with the sock.

People love socks that reflect the things they like. Many airports have stores that sell nothing but socks – socks with animals, sayings, pictures of people and much more. Now, you can go them one better by printing socks that not only have pictures of their hobbies, sports or any number of other things but their name to boot!

All socks are imprinted one side at a time. They are easy. A quick spray with ProSpray and press the first side. Before pressing the second side, pull the sock around the cardboard or jig just enough to insure there won't be a white line and press the second side.

Not all socks are done in exactly the same way, temperature or time, so be sure to check the Condé website for the latest information for the specific sock you are working with.

Basically, there are two types of socks on the market. Although both sublimate very well, the ones on the left, The Sublime brand, come with a cardstock insert already in the sock. This makes the sublimation process much faster and not having to insert a template inside the sock. The cardstock can be left in the sock afterward to make a nice presentation to the customer.

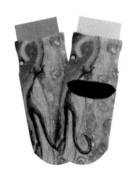

Ankle sock. Note the cardstock inserted into the sock.

Crew socks, also with cardstock inserted.

Knee socks also come with cardstock already inserted.

PART TWO
SECTION 18

"The value of an idea lies in the using of it." -Thomas Edison

SPECIALIZED PRODUCTS

There are more and more specialized products coming into the sublimation world all the time. Perhaps the oldest is the Mates product, which is a self-adhesive product that comes in gold, silver, clear and white. This material requires some special handling. It makes great labels and can even be applied to drinkware and washed in a dishwasher (no high temp however). It can't be microwaved or cut with a laser, however.

The newest product is from a company called Siser. It is a sublimatable film that can be applied to fabric. This allows sublimators to work with most any fabric, including cotton.

Other products include Polyester ribbon for making bookmarks, award ribbons and sashes for all kinds of uses.

A unique and fun product is the SubliSandal. It is a flip-flop that can be sublimated. These are great for vacations, ocean-side weddings and just for fun.

New products are always coming and will be added to future volumes of this book but the latest and greatest can always be found on the Condé website. Just click on "New Products".

To make a SubliSandal. just sublimate, pop out the bottoms and attach the straps. In about 5 minutes, they're done.

Diaries and notebooks make great gifts.

Flags for yard or car.

Towels of all kinds and sizes are available.

142

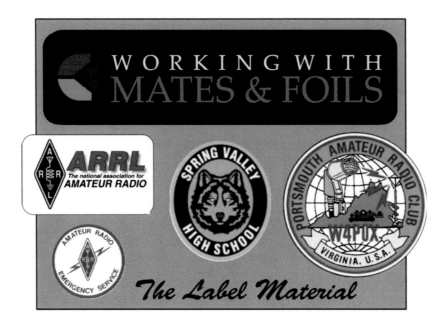

"Success is the sum of small efforts, repeated day in and day out." -Robert Collier

Mates, or any thin self-adhesive sublimatable material for that matter, fall into a category all by themselves. Mates is a terrific money-maker but there are a couple of tricks you need to know to be successful.

I use a lot of Mates. It is my favorite material to work with because it is, by far, my biggest money maker.

Mates can be however, a little frustrating to make. Small pieces are usually no problem. Just stick it in the press and it will come out fine but larger pieces like the 8.5"x11" sheets are a different story.

The bad things that usually go wrong are:

1. The sheet rolls up into a scroll and can't be flattened back out. The "sticker" will still work fine but working with it while still on the carrier sheet can be a challenge.
2. Ghosting. Two images printed on top of each other.
3. Moisture resulting in wisps of color, usually off to one corner of the image.
4. The material comes out permanently glued to the cover sheet.

Mates comes in sheets but also in pre-cut 2" disks.

Below are the steps to make full sheets of the Mates material that will avoid the problems listed above.

1. This is probably the only product where you use two Teflon sheets, one on top and one on the bottom. Because the Mates material is made up of several layers of film plus a layer of adhesive and a carrier sheet, it is not unusual for some of the adhesive to squeeze out onto a cover sheet and glue itself down. This is why we exchange the usual paper cover sheet for a Teflon sheet on top and bottom. It is needed on the bottom to protect the rubber pad on the stage of the press and on the top to protect the heating platen.

2. Using two sheets of Teflon instead of an absorptive sheet of paper as a cover sheet introduces far more moisture into the process than with other products. This shows up in two ways: One, you will likely hear a squeak when you close the press. This is moisture escaping from the product and the

Mates is an ideal material for making self-adhesive labels, stickers and decals.

transfer sheet. Two, you may see a wisp of color, usually at a 45° angle from one or more corners of your image on the finished product. If you don't need the material outside your image, that's no problem but if you do, you will have to fight to get rid of it. The steps below will help you do that.

3. Just before you are ready to attach the transfer to the Mates material, it is helpful to pre-press it to remove as much moisture as possible. To do this, lay both the Mates material (face up) and the transfer (face up) on the stage of the heat press and move the heating platen to within 2" or 3" of them. Allow them to rest this way for 10-20 seconds.

4. Immediately after removing the transfer and Mates from the heat press, adhere them for pressing. This can be done two ways: One, you can spray a very light coat of spray adhesive onto the transfer, put them together and place them in the press. The other way is to use heat tape. With this method, it is imperative to place two pieces of tape *on the same side* of the transfer. Do **NOT** place tape on opposite sides of the transfer! Doing so will often cause ghosting as the Mates material will shrink slightly when being pressed. It really doesn't matter if the transfer is face up or face down, but I prefer face down.

Although not normally recommended, this is one product where you should use two sheets of Teflon.

5. Place the transfer with the Mates material on top of a sheet of Teflon and cover with a second sheet of Teflon and press with medium to heavy pressure for about 45 seconds. Open the press slowly after the timer goes off and remove the top sheet of Teflon. Using a heat glove, remove the product and place it on a Kool Plate (if you have one) or a flat surface to cool. To reduce the material's tendency to curl into a scroll, place something heavy on top of it while it cools. I use the base from a trophy but even a rock from you garden will do the trick.

To cool the foil, lay it on a flat surface or a KoolPlate and place some weight on each sheet until cool.

6. After the Mates material has cooled to the touch, I stack it facedown and place yet another weight (I use a brick) on it until I am ready to package or use it. The Mates material will eventually flatten out almost completely but it takes weeks for that to happen so it is important that your customer understand the curling does not affect the Mates film itself, only the carrier sheet it is adhered to. Once the Mates is removed, it will be flat and can be adhered to any surface that is flat or cylindrical. When adhering

Once cool, place a weight to help flatten the material.

the material, it can be positioned and then removed multiple times as needed but once left in position for a few hours, it becomes permanent. Of course, when applied to paper or similar surfaces, it may not be removable.

NOTE: For those who own a laser engraver, the Mates material contains PVC and should never be cut using a laser engraver. Mates has a close cousin called Rowmark Lights which is not sublimatable but is laser engravable; it does not contain PVC and therefore, can be cut with a laser.

First and foremost, this is not typical vinyl in that it DOES NOT CONTAIN PVC. This means heat, even from a laser engraver will not cause it to release dangerous Poly Vinyl Chloride into the air. PVC, when heated, releases fumes that can be deadly. Never laser cut anything that contains PVC!

Now that we have cleared that up, let's talk about one of the most exciting products to come into the sublimation industry in years. It allows you to sublimate on a sheet of film and then transfer it to a garment.

For complete instructions, go to the Condé website but below is an abbreviated overview:

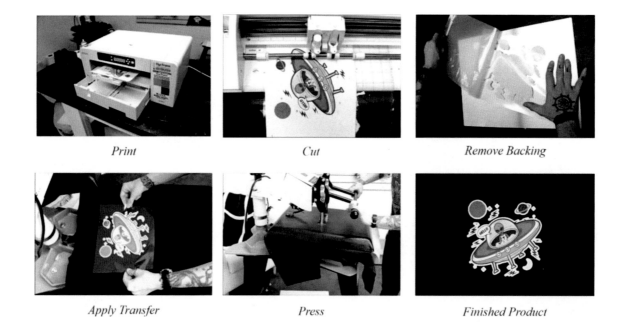

Print   *Cut*   *Remove Backing*

Apply Transfer   *Press*   *Finished Product*

Satin and Grosgrain Polyester ribbon opens up sublimation to all kinds of possibilities. Above is an example of a "Cheer Ribbon" (a hair bow for a cheerleader) which can be made using sublimation and some 3" wide Polyester ribbon. Instructions can be found on

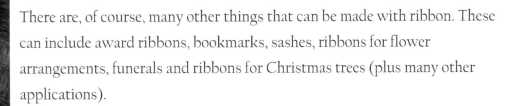

CondéTV. It is an easy product to make and carries an excellent profit margin with a selling price of $20 or more for each custom ribbon and a material cost of only about $3.

There are, of course, many other things that can be made with ribbon. These can include award ribbons, bookmarks, sashes, ribbons for flower arrangements, funerals and ribbons for Christmas trees (plus many other applications).

Ribbon is easy to sublimation. Just check out the instructions below:

Hover transfer under open heat press for 10 seconds to dry excess moisture.

1. Cover the bottom table of the press with a sheet of protective paper.
2. Secure transfer to substrate using ProSpray.
3. Place substrate face down, with attached transfer face up, on top of protective paper on bottom table.
4. Top with protective paper and press for 90 seconds with medium pressure.

**L
A
N
Y
A
R
D
S**

Lanyards for name badges used as company IDs, for conferences and many other applications, can be sublimated and secured to a number of attachments.

Both vertical and horizontal badges are available, as well as badges made from FRP and metal. Badges can be one-sided or two-sided. To remember how to make FRP or metal, check out the previous chapters.

To make the lanyards themselves, treat them like any other piece of cloth. Lanyards are ¾" wide and 36" long. Although this is too long for most heat presses, they can usually be made in two parts with the seam in the middle where it doesn't really show. With a little care in the design stage, especially if the background is left white, no one will ever know it was made in two parts.

To make the lanyard, spray with some ProSpray and drape over the transfer. It should be made face up in the press. This is accomplished by using two pieces of heavy cardboard as backers or hardboard (I recommend hardboard) and building your sublimation sandwich on one sheet of backer. When ready to press, cover with a protective sheet and cover with the second piece of backer. You can now flip the entire sandwich over, lay it on the press and gently slip the backer boards out of the press. This leaves the transfer face down and the lanyard face up in the press.

I find it difficult to hold the lanyard in the exact spot over the transfer, so I built a simple jig to align the lanyard and hold it in place. This can be done with a piece of hardboard and some strips of aluminum.

By carefully spacing the slots where the lanyards will lay, you can create your design in CorelDraw so it matches the layout of the jig. This allows making several lanyards at the same time and reduces the chance of them moving during the pressing process.

Press lanyards for 45-60 seconds with light to medium pressure at 400° F.

BEFORE PRESSING
BACKER BOARD
PROTECTIVE PAPER
TRANSFER FACE DOWN
LANYARD FACE UP
PROTECTIVE PAPER
BACKER BOARD

LEFT: Getting a lanyard ready to press uses two backer boards to stabilize the sandwich while flipping it over.
RIGHT: Once the sandwich is in the press, carefully slip out the two backer boards leaving this configuration.

IN THE PRESS
PROTECTIVE PAPER
TRANSFER FACE DOWN
LANYARD FACE UP
PROTECTIVE PAPER

What will they think of next? Air fresheners for car or home to cover up those awful odors like the smell of McDonalds after you eat in your car. Or pet odors in your home. Whatever it is for, air fresheners are more fun when they are personalized.

These are great for company logos, organizational logos, pictures of a church or landmark. Because they are thin and light, they are great for mailing to clients or group members. Use them as a date reminder or to remind people you have changed your phone number or moved.

These are great to put pictures of your pet(s) or even a grandchild. Imprint them with sports equipment or something to do with a favorite hobby.

Because these are very inexpensive, they make great promotional items and chances are, we can all use one of these somewhere in our car, home or office. Or, perhaps in a closet where shoes are stored.

Each sheet comes in a 7x10.375" sheet with the fresheners punched so they pop out easily. They also come with a plastic bag and string to make them complete. All you add is the scent. A few drops of Essential oils and it is ready to go to work for you or your customer.

TIP: Make samples of each design and scent them with cinnamon and hang them around your showroom. People love to smell cinnamon – it reminds them of Christmas, home cooking and all that goes with the holidays.

Essential oils are available from Amazon and many other stores.

But, there's more!

You can also get this material cut into 3D ornaments. These fun cutouts can be sublimated and made into really unique products.

These can be sublimated on both sides but should be sublimated one side at a time. Use ProSpray to hold the transfer in place and sublimate at 400 F with light pressure with the felt face up and the transfer face down. Use a protective sheet of paper top and bottom.

PROTECTIVE PAPER
TRANSFER FACE DOWN
FELT FACE UP
PROTECTIVE PAPER

Stacking order for all felt products.

PATCHES

There are a number of sizes and shapes available.

Think hobbies, organizations, clubs, schools, churches, businesses and every kind of sport. They all love patches.

Having a patch made the traditional way takes time, usually involves a setup fee and always a minimum number of patches. You pay by the number of colors and the number of stitches. What's more, all the patches must be exactly the same – no personalization possible.

None of that is true with sublimation.

- Customer wants to put a different name or number on each patch – no problem.
- Customer only wants one patch – no problem.
- Customer wants a photo or logo – no problem.
- Customer needs just a few extra after initial order – no problem.
- Customer wants lots and lots of colors – no problem.
- What's more, there is no setup fee – unless you want it.

Hobbies and sports like skydiving, SCUBA diving, swimming, archery, shooting (guns), hunting, pet shows,

SCUBA diving patch.

skating, modeling, crafts, travel, hiking, running, camping, motorcycles, BMX and bicycling, ham radio, cars and trucks, landscaping, Bridge and other card gaming groups and probably a thousand more, are all potential markets for patches. People like to belong, and they like to make that known, so others can ask about their interest. Organizations, churches, schools and businesses are also potential markets.

These are made much like any piece of cloth with two exceptions: One, a sheet of Teflon should be placed under the patch (remember, there is glue on the backside) and you should use heavy pressure with patches. So, the patch is made face up in the press with Teflon underneath and protective paper on the back of the transfer. Time is 45 seconds at 400 F and heavy pressure. Open the press gently and allow patch(es) to sit for a few seconds before moving them.

PROTECTIVE PAPER
TRANSFER FACE DOWN
PATCH FACE UP
TEFLON SHEET
PROTECTIVE PAPER

Stacking order for heat seal

We place mousepads in the Fabric Section because most are actually cloth adhered to a piece of rubber or foam.

Mousepads have been around an entire generation now. Everyone seems to have at least a few around the house or office but the interesting thing about them is, people still like getting new ones – especially if it's personalized with their name, favorite hobby or company logo.

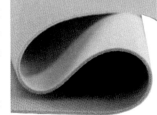

Typical mousepad material.

Mousepads come in a variety of sizes and shapes as shown above. They also come in different materials and different thicknesses. Most unique or custom shapes come in 1/8" thickness while many standard size pads are ¼" thick. They also come with the rubber back in one of two colors – black or tan.

The 1/8" material is available in sheets and can be cut with an X-Acto knife or laser engraver so you can make small quantities of specialized shapes. For larger quantities, Condé will be happy to make them for you. Just give us a call.

MouseMates are waterproof and high definition.

Most mousepads are made of a rubber compound with a sheet of Polyester fabric adhered to it but there are a couple of alternatives.

One is the MouseMates product. More information is available on the next page. This mousepad is made with a rubber black backing approximately 1/8" thick but has a special high gloss film adhered to the rubber that, when sublimated, produces a washable, high resolution image.

UNISUB Memo Boards make great mousepad fora super harsh environment.

A product that is no longer marketed as a mousepad but can certainly be used as one, is the UNISUB hardboard memo boards. These have nice rounded corners and have the super hard UNISUB white coating that produces a high-resolution image and is also washable. It can also be marked on with a Vis-à-vis marker and then the marker removed with water. To make these even nicer, place 4 silicon rubber feet on the back.

To produce any of these products, use some ProSpray to secure the transfer, then place the pad face up in your heat press and press with light to medium pressure for one minute.

WORKING WITH
MOUSEMATES
PLACEMATES
MUGMATES

This product comes from Rowmark, a major manufacturer of engraving plastics. It is a rubber-based material with a flexible high gloss surface in either gold or silver.

When sublimated, it produces an extremely high-resolution image. It is waterproof and very durable. Grime, dirt and even markers can be removed easily with water and a household cleaner, so it makes great placemats, mats for pet dishes, coasters and mousepads.

The material can also be used with Vis-à-vis markers and cleaned with water or with permanent markers like a Sharpie and cleaned with mineral spirts.

The coasters are inexpensive enough they can be used as a promotional product that will stay on the recipient's desk for years. All you have to do is imprint it with their name or company logo. People almost never throw out something with their name on it!

These products take about a minute to make at 400° F with light to medium pressure. To print these, place the product face up in the press and use ProSpray to secure the transfer. Be careful, these products retain heat for a long time and can cause a serious burn if handled without a heat glove.

WORKING WITH FLAGS, BANNERS & PENNANTS

Sublimation works great for all kinds of flags, banners and pennants. This includes garden flags, car flags and even full-size flags, provided you have a press and printer large enough (Condé is always happy to do the large ones for you).

School pennants are always a popular gift. Try imprinting a child's photo along with their school logo. In the infamous words of the Beach Boys, "Be proud of your school".

Flags come in both a single-sided and double-sided version and are printed the same as any other cloth product with one exception. When doing the double-sided products, a sheet of paper must be placed between the two layers of fabric, so the dyes don't pass through to the other side.

Double-sided flags come pre-sewn and ready to print. Both sides can be printed at the same time or you can print each side separately.

Car flags are attached to the car window using plastic pole that fits over the top edge of a car window and can withstand most in-town driving. Flags should be removed when traveling at high speeds.

Example of double-sided car flag.

Car flagpole.

Garden flags are very popular and come in a couple of sizes. Poles are also available for them. These have an extra-large market, since the same person may purchase one for each season, each holiday or various special occasions such as graduations, birthdays, etc.

Unless imprinting both sides at once, place the flag face up in the heat press. Affix the transfer using ProSpray. Cover both top and bottom with clean paper and press with medium pressure for about one minute at 400° F. Open the press gently and allow any cloth item to cool for a few seconds before moving it.

The newest flag material being offered is SubliLinen. This makes an excellent material for flags, placemats, tote bags, aprons and a host of other products.

SubliLinen 2-sided Flag

SubliLinen Apron

LUNCH TOTE

MESSENGER BAG

ARM BAND TO HOLD
MEDIA PLAYER

HANDBAG

EYEGLASS STRAP

COSMETIC BAG

BEVERAGE HUGGER

ICE POP
HOLDER

LAPTOP SLEEVE

LUGGAGE FINDER

WORKING WITH NEOPRENE

Neoprene is one of those surprise materials. It is the same flexible material that is used to make wetsuits for SCUBA diving. This material is extremely durable and when made in white, sublimates very well.

In the Condé register of products, it is used to make coasters, cup huggers, eye glass cases, wrist bands, laptop bags, checkbook covers, business card cases, cosmetic bags along with a variety of other style bags, including a handbag, and my very favorite, a luggage finder.

The fabric is also available in sheet form so you can put your creative juices to work.

These products are inexpensive and very easy to make. These are great as gift items and some are perfect for use as a promotional product you can give away to promote your business.

These items are all made face up in the heat press with light pressure at 400° F for 1 minute. Use ProSpray to hold the transfer in place.

Neoprene is used to make wetsuits for SCUBA diving.

Cut and Sew is the term we use for people who use a pattern to cut out a garment, sublimate it in pieces, then sew it together. This is how commercial manufacturers do most of the Polyester products we wear every day.

Really large operations use printers and presses as much as 12' wide. Roller presses are often used so fabric can be printed and immediately pressed. Larger operations usually print the ink directly to the fabric rather than using a transfer sheet.

Many of the smaller sports garment companies use this method to custom make all kinds of sports uniforms. This process allows every inch of the garment to be sublimated either in a solid color or design.

Just because you don't have all the equipment to do this process doesn't

Custom garments like these are usually done with cut & sew sublimation.

mean you can't sell cut & sew garments. There are a number of sources that will gladly wholesale these to you. Check with your Condé representative for details.

PART TWO
SECTION 19

*"To succeed in business, to reach the top, an individual must know
All it is possible to know about that business."* -J. Paul Getty

FABRICATING YOUR OWN BLANKS

People with the capability of cutting the various materials will want to know these tips and tricks to cutting metal, FRP, hardboard and other common materials. Remember, whatever you make has to have a sublimatable coating so it is usually necessary to start with a piece of material that has been prepared for sublimation and then just fabricate it to your own specifications. Trying to coat your own substrates is an exhausting process and just isn't practical.

Cutting Metal: Most of the metal used in sublimation is thin (.018-.020") and can be cut easily with a metal shear. These shears are fairly inexpensive (starting under $400 and going close to $4,000 for a colossal model). For most shops, the $400 model is more than enough. Shears can be ordered to have a blade for cutting one of two types of material: metal or plastic. Of course, you want one for cutting metal. There is nothing currently sublimatable that can be cut with a plastics blade that can't be cut with a metal blade.

There are a couple of things you should know about cutting metal: When metal is cut on a shear, it will

This Accucutter 2001 EVO shear has been completely redesigned.

probably not cut perfectly square. This is because of a phenomenon that occurs as the blade passes through the metal. Good shears try to compensate for this in a couple of ways. The best way is to buy a shear that has a hold-down bar that forces the metal to stay in place and not twist when cut. But these presses cost around $1,000 and are out of the budget and the need of most sublimators. The cheaper shears approach this by knocking the ruler out of square a tiny bit and this pretty much solves the problem. The final and most important thing to do to insure straight, square cuts is to keep a sharp blade. Replacement blades can be purchased for all shears and shear companies offer a sharpening service as well.

Second, shearing metal should always be done face up. This is because sheared metal has a burr up and a burr downside. A quality job will require burr down on all four sides, so it will be necessary to cut or trim each piece of metal on all four sides.

This top-of-the-line Accucutter 4001 shear comes in several sizes and can even be air operated.

A few sublimatable metal products use .035 or .050" metal. These cannot be cut with the less expensive shears. If you want to cut these materials, you will need to invest in a hydraulic press in the up to $4,000 price range.

Finally, shears can be very dangerous when not used properly. Most shears have safety guards to keep fingers clear of the blade, but not all. Regardless of the brand, improper use of a shear can remove fingers! These things are extremely sharp.

Cutting FRP: There are several ways to cut FRP: It is said by many that FRP cannot be cut with a laser. That is not true. A CO_2 laser will do a wonderful job cutting FRP in a single pass. What people are referring to when they say it can't be laser cut is the black goo that is left on the edges of the FRP after being cut. If you are willing to clean the residue off with a piece of 220 grit sandpaper, there is no reason you can't cut FRP on your laser. There are no chemicals in FRP that will produce dangerous gasses or damage mirrors.

FRP, when cut with a laser must be sanded to remove a black goo

There are a number of ways to cut FRP with a rotary engraver. Because of the 3/32" thickness, the cut should be made slowly with a sacrificial sheet underneath (I recommend it be at least 1/8" thick). Depending on the type of edge you desire, you can use a "V" cutter (plastic cutter) ranging from .010 to .030" and end up with a sharp beveled edge. If you desire a straight edge, an end mill cutter will do a good job. These cutters come in a variety of sizes but I recommend a .010 or .015" cutter. A word of caution: Be sure you have properly adjusted the height of your cutter before starting your job. End mills are brittle, and if maladjusted and if it cuts through the FRP and sacrificial sheet to hit the metal table, it could break. If it does, the tip will fly around the room like a missile. Safety glasses are a must when using end mill cutters! To hold the FRP products in place, you will have to use lots of double-sided "table tape". Each piece that is to be cut out should have at least a couple of pieces of ½" tape. The larger the piece, the more passes it should have. When FRP is cut using a rotary engraver, the spin of the engraver causes the FRP to want to twist as it just about finishes the cut. This can be avoided by using plenty of table tape.

Cutting FRP with a table saw or band saw is very dangerous and not recommended. If you do try this, insure there is no "chatter" when being cut. Use a very fine-toothed plywood or plastics blade. FRP can be cut with a safety saw like those used by engravers to cut plastic.

Cutting Hardboard: One material used a lot with sublimation is hardboard, usually in 1/8" thickness. Except for the special coating, this is the same hardboard you buy at a hardware store and can be cut in the same way. If you have a laser engraver, it is easy to cut this material into any shape you want. If the material has a protective coating on it, leave it while cutting. If not, residue can be cleaned off with alcohol, Simple Green or a laser cleaner. A light sanding with 220 grit paper will likely be needed to finish the piece. If you have a rotary engraver, you can use the same steps as cutting FRP but will find it is a bit more difficult to hold the product in place. Table tape probably won't do the job so you will have to use some type of T-clamp to hold the piece(s) in place. Using a table saw or band saw to cut small pieces is ill-advised but if you do, use all safety devices, control any chatter and use a fine-toothed blade.

The best way to cut hardboard is to use a "safety saw". These are fairly expensive (around $2,000) and are capable of cutting up to ¼" material with no chatter and no danger to the operator. These cut perfectly straight edges and square corners and will not chip the sublimation coating.

Cutting MDF: MDF (Medium Density Fiberboard) is made up of many layers of paper pressed together with glue. It can be fabricated like fine wood. It can be cut, sanded, routed, and beveled with virtually no need for sanding. It can then be painted (edges) and sublimated. Because MDF is between ½" and 1" thick, most lasers are not going to be a viable means for cutting the material. In this case, probably short of a table saw or band saw is going to do the trick. Like any job, use all possible safety guards and a fine-toothed blade. Passing the material through the blade very slowly will help prevent chipping of the sublimatable surface. Adding masking tape or painters' tape to the edges prior to cutting may also help prevent chipping.

Cutting DyeFlex Plastic: The best way to cut DyeFlex plastic is with a laser engraver. Medium power and high speed should provide a clean cut. Too much power may mar the surface.

To cut DyeFlex with a rotary engraver, use the same basic setup as with FRP. A sacrificial sheet under the DyeFlex is mandatory along with plenty of table tape. Cut the material face up using a "profile" cutter of a .020" cutter allowing the cutter to just barely pass through the material and into the sacrificial sheet.

DyeFlex can also be cut on a shear (metal or plastic). Plastic shear is preferred of course, but a metal shear will also work. It can also be cut with an X-Acto type knife. With this method, don't try to cut all the way through the material; just a deep scratch. The excess plastic will easily snap away. Other methods of cutting include a paper shear or roller shear.

Cutting Mousepad Material: Mouse pad material comes in a variety of thicknesses beginning at 1/16" and 1/8" which can be cut with scissors, an X-Acto knife or a laser engraver. The thicker material is usually ¼" or ½" and can be cut with a laser or X-Acto type knife. ¾" material and above will require multiple passes with a utility or X-Acto knife or a laser engraver, if you have one powerful enough.

Cutting Neoprene (wetsuit material): This material can be cut using scissors, or a knife but it can also be cut with a laser engraver. When cutting with a laser, it is advisable to use as little power as possible and air assist to lessen any contamination on the surface of the material.

Note to laser users: Every laser engraver is different – some drastically. Because of this fact, it is impossible to list actual cutting settings for each brand or type of laser. Cutting speed of most lasers should be between 5% and 20%. To determine the power setting, try a trial cut on a scrap piece of DyeFlex with 50% power and adjust accordingly. Use air assist if available. For large jobs, a cutting table is preferred but not required.

PART TWO
SECTION 20

"Dream big, work hard, stay focused & surround yourself with good people." -Unknown

ADDING ENGRAVING TO THE MIX

It is rare that you should ever want to engrave a sublimated product – there just isn't any reason to. All the information can be imprinted at one time when making the badge, tag, plaque, etc.

However, there are a couple of reasons why you might want to engrave a sublimated product after it has been sublimated. They include:

Needing to award a plaque or other gift item but not having the name of the recipient until after the presentation.

Someone insists they want gold or silver included in a name badge or plaque.

Of course, having to handle a product twice to obtain a metallic element of a product merits a significant up-charge. You should not feel obligated to offer this service without being compensated handsomely.

Engraving FRP, Hardboard or MDF Board: These all engrave about the same and can be marked with either a laser engraver or a rotary engraver. Don't be surprised if you have to make multiple passes with a laser. This is because the UNISUB coating is so hard, it resists the heat of a laser beam. Several quick passes however should get the job done. Unlike cutting FRP, there is no significant residue left behind when FRP is only being engraved. The gooey residue found when cutting FRP is from the fiberglass, not the topcoat (which is all you need to cut through).

To paint fill a sublimated product, it is ideal to have about .010" of depth in the engraving. More is better, at least to a point. Depending on the depth you have to fill, a number of paints can be used. If gold or silver is the objective, consider the gold and silver ink pens artists use. Just paint over the engraved area, allow to almost dry and wipe off excess with alcohol or mineral spirits.

This Chessie logo was laser engraved on a UNISUB paper weight and paint filled.

If you are using a rotary engraver, the depth is not an issue. Use a standard plastics cutter and nosecone if you have one. The size of cutter is unimportant so far as the material is concerned. Paint filling this type of engraving should be much easier since you can have a deeper engraving, but the same metallic paints or inks can be used as mentioned above.

Engraving Metal: A laser engraver is pretty limited when it comes to engraving sublimation metal. I have had some success with the non-UNISUB metals but prefer using a rotary engraver for this task. Diamond drag or "scratch" engraving produces the best outcome as it can pass through the coating on any sublimated metal. Rotary (burnishing) engraving works pretty well on non-UNISUB metals so long as a small tool is used (.005"-.020"). Larger tools tend to skip over the harder portions of the coatings as do all cutters when used with the UNISUB metals. If you try using UNISUB metal, expect to have to use lots of pressure and multiple passes.

Tip: If you are going to engrave metal after it is sublimated, include in the original design a box or other solid colored element where the engraving is going to be. The dark background makes the engraving much easier to read and does not affect the level of difficulty of engraving.

PART TWO
SECTION 21

"If you don't build your dream, someone will hire you to build theirs" -Unknown

MAKING ADA COMPLIANT SIGNAGE

Can sublimated signage be ADA compliant? Well, yes and no. On its own, it cannot. ADA signs require very exacting tactile lettering and Grade II Braille. This cannot be accomplished with sublimation alone. If you have a laser engraver and/or a rotary engraver however, you can marry the multiple methods together to get a beautiful sign that is cheap to make and not too terribly labor intensive.

ADA regulations require that all ADA signage have tactile letters that are raised 1/32" from the surface of the sign. They also require the tactile letters be highly contrasted with the background directly behind them. At one time, it was understood that the entire sign be of a single high contrast color, but that is no longer true. This opens the door to using logos, artwork and graphic designs on the sign – so long as the tactile portion of the sign has high contrast. Of course, it must also have Grade II Braille in a specific location on the sign. To learn all the specifics of making and hanging ADA signage, visit www.ada.gov.

To fabricate an ADA sign, here are the options: First, sublimate the sign in accordance with the size requirements. FRP or MDF board is commonly used to make signs (metal can be used but will require that Braille characters be made in a piece of plastic and adhered to the face of the sign [which is legal]).

Other than that, all signs are made in the same manner. After sublimating the background, it will be necessary to create the tactile letters. This can be done with a rotary machine using a profile cutter, but is easier on a laser since the regulations require the letters have straight (flat, non-beveled) edges. The special ADA applique material is available from distributers who sell engraving plastic. The material must be matte (non-reflective) and 1/32" thick. Cut a piece of the applique and place it over the area where it should be and cut with your laser. Do not press the self-adhesive applique down hard as it will only make it more difficult later. After cutting the letters out, remove the excess immediately and press down the remaining letters.

Note the Braille that has been added to make this an ADA compliant sign.

The process with a rotary engraver is exactly the same as a laser. Adjust the cutter until it just barely passes through the applique plastic.

The Braille can be added a couple of different ways. There are companies who make Braille strips for you or you can produce the Braille yourself using something called "Raster Dot". With this method, you drill holes into the face of the sublimated sign and manually insert tiny colored beads into the holes. The beads, or dots, are held in place by friction and when done properly, will expose the required 1/32" of height along with the rounded surface now required by ADA regulations. These holes can be cut with a laser, but it is a bit more demanding in that the dots must fit tightly and expose 1/32" of themselves after being set. Although you will have to experiment with your laser, I can use a filled circle with a hairline outline that is .009" in diameter to obtain the right size hole in most materials.

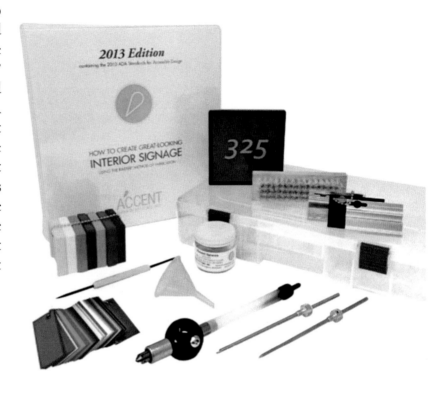

Raster Dot kit from Accent Signage has everything you need except the engraver.

"All of our dreams can come true - if we have the courage to pursue them." -Walt Disney

INTRODUCTION TO PART III – PROMOTION

Here's a hard bit of truth: Even if you are the best sublimator ever on the planet and you don't know how to market your products, you aren't going to sell much and if you don't sell, you don't make a profit and if you don't make a profit – well, you can see where this is going.

"I don't like selling". I hear it all the time. People don't want to be like the stereotypical used car salesman, who pushes his way in the door talking as fast as he can or the Fuller Brush salesman (let's see how many of you remember them), who sticks his foot in the door to get you to let him in.

It has been said before, but it is worth repeating, "Sublimated products will sell themselves". You don't have to use strong-arm tactics or trickery to sell this stuff. All you have to do is show it – but you have to show it at the right time, in the right place, and to the right people – that's the tricky part.

Trying to sell a car salesman a purse or a teetotaler a shot glass just isn't going to work. As author of the book, "125 Ways to Make Money with Sublimation", I have tried a lot of ways of showing (not selling) sublimated products to people. Most worked, a few did not. In the book, I shared what I learned about more than 125 of them, the products that I found appropriate and even designs I used to make the sale. Of course, trying 125 of these would drive you to distraction, but picking out three or four and trying them is quite sensible. If you find one that isn't working out, drop it and move on to another. That's what "selling" sublimated products is all about. The more people you show the products to, the more sales you are going to make – it is as simple as that.

In this section, I have tried to provide you with a mountain of information. You won't be able to use it all, nor should you. Pick out what you think is right for you and your company and start there.

Whatever you do, don't let the idea of selling scare you. Our job isn't to sell anything. It is to help solve a person's problem (fulfill their need). They need a gift or want a new T-shirt. We just show them what we can do and presto, a sale is made.

An old friend of mine used what he called the three-foot rule. If he got within three feet of someone, he started his pitch telling people what he did for a living (it wasn't sublimation). Some people thought he was crazy but really, he was crazy like a fox. You see, he loved what he did. He was very enthusiastic about it and it showed. He couldn't wait to tell (show) someone (anyone) what he did.

That's what I would wish for you. That you be so excited about sublimation, you just can't wait to show someone what you can do. If you have that kind of excitement, I promise, you will do well.

Good luck!

PART THREE
SECTION 2

"A satisfied customer is the best business strategy of all." – Michael LeBoeuf

THE BEST NEW CLIENT IS THE ONE YOU ALREADY HAVE

No, this isn't just double talk. Many entrepreneurs fall into a trap of always trying to get new customers. Some spend a lot of money on advertising and gimmicks to bring in a new face and that's fine – to a point. It's always good to see a new face.

Sometimes however, we forget that the best customer is always the one we already have. They feel comfortable with us and the quality of work we offer. They think they know what products we offer – and that's the problem, they really don't and that's our fault.

Each time a customer comes in, we should show them something new. Keep your showroom constantly changing. You don't always have to buy new products, just move things around a bit. Customers usually enter a showroom with tunnel vision and actually see only one portion of the room. Move stuff around on a regular basis and it looks new to returning customers. I did this for years and often heard, "I like to come here. You are always adding so much new stuff". The truth was, I hadn't added anything at all. I just moved it around.

One of the things you may want to do when you start your own business is to identify some products you can sell that you don't actually make yourself. Screen printed coffee cups is a natural; since you do short order coffee cups in house, why not sell the large orders as well. You get 40-50% profit and you don't have to lift a finger. Pens, calendars, bronze shoes and bronze signs. The list goes on and on and it doesn't cost you a dime to sell any of them.

Constantly having new items to offer allows you to touch more areas where your existing customers live, increase sales and not have to waste money trying to find that illusive new face.

Don't misunderstand me. You have to build your clientele and that usually requires advertising - which is expensive. The trick is to find ways to promote your business that don't cost an arm and a leg. I have known companies that, without legalizing it, spent hundreds of dollars to get one customer and that guy only bought a $5 item!

This is usually the result when you just throw money at the problem. Listening to the long list of people who are constantly telling you their "something" will build your business, are not your friends. Friendly as they might seem, they are just salespeople trying to sell you website design, hosting, social media support, the perfect ad on the front of some flyer, or school newspaper. Although some may be able to legitimately help you grow your business, most are full of empty promises.

The clients you already have however, are birds in the hand and can be used, not manipulated, to help you grow your business. Ask them to tell their friends, visit your Facebook page and post something nice or allow you to use some quote or picture of theirs on your Facebook page or in your shop.

Although "Word of mouth" advertising takes a lifetime to develop, it has to start somewhere – why not here?

Try coupons that offer an incentive to repeat customers or coupons they can give away to tell others about your business. To be sure, develop an Email list, so you can send occasional information describing your specials or sale items for the month. If you can, find out when people have birthdays or anniversaries and drop them a card or email of good wishes.

In short, build a personal relationship with your customers when possible. Learn their names and try to remember specific things they tell you about themselves, their work or their family and ask about them on their next visit. Don't make a major deal out of this like some people do with special software to track every detail they can obtain. Just be genuinely interested. That will be enough to let them know you care and that you were really listening to them.

Not only can existing customers be encouraged to buy more, they happily tell others about you – just because you care.

When you do see a new customer, always ask how they learned about you? Was it a friend, the Yellow Pages, advertising, your website or just saw your sign while driving by? Track your answers to see what is working for you and what isn't.

One of the biggest mistakes new shop owners make is buying advertising in the form of school papers, football programs, etc. We justify our bad business decision by saying, "we want to support the community" and that may be fine, but be aware you are doing it as a gift to the school because it probably won't bring in a dime. I made a policy (after wasting a ton of money on school advertising) that I would create a policy of buying up to 10% of whatever the school spent in my shop. What I found out was that most schools who were asking for money, were buying their stuff somewhere else and never spent a dime with me. Money saved. Lesson learned.

Coca-Cola spends billions on advertising worldwide. They can afford it and they know that name recognition for them will eventually pay off. Walmart, Target and a thousand other businesses do the same thing. We can do that. We can't play on the same field they do. We have to know what it is costing us, per customer, to run advertising campaigns. Although name recognition has value, it doesn't work for us the way it does for Coke. We need a faster return on our investment and the only way to figure that out is to ask questions - so don't be bashful.

PART THREE
SECTION 3

"Who you are tomorrow begins with what you do today." -Tim Fargo

DON'T KNOW WHERE TO START? FOLLOW YOUR PASSION

Don't know where to start? Most people don't, but I have a suggestion. Start with whatever you are passionate about.

What makes a product special is when it has a picture of the customer's horse or car, etc.

For example: If you love horses and horse shows, perhaps a line of products you can sell at the various horse shows, in shops that cater to horse people, or over the Internet through a website, on Etsy, eBay or Amazon.com.

If your love is cars, consider renting a booth at a car show and offer a line of products where people can have a picture of their car and themselves imprinted.

The same is true if anything you enjoy doing. Sewing might mean sublimating squares for quilts, or if you are into pet shows, offer items with a person's pet(s) on them. If you like craft shows, design a series of products that look antique. The same advice goes to those who enjoy SCUBA diving, airplanes, motorcycles, BMX, any sport or hobby, only to mention a few possibilities.

Don't forget the opportunities at your church or Synagogue. There is always something you can offer fellow members such as license plates, key chains, wall hangings and shirts containing a picture of your church. Perhaps do it as a fundraiser so the church can reap a little of the profit.

For additional ideas, check out the rest of the Promotion Section. If you can't come up with something you like, ask your Condé representative. Chances are, they can give you some ideas you would never think of.

Don't forget your place of worship.

166

PART THREE
SECTION 4

"The purpose of a business is to create a customer who creates customers." - Shir Singh

LAGNIAPPE – ADDED VALUE

According to the all-knowing Wikipedia, the definition of "Lagnappe" is as follows:

> A **lagniappe** (/ˈlænjæp/ *LAN-yap*, /lænˈjæp/ *lan-YAP*) is "a small gift given to a customer by a merchant at the time of a purchase" (such as a <u>13th doughnut on purchase of a dozen</u>), or more broadly, "something given or obtained gratuitously or by way of good measure."

Someone once said, "people buy from people" and it's true. Think back over some of the purchases you have made recently (online purchases excluded). Chances are, one of the reasons you bought that car from a specific dealer was the personality of the salesperson. Or, even with small purchases, it is likely you go to stores where the sales staff are friendly and if you go often, you probably search out a particular person to wait on you. We like dealing with people who are friendly, trustworthy and knowledgeable.

One way to capitalize on that fact is to use lagnappe. Include with each order a little something extra to say, "thanks". Some people use the buzz word, "Added value" and that can be it: Going the extra mile to get an order out quickly or to include something extra – a promotional ink pen or key chain.

It can also include sending a "Thank You for Your Business" note in the mail (Speedy Sign-a-Rama is one chain that takes advantage of this idea), or including an "exclusive" coupon toward their next purchase (CVS uses this one a lot).

A smile and handshake go a long way in customer appreciation, but a token can go even further.

There are a thousand ways to take advantage of lagnappe and it doesn't matter which one you use but giving a little extra can go a long way in building a relationship with a new customer. Take the time and make the effort – remember, people buy from people!

PART THREE
SECTION 5

"All progress takes place outside the comfort zone." -Michael John Bobak

125 WAYS TO MAKE MONEY WITH SUBLIMATION

One of the unique things about sublimation is many people became successful because they found a niche or several niche markets and focused on those rather than trying to be all things to all people.

A niche is a very narrow band of products or customers that is usually too small for most people to notice. For instance, there isn't a huge market to sell to Ham radio operators. Although there are thousands of operators around the country, the problem is, only those thousands will ever be your customers. This is both good and bad. The good is you aren't likely to have much competition and your customers have few options. The bad news is that you have a limited number of potential customers and you must make the most out of finding them (or helping them find you), and being flexible enough to adjust to their individual needs.

Through the years, I have worked with a number of small groups (niches) and have always enjoyed going after them; seeing what works and what doesn't and moving on.

As a result, I wrote a manual called *"125 Ways to Make Money with Sublimation"* which outlines niche markets

and how to reach them, what to offer them etc., but also business concepts specifically for sublimation. Written in 2006, it is beginning to show its age and a revised edition is in the works. I am proud to say that Condé Systems is one of the distributors and has been a strong supporter of the manual.

To make the manual even more helpful, it comes with 2 CDs filled with layouts for each chapter of the book. These can serve as samples or be altered and used as actual products. All the layouts are done in Corel 8 so they open on any Corel version after that. If you have an earlier version of Corel, for heaven's sake, it's time to upgrade!

One of the things you will probably discover as you read the manual is that most of this information is just common sense. "I should have thought of that" will be a repeated phrase. Don't feel bad, most of them I didn't think of originally either. Most came to me by a customer asking a question, or even by accident.

I have served some of these markets for a decade or more while others have come and gone. I don't have time to reach out to all these, so I tend to focus on those that bring the most repeat business and let the others rest. What I find is that one market will be hot for a while and then fizzle. Just as it fizzles, another market will pop up and run hot for a while. This cycle has repeated its self for 15 years. It has taught me not to overstock on products for any one market.

"125 Ways" was a labor of love. It started out as "25 Ways" but the more I wrote, the more niche markets I remembered. Since 2016, a few of the markets have gone away but others have taken their place. I probably won't change the name of the book when the new version is released, but I expect it will be closer to 150 Ways with the addition of all the new phone covers, tablets, wood products, glass products and new garments.

I hope you will pick up a copy and put it to good use. *"There's money in that-there book!"*. Pick out several niche markets and go after them. It really is a great way to grow your business.

PART THREE
SECTION 6

Some people dream of success while others wake up and work." -Unknown

USING SOCIAL MEDIA

First there was Google, then Facebook, then Twitter followed by Pinterest and Snapchat and Periscope and about fifty more according to Wikipedia. If you listen to the voices of the Internet, you can't be in business unless you subscribe to all these wonderful, all-powerful, social media outlets.

The truth is, as best as I can discern it, the need to be on Social Media is a mixed bag. On the one hand, I hear people telling me how wonderful Social Media is and on the other, I hear just as many or more telling me how much time and money they wasted on these platforms and never saw a dime in return.

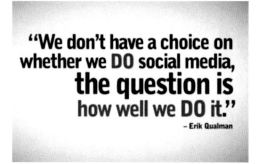

Art by Postific.com.

So, what do you do? As a new business, do you invest your time and energy in all these activities or do you pass?

I have always encouraged start-ups to use what I call the "wet toe technique" or the "three finger approach" to marketing. Essentially, this means to try a little but don't over invest yourself in any one approach unless you see a positive response. Select one of the Social Media platforms and build a Facebook page or Twitter account and begin to work it. Don't try to sell on Social Media, that's a "no-no". Rather, just talk about a product or your new business and how fascinating the process is. Post pictures of you making something or a shot of your "very first product". These are the kinds of things people want to see on Social Media.

While you are testing Social Media, give equal time to a couple other techniques such as cold calling, having a house party, small ads in the local paper or some radio spots. See what brings results and follow that technique for as long as it produces. When it stops producing, move to something else. If none of the things you try produce results, dump them all and try three or four different attacks.

The problem with Social Media isn't that it is so expensive in dollars but in time. It is easy to justify to one's self that spending hours on end posting on Social Media is working but that's not really true. Working means producing results. No results, move on. You may revisit previous techniques later but for now, spend your time on what produces sales. Social Media can be a trap that eats up a ton of time. It is easy to get caught up in the excitement of social media.

There are now companies that offer their services for handling your Social Media needs. These are expensive and probably unproductive. Most are cottage industries, not legitimate marketing groups and how much could they understand about your business?

What works best on Social Media is conversation, not selling. People want you to talk about your life, your family and your business. If you are excited about your new business, talk about it, show pictures of it, but don't try to sell products. One way to "sell" without selling is to spotlight a product in a post. For instance, my wife recently took a sublimated purse to a social event. Lots of people ask her about it. That makes for a great post, "My wife got lots of attention with her new sublimated purse at the xyz event last week. People couldn't believe the images were so vivid.". That's selling without selling.

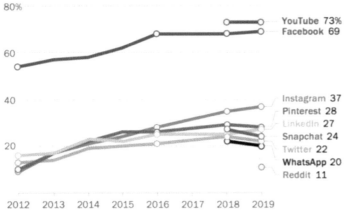

Facebook, YouTube continue to be the most widely used online platforms among U.S. adults

% of U.S. adults who say they ever use the following online platforms or messaging apps online or on their cellphone

YouTube 73%
Facebook 69
Instagram 37
Pinterest 28
LinkedIn 27
Snapchat 24
Twitter 22
WhatsApp 20
Reddit 11

Note: Pre-2018 telephone poll data is not available for YouTube, Snapchat and WhatsApp. Comparable trend data is not available for Reddit.
Source: Survey conducted Jan. 8-Feb. 7, 2019.

PEW RESEARCH CENTER

Comparison of various social media platforms. Research and chart by PEW Research, www.pewresearch.org.

So, back to Social Media: What should you do? Dive in or ignore it? I suggest you set up a business page on Facebook and begin collecting "Friends" so you can do an occasional post (the professionals suggest three posts per week). If you like, you can also set up a Twitter account and use the same material to post there. Remember, every minute you invest in Social Media, you are taking away from something else, so invest wisely.

Here is a list of the most popular Social Media options and thanks to Jennifer Cox, President of National Network of Embroidery Professionals, (some very helpful information you will need if you are going to interact with these sites). Each site has very different requirements for posting pictures. Jennifer has graciously provided that information for us in an Internet posting which appears below and is reprinted with her permission:

"As George Michael says, "If you're gonna do it, do it right!" (For those of you that are either too young or too old to not recognize the lyric, sorry for a reference that makes no sense).

Social media is here to stay. Facebook, Twitter, LinkedIn, YouTube, Pinterest, Instagram – and whatever comes next...

And more importantly, your customers are USING SOCIAL MEDIA DAILY! If you are going to participate in social media, why not put your best foot (or image) forward, and make it worth the effort?

All of these platforms LOVE images. We work in an industry that is all about color, texture, style, design. All of these elements come across well in images. It is a match made in heaven!

Just think how much easier you have it to maximize your impact on social media than business owners in other industries! How about a plumber, for example? Yet there are plumbers out there that are ROCKING social media. And there are apparel decoration professionals that are not having any impact on social media. Do not be that person!

To help you become a social media ninja, here are some cliff notes to make it easier and faster for you to create great looking image-based posts that will display well. The information listed below is measured in pixels and is width x height. The image sizes listed below are correct as of January 2016."

Facebook

Cover photo: min. size 399 x 150; max. size 851 x 315

- Your profile photo: min. size 180 x 180; max. size 360 x 360
- Link images: min. size 600 x 314; max. size 1200 x 628
- Photo post image: min. size 504 x 504, max. size 1200 x 1200

Twitter

- Header photo: 1500 x 500
- Your profile photo: min. size 400 x 400; max. size 500 x 500
- Tweet images: min. size 440 x 220; max. size 1024 x 1024

LinkedIn

- Profile banner photo: min. size 1000 x 425; max. size 4000 x 4000
- Profile avatar photo: min. size 200 x 200; max. size 4000 x 4000
- Post photo: 698 x 400
- Company cover images: min. size 646 x 220
- Company logo image: min. 300 x 300; max. 400 x 400

Pinterest

- Your profile photo: min. size 165 x 165; max. size 600 x 600
- Pin images: min. size 80 x 80; max. size 736 x unlimited
- Board cover images: min. size 217 x 147; max. size 736 x 498

Instagram

- Your profile photo: min. size 110 x 110; max. size 180 x 180
- Photo Post image: min. size 1080 x 566; max. size 1080 x 1350

YouTube

- Channel art photo: min. size 1546 x 423; max. size 2560 x 1440
- Video thumbnail photo: min. size 640 x 360; max. size 1280 x 720
- Channel icon: 800 x 800

PART THREE
SECTION 7

"If you can't dream it, you can't do it." -Walt Disney

FUNDRAISING WITH SUBLIMATION

Before you try to sell the fundraising idea, it is important that you understand the way fundraising typically works. In most cases, candy, wrapping paper, candles, etc., there is a minimum number of items the company must purchase. This is especially true if there is any kind of personalization involved. Whoever is doing the fundraising must pay for the entire order up front along with shipping (which is usually inflated) and must cover any loss through damage, thief or loss. Anything not sold cannot be returned. In most cases, all sales are final. The typical sales price is usually split 50/50 which really isn't 50/50 at all since the buyer has to cover all the shipping and losses. For example, for an order of 250 candy bars, the cost might be fifty cents each plus $30 for shipping. That means they have to sell 60 candy bars before they make a dime! The remaining 190 candy bars should bring in $95 profit, less losses. Finally, is the hard and cold fact that more often than not, the people who buy candy bars and such, buy it because they want to help a kid who is stuck with selling this stuff.

Most non-profit organizations are looking for ways to make money.
Photo curtesy of Bplans.com.

When offering sublimated products as fundraisers, the profit margin will be less, probably 25-40% depending on the product and the size of the potential order (this is entirely up to you). In return for the smaller percentage, they don't have to pay anything up front since there is no set up fee and you make the products only as they are ordered and paid for – they get paid in full, and you get paid in full with each order. There is no shipping since you are probably local and someone can either pick them up or you can drop them off (again, your choice). In some cases, you might be asked to ship each order to the end buyer which is added to the price at both ends.

This approach allows organizations of all sizes to participate in your fundraising program. The only difference between a large and small organization might be the percentage you elect to share with them.

To whom do you offer this service? Churches are a great place to start your fundraising program. The members love to have things with a picture of their church on them. Prayers and other religious sayings are also popular as are license plates with the church name. Fraternal organizations are another great place to start. Class reunions, clubs of all kinds, hobby groups, tourist attractions and of course schools – all kinds of schools – kindergarten through college.

What are the advantages of working with you? They have nothing to lose and they put zero money at risk. There is no minimum order and, in most cases, no shipping. Your products may well become collector items or family heirlooms as opposed to a candy bar or wrapping paper.

Best of all, the products you produce for sale are products people actually want.

What do your charge? Setting a price depends on a number of factors: One, what does it cost to make the product being offered? How many are they likely to sell? How long does it take to make the product? How much waste are you likely to suffer? What is the normal retail price of the product?

Some sublimation products afford us a 600% margin or more. Others are far less. If you have a product with a 600% margin, you can easily offer 25%, 33%, 40% or even 50% discount, based entirely on what *you* want to do. If you are selling to your own church for instance, you might go the entire 50% while other customers you might only give 33%. Here is a rough idea of how I determine my lowest possible price; it isn't scientific, but it has worked over the years. If a product costs me $5 to make (labor, parts, etc., included), and the retail is $15, I might go as low as $10. Here is the logic: If I make one wrong and have to remake it, my cost will be $10, the same as the selling price so I will break even on that one. Most, however, I won't do wrong, so I make $5 on each of those. If the item cost $10 to make and only sold for $15, I would be $5 in the whole for each one I messed up and I find that unacceptable.

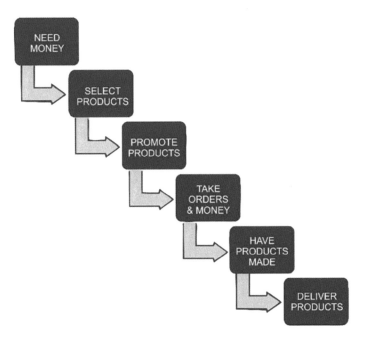

Here you can offer products with no minimums, custom made and personalized and no up-front investment.

What products should you offer? That is entirely up to you and the customer. Shirts, coffee cups, travel mugs, ceramic tiles, trays, keepsake boxes, license plates, picture frames, coasters, wrought iron items, mouse pads, kitchen mitts, flip flops and socks make up a good list of popular items. Avoid really inexpensive items like key fobs just because there isn't enough profit involved unless that is a very large quantity involved. Studies have indicated that there are certain points where people think twice before throwing down money. They are $5, $10, $15 and $20. This is why you often see products selling for $4.99. It is only a penny from the natural barrier of $5 but to the brain, it sounds like it is less and therefore a good deal.

How do you get paid? What you do with your finances is, of course, your business. However, a word of advice: Credit kills. Your customer is (or should be) collecting money for your products when they take the order. Therefore, there is no reason they can't pay you when they place or pick up their orders. There will be some companies you will have to carry on credit but try to avoid this at all costs – especially since you are already discounting the product. Insist on cash, a check or if you have to, a credit card over credit. Even paying a credit card processor 3% is better than carrying an account where you may never get paid at all.

PART THREE
SECTION 8

"Yesterday's home runs don't win today's games." -Babe Ruth

SPECIALIZED MARKETS

Specialized or target markets are those you go after in a specific way. Let's say you want to service local restaurants with name badges. Name badges make a great target market since almost everyone in business uses them. To begin, you need to visit the manager or decision maker of the business and show him the advantages of using sublimated badges over what they are using now. Find out, if you can, what they are currently paying for badges and how long it takes to get them (many suppliers are notoriously slow). If you can obtain this information, you have a leg up on the competition. If not, that's okay, just sell the badges on their own merits: Almost impossible to damage, full-color with logo, multiple sizes, shapes and styles, won't be damaged when run through a washing machine (except perhaps for the finding which you offer to replace free of charge), and can be written on with permanent marker for temporary or new employees and the price is right.

Determine how orders are to be taken and delivered: Fax, email, phone for ordering and delivery by mail or hand delivered.

Obtain a clean copy of their logo and settle on a design and you have a long-term customer.

Although it is difficult to get to the right people for the chains and big box stores, even they are potential customers in that many allow their managers to spend money on things like name badges. Certainly, "mom and pop" type businesses such as hardware stores, restaurants, picture framers, hospital and medical staff, medical students, pet stores, groomers and vets, clothing stores, airport personnel, schools, class reunions, florists, photographers, sales clerks, military reserve units, opticians, customer service representatives, sign & banner salesmen, automotive salespeople, attendants at gas stations and convenient stores, grocery store clerks, daycare workers and even churches, only to mention the obvious.

Wedding supplies can be sold through shops that specialize in wedding supplies, religious bookstores, card shops or at one of the wedding tradeshows (so common around the country).

Industrial applications make a very lucrative market with DyeFlex plastic, Rowmark Mates or even metal and FRP. Offer all kinds of labels, tags and safety stickers as well as electrical legends for motors and similar electrical gear, tags for breaker boxes and light switch covers can be sublimated for high profit.

These target markets are many and diverse as almost everyone in business wears or should wear a name badge. The big complaints about badges, other than many people say they don't like wearing them, is that they scratch too easy, they aren't available in color, they won't survive the washer and dryer, they cost too much and they take too long to get. With sublimation, you can solve each and every one of these problems. You can even reduce the number of people who say they don't like wearing one by giving them a nice-looking product.

There are any number of targets you can establish. The pet market is huge and lucrative. Pet memorials in the form of a keepsake box or plaque, collars and leashes, pet bows and mats, coffee cups and shirts can be sold through any number of resellers, not just pet stores. Set up a booth at a local pet show or anywhere people might take their pets.

The school market is an interesting one. Schools need all kinds of things. Awards to be sure, but also labels, things they can sell through their school store, labels for athletic and band equipment, shirts, hats and coffee cups. Ribbons and plaques may be the most common request for special activities and don't forget UNISUB does offer some unique trophies you can put team pictures on. Also, many schools hang pictures of honor students or sports winners in their hallways. Chromaluxe™ is a great way to offer this service much cheaper than professionally framed photographs.

Another target market with schools is usually done in conjunction with the school photographer by offering a number of sublimated products using the digital photos sold to parent. The photographer can include in the information sent home to parents, a form so they can order coffee cups or other products with their child's picture on them.

Just look around. There are target markets everywhere. Consider what hobbies you are involved in. I am a certified scuba diver. Did you know that FRP works great as a "chalk board" under water when used with a grease pencil? Did you know that after you spend weeks training for your first certification, the only thing you get is a paper card? You want to bet there isn't a market for a nice plaque for people to hang on their wall after doing all that work? You bet there is!

I am also a Ham radio operator. Until I became a Ham, I never thought of the many products that Hams like to buy that can be sublimated. Shirts, hats, signs and license plates with their call letters, maps, charts and coffee cups, only to mention a few.

These markets differ from the fulfillment markets discussed in another chapter because these are retail (although you may opt to discount some of the products), not wholesale. The buyer in this case, does not necessarily get a discount and typically pays from price for whatever he orders.

In the chapters that follow, we will consider several of these specialized markets.

NAME BADGES

If I had to pick my favorite product, it would be the name badge. I have done many videos talking about my love affair with the lowly name badge! Why? The name badge business is severely underrated as it enables you to provide businesses with high quality, durable, and attractive name badges. A surprising number of businesses do not use name badges solely because it is too much of a hassle. This provides you and others in the sublimation business with an opportunity to go out and gain a massive number of clients with a product as simple as the name badge. The badges have a scratch and fade-proof epoxy coating and come with the choice of a pin or magnetic backing.

Our Fiberglass Reinforced Plastic (FRP) badges can be custom-cut into almost any shape or size. Using the latest, top of the line printers and heat presses, you are capable of producing impressive, high-quality, and professional name badges. Just a few of the places that could benefit from this business for example are hospitals, nursing homes, retail stores, restaurants, or companies like UPS or FedEx.

To get the word out about this product you should utilize all of the possible avenues, such as creating a website and making it accessible through social media, by making flyers, and by going from business to business with a display board that showcases exactly what each name badge looks and feels like, along with a price list and samples of all of the different colors, shapes, sizes, finishes, and materials. This makes it quick and easy for the client. Businesses will almost always choose the cheapest or most convenient companies do business. If you approach them, make the ordering process as simple as possible, and have reasonable rates, you can expect your client list to expand at a surprisingly rapid rate.

As your name badge business grows, you may want to begin using jigs to speed up production. These specially cut boards hold up to 15 badges at once without having to use heat tape or spray to align them in the press. In a test done years ago, we found that 425 badges could be made in a single hour by one person using a jig! Jigs are produced by UNISUB for all their badges and are available from your Condé representative.

Badges are available in both FRP and metal. The metal badges allow you to offer true metallic badges, which many companies prefer. They all sublimate the same and cost about the same. If you have a metal shear, you can also buy the metal in sheets and cut your own badges in whatever size you need. Metal badges are available in bright gold and silver, satin gold and silver and white in both matte and gloss.

Another add-on are the gold and silver frames available for some sizes and shapes of badges. These add a bit

of class to a badge but not much money. They are especially appreciated by professionals such as Realtors, bankers, insurance salesmen – anyone who dresses "business formal".

LANYARD BADGES

Sublimatable Lanyard

Break-away Clips

Horizontal Badge

Vertical Badge

GIFT SHOPS

To sell to gift shops and most tourist locations (see Museums & Tourist Destinations), you will need to develop a wholesale side of your business. Wholesale doesn't mean you have to give a 50% discount (called "Keystone"), but you will have to give enough discount to motivate the gift shop to want to buy and sell your products.

In most cases, about 25% is enough, although there may be some products you can give more or less.

Tin with logo.

When selling to a gift shop, you will probably want to establish set designs without additional personalization. The items might be personalized to the gift shop or the location but not to the individual who buys them.

Like some of the other clients you might go after, many gift shops can't afford to invest in a gross or more of a single product, so your offering to sell small quantities at a time becomes very enticing to them.

Some of the items you might offer include shirts, scarfs, key chains, cups and travel mugs, trailer hitch covers, jewelry, pet products, dog tags (for people, not pets), tins and cell phone covers.

Many restaurants have small gift shops.

SELLING ON AMAZON, EBAY & ETSY

An excellent way to get your business started is to offer your products on Amazon, eBay or Etsy. For the most part these are all free unless you sell something. When something sells, they will collect the selling price, deduct their share and at the end of the month, deposit the remainder into your account.

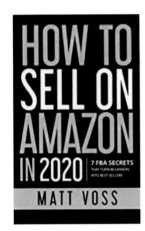

It does take time to get your product ready to sell. A good photo has to be taken (Amazon required a white background). Each company has some requirements for photos and text, but they are simple to learn.

I prefer Amazon, personally, because they appear to be more professional, but I have had luck with all three.

The biggest thing to remember is not to forget shipping. Normally, you have to foot the bill for shipping unless you specify otherwise. Amazon automatically adds $3.95 for shipping. If you want to change it, you will have to create an Excel spreadsheet and submit it to Amazon.

This book is free for Kindle to Prime members.

eBay is probably the simplest one to setup since you can set your price and shipping all on one screen.

The secret to all of them is to have a good image and a clear explanation of what it is. Amazon now offers the ability to offer personalization. They will also inventory non-personalized items for you so they can be sent using Prime shipping, but there is a fee for everything, plus you can't personalize, and you tie up inventory.

If you do sell on these, it is important you ship as soon as possible. Even one bad review and you may never sell anything again. Many sellers ask customers to contact them first, before writing anything but a 5-star review. It's not a bad idea.

Just one of many books on selling.

ATTACKING THE AWARDS MARKET

"During my live training, I often direct this question to Awards shops: Should you sell Lady's purses? Of course, they know that it is a trick question but the reason behind the answer is simple. One of the key decision makers in team sports is the team Mom. What if you sell her a purse with the team's photo on it? Do you think you can solidify her business until the end of time? I think so. This tip is really about putting all the other tips in practice. For example, most folks in the Awards industry never make sales calls. Hard to believe! But getting out of the shop will open your eyes to many new opportunities. Continuing my rant on awards folks, I almost lose it when they speak of a slow season around the Christmas holidays! This would be their busiest season if they have had stepped out of their comfort zone and grown their photo gift business!"
-David Gross

What is an award anyway? Is it a trophy? A plaque? A glass obelisk? Actually, it's all of these and none of these. An award can be anything that has the words, *"Presented To"*, *"Awarded To"*, *"In Recognition Of"* or even *"Thank You"*.

Although it's true that the first thing that comes to our minds when we hear the word, "Award" is a trophy or plaque, almost anything can be an award if we want it to be. A trip can be an award. Cash can be an award and so can a decorated shirt, coffee cup, clock, clipboard or just about anything else.

Now, having said that, where do you look to get in on the very profitable awards market?

Awards are used by just about everyone. Companies give "Employee of the Month" awards. They recognize people for longevity or retirement. Companies *love* safety awards. These awards, and many others, apply to any company of size and even some very small companies. All you have to do is ask what kinds of awards they give and then give them an alternative. Most companies that give awards like these are bored to tears with the "same ol' stuff" and will welcome some change.

Schools, clubs and fraternities use awards as well. These tend to hang onto the trophy concept, mostly because of price, but that's okay since you some interesting shaped trophies from UNISUB. You can also try to introduce shirts and other items as a change. Clipboards make a great gift or award for coaches and cups make the perfect teacher's gift or award.

Sports teams generally give participation awards at the end of the season along with MVP, Most Improved and so on. Here is a place where the UNISUB trophies can shine with a picture of the team on each trophy along with an inset of the recipient. It is an award a child will cherish for a lifetime. Can you do more elaborate awards? Of course, you can. Sublimatable acrylic is top-end, as are full-color plaques. If you are a trophy dealer, you already have a source for thousands of beautiful glass awards, loving cups and even trophies that can hold an "engraving" plate in full-color – a nice change from the ho-hum traditional engraving plate.

Megaphone trophy by UNISUB allows for multiple photographs and text.

Got a big order for trophies? Consider this: Rather than engraving all those metal plates and having to cut them all, put tape on them all and adhere them to a trophy. Why not sublimate them on self-adhesive film? You can cut them apart with scissors and they will stick right on. It will cut your labor by 2/3's.

Remember too, you can make your own 2" disks with sublimation, so any trophy or plaque that calls for a disk can be full-color. No more stocking hundreds of disks. You can make most of them yourself as you need them. (I say most because you can't make copyrighted designs such as D.A.R.E., Scouts and some other logos that are carefully controlled by their owners.)

For the adults in the crowd, why not a bottle of wine? Of course, you can't sell the wine but you can make a wine box or carrier announcing what the reason for the award is; or if it is a gift, you can do something to show, "*Happy Birthday*", "*Merry Christmas*", "*Happy Anniversary*", etc.

Having a Base shape is perfect for a baseball award.

This round award from UNISUB is perfect for any ball sport.

One additional approach that isn't exactly an award but more of an appreciation gift is something for a company's customers – perhaps at Christmas, or for an extra special order. These can range from a coaster to a keepsake box, clock, desk item, phone cover or mural.

Weddings & Wedding Shoppes

Weddings are a landmark experience in people's lives and any such time is a perfect time to offer sublimated products as a remembrance.

Plaque for mother of the bride.

Long before the actual wedding comes the first opportunity to sell. Most couple send out a "Remember the Date" magnet about 3-4 months before the wedding. UNISUB makes refrigerator magnets that are light, thin and therefore inexpensive to send in the mail. Of course, if you have the right equipment, you can make your own with DynaSub metal and some magnetic material.

Most weddings have a wedding party - Bridesmaids and Groomsmen. It is traditional that these folks are given a gift for participating. This is a perfect opportunity for sublimation. Jewelry or a keepsake box for the ladies and a flask for the gentlemen.

The reception brings additional opportunities. Most weddings include a gift for each person who attends. Coasters are ideal for this. They are inexpensive, easy for the guest to carry home and can have a picture and personal message from the wedding couple. Some weddings use name badges, so sublimated badges with a picture of the couple works for them while stemless wine tumblers work great for the big toast.

Coaster for guests to take home.

Save-a-Date magnet.

Of course, there are any number of other items that might work, including gifts for the bride and groom to help them set up housekeeping or to take with them on their honeymoon. Travel mugs, photo panels, tins filled with candy (or money), luggage tags with the bride's new name is always special, placemats for their table, only to mention a few.

You can sell these in your storefront (if you have one), or you can take orders at Wedding shows held around the country. You can also wholesale to any local wedding shops on a wholesale basis.

FLEA MARKETS

Everyone seems to love Flea Markets. They come in all shapes and sizes. Some are indoors and climate controlled and some are outdoors – rain or shine. Some are in permanent locations and some are just held in an open field. Take your pick.

You will need a portable heat press, the Virtuoso SG400, a laptop, a smartphone and a table to set it all on.

With those, you can go anywhere there is electricity and set up a booth. You can add a tent if it is outdoors, backdrops, lights, signs and table covers if you like.

Flea Markets are a great place to set up a green screen (see section about green screens) and provide people with a box of old hats, scarves, coats, etc. so they can play dress up and have their picture taken, then placed on a shirt, cellphone cover, or any other product you want to offer.

The secret with Flea Markets is to keep it simple. Don't take too many product lines. Pick several items you think people will like and focus on them.

You can get as fancy as you want with a sublimated tent, table cover, flags and backdrop. Tents start about $100.

CONDÉ KIOSK

Typical kiosk found in a mall

For folks that have a store front or do mobile events, I suggest you add my iPhone Kiosk to your booth. In its simplest form, my iPhone Kiosk is a convenient way to get a photo from an iPhone transferred to your PC. You can send the photo to a folder on your desktop or have it automatically open in a program like PhotoShop Elements.

This is a great way to sell shirts, phone covers and many other items in your storefront but is also an easy way to take your business "on the road" to car shows, sporting events, flea markets, school carnivals and more!

To help you get started, I have several CondéTV videos about the Kiosks we offer as well as one by Condé employee, Jeff Butler, who shows how to make the neat phone case display rack shown in the picture.

To learn more about my Kiosk or to set one up yourself, just call our Support Department.

For those who want an even more sophisticated version of the Kiosk, we also offer one that automatically prints the image sent to your computer. Nothing could be easier than that!

Condé employee found selling phone covers at a flea market both fun and profitable..

SCHOOLS & UNIVERSITIES

Selling to schools and universities will often mean selling to their gift shops (See "Gift Shops") but not always. You can also sell to the sports programs, individual clubs, Sororities and Fraternities, or directly to the school.

Selling to high schools and below is very different than selling to a college or university. One big difference is that few high schools have logos or mascots that are copyrighted or trademarked (licensed) while most colleges and universities are. Always check to be sure you know what you are working with, especially if you aren't selling directly to the institution or one of its entities.

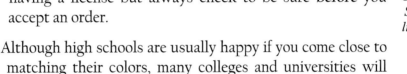

Elementary and High Schools usually don't license their logos but always check to be sure.

When selling to a school, its sports program or gift shop, usually means you can reproduce their logo, mascot, etc. without having a license but always check to be sure *before* you accept an order.

Universities like Marshall are very strict about the use of their logo, mascot or even a photo of their buildings.

Although high schools are usually happy if you come close to matching their colors, many colleges and universities will demand exact color matching and will provide you with PMS numbers to work from (See section on Color Management). In these cases, you may have to provide samples of the finished product for approval. Should you have to do a color match, you should charge for each color matched ($35-50 is typical).

CAUTION: If you make up samples using a licensed logo, either leave them with the school or if you take them with you, *do not sell them!*

If you want to make colleges and universities a main part of your business, you will need to buy a licensing agreement. This is usually handled by an agency and not the school. This can be an expensive and time-consuming process. To learn more, contact the Collegiate Licensing Company (CLC) in Atlanta, GA. Their website is https://licensing.gatech.edu/licensing/clc.

What will happen if you produce products using licensed images and sell them to the public? First, you may receive a "cease and desist" letter from an attorney. If you continue, you can be sued or they can actually come in and confiscate your equipment for the purpose of putting you out of business. It is a very serious infraction.

MUSEUMS & TOURIST DESTINATIONS

One of my favorite spots in the entire world is Cass Scenic Railroad, nestled in the hills of West Virginia. There, 100-year-old Shay steam locomotives attack the second highest mountain in the state. I have books about it, videos about it and hundreds of photographs. I can't seem to get enough.

Perhaps you have a special museum or tourist destination, as well. If you do, you probably have all kinds of memorabilia around your house.

Buying these items for resale is difficult for many such destinations because they are close on funds and full-color items they can sell are both limited and expensive because they have to buy in such large quantities. There is something you can do to help. You can offer hundreds of products in full color without expensive setup fees or minimum quantity requirements. The image top left is actually a mousepad I have sold off and on for years.

Anyplace people might visit on a weekend or holiday is fair game. Chances are, you can offer them all some products they would like to sell but don't have a source for. License plates, shoutboxes, mousepads, coffee cups, travel mugs, air fresheners, ornaments, sun catchers, key chains and bag tags (only to mention a few).

Most such places have someone who oversees the giftshop. Many such shops are actually run by people outside the museum, park or tourist destination. This is probably the person who places the orders.

While visiting the site, ask to meet the store manager and set up a time when you can show them some products or take some products with you that you think might be of interest. You might even offer to leave a few so they can see for themselves how they sell.

This mousepad shows another great museum on the East coast - Kitty Hawk on the Outer Banks of North Carolina.

Most important of all, follow up every few months. Things change. A store that wasn't interested today might be very interested down the road. Don't be discouraged!

THE PET MARKET

The pet market in the United States is a Twenty-one Billion Dollar per year business. People love their pets so much, they will go without food themselves in order to care for their pets and their pets include everything from the typical dog and cat, to the exotic snake or bearded dragon.

Pet Tag

Bearded Dragon

Ironically, sublimation has been slow to claim this market, so there is plenty of opportunity for whatever level you may seek. You can sell direct to customers through a website or local advertising or through outlets like Amazon, Etsy or eBay. You can also arrange to take orders from local pet stores, veterinarians, and animal hospitals.

When you think of pets, what do you think of? Pet tags perhaps? Pet tags are fine, but they just touch the tip of the pet market. Think bigger. Think pet bowls, feeding mats, leashes and collars. Think urns and memorial plaques. Think shirts with pet photographs.

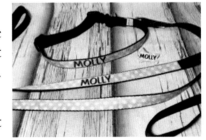

S. Russell used the "sell by batch" concept when making this trio.

While you are thinking about markets, don't forget about selling wholesale to photographers. They often take pictures of pets and might welcome the opportunity to sell coffee cups, key chains and a host of other products with the pet's picture on them.

Last, but not least, there are pet shows that cover everything from dogs to exotic pets and these people spend inordinate amounts of money in travel, lodging, meals, entrance fees and grooming. Most would welcome the ability to have their pet's picture placed on any number of sublimated items.

Shout Box

Pet bowls in two sizes

189

CLUBS & FRATERNAL ORGANIZATIONS

There are thousands of clubs across the United States and a number of Fraternal organizations as well. Most people belong to at least one club and some surveys indicate that about 50% of adults belong to at least one Fraternal group.

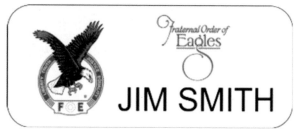

Fraternal organizations love to show off their logos and most clubs do, too, and where there is a color logo, there is an opportunity to sell name badges, license plates, beverage cups and lots more. As for the clubs that don't have a logo, make one for them.

To sell to clubs and Fraternal organizations, you probably need to talk to whoever runs their meetings (President or whatever title they assign to that person). They may refer you to someone else, but start there.

Typical name badge used by the Masons groups.

If you belong to one or more of these groups, you already have an inroad to selling them products. If not, make up some samples and give them to the President or whoever he/she refers you to and let them show them to other members.

Name badge for an F.O.P.

One way to entice groups to work with you is to offer them a slightly reduced price so they can mark it up and keep some of the profit for themselves.

As usual, one of your biggest selling points is that there is no minimum order. Many groups don't have the money to invest in a gross of anything so an "order as you go" and "pay as you go" arrangement works well for them.

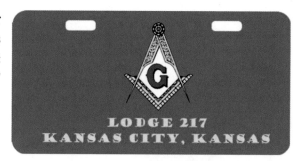

Simple license plate for Masons group.

HORSEBACK RIDING PAINTING SKYDIVING DANCING ART
FISHING **HOBBIES** *MUSIC*
SCUBA DIVING BOWLING GARDENING **MARTIAL ARTS**
PHOTOGRAPHY BILLARDS COOKING

Are there a thousand different hobbies people enjoy? Probably. They range from bowling to shark diving and everything in between, and people are passionate about them.

Anything people are passionate about is a great opportunity for sublimation. If they love their hobby, they will want a T-shirt or coffee cup to display it. Oh sure, people can buy generic shirts and cups (and most anything else) with a generic picture of their hobby on it but that really isn't what people want. They want a picture of THEIR car, boat, garden, horse or whatever it might be. Likewise, they want their name and picture on it as well. And why not?

UNISUB ChromaLuxe photo panel.

With sublimation, you can easily fill the bill.

Laptop sleeve.

A great way to capture the hobby market is to attend the various shows in your area. I once met a man and wife who bought a big RV to drive around the country going to various shows. The living room of the RV had been converted to a sublimation workshop. Of course, you don't have to go to those extremes but having a portable setup you can travel with is ideal for attending whatever show, competition or event where you might want to sell.

You can also sell through hobby shops; Marshall arts studios, or wherever else people go to purchase supplies or get training for their particular hobby. And don't forget clubs. Almost every hobby has clubs scattered across the country. You can wholesale to them or setup a stand and take orders during one of their meetings.

Possible products to offer include cups and travel mugs, shirts, ShoutBox and all other picture panels, tote bags, laptop bags, beverage huggers, key chains, bag tags, garden signs, shirts, socks and many more.

Bag tag.

Cellphone cover.

There are many types of shops that can resell your products such as this framing shop.

SETTING UP A FULFILLMENT BUSINESS WITH SUBLIMATION

Fulfillment, or wholesale, if you prefer, is a great way to sell sublimated products through other retailers, especially if you don't have a retail facility yourself. It is like having multiple locations without all the hassle and expense of actually having satellite locations. This type of business model works especially well if you don't have a storefront, in that you can sell out of garage or basement, and no one cares so long as you produce a quality product.

Of course, you won't make as much money per item as you would selling retail, but then chances are, you would never have the opportunity to sell to so many people anyway, so things balance out in the end. You can still sell retail yourself so long as you don't go after the same customers your resellers have.

There is really nothing special to setting up a fulfillment business. You will, of course, have to make contact with several retail facilities that might like to sell your products and there are many: gift shops, novelty shops, tourist shops, wedding shops, baby shops, photographers, pet groomers and vets, engravers and awards shops, schools of all kinds, picture framers, sign shops, embroidery shops, wedding shops, screen printers.

Privately owned pet stores are a great place to sell sublimated products.

Another way to set up a fulfillment business is to enlist women who sell other products (like Mary Kay) to include your products in their offerings. You can facilitate this with a couple of nice samples and some catalogs. Let them take the orders, obtain the photographs and text and forward it on to you. When complete, they can deliver the product to the customer.

Like most sublimation endeavors, the hardest part of being a fulfillment company is deciding what products you will offer and what you will charge. You have to discount each product enough, so it is worth the reseller's time and trouble, yet, you have to cover all your costs, including a profit. Some products may not be profitable enough to use for fulfillment, but the vast majority are.

There are a couple of ways you can set your prices. You can either offer an across the board discount or you can create a price list, which is what I recommend. This way, you can control your profit margin and factor in such things as breakage and shipping and labor, since not all products will be equal in these areas.

To entice resellers, you need to be willing to relinquish at least 25% off the retail price, and more, when possible. Less than that just isn't worth their trouble. One way to further increase the percentage is by encouraging them to sell multiple items that use the same artwork. This saves you time designing the second product. For instance, should a customer order a single coffee cup, it will cost you "x" amount to buy, ship and make that cup. If they order two that use the same basic artwork, your time and investment is much less so you can pass that on to your reseller as a motivator to sell the extra cup(s). He can then pass that savings on to his customer or keep it for him or herself. I call this a "two fer" where one item may cost $15 but the customer can have 2 for $25. Remember, the most expensive element of your business is the time you spend behind the computer designing a product. When you reduce that time, you make time for the sale and design of yet another product. Time IS money.

Gift shops of all kinds are a great place to wholesale your products.

There are several factors that have to be worked out with being in the fulfillment business, such as, "do you deliver the products, or do they pick them up?". How do your resellers pay for the products they order? Do they pay upfront, when the items are delivered or after they get paid? How do you handle mistakes such as misspellings? What about rush orders and what about additional discounts for large quantities? Who pays for samples and how much (samples are usually either provided free or at cost)? And finally, how do you reward those resellers who send you a ton more orders than those who don't. They will expect, and deserve, something extra.

GO EXPRESSION BY SAWGRASS

New from Sawgrass: It's like a business in a box. Register on the Sawgrass website under "The Sawgrass Network" and you're in business! Make products for other people who either don't have equipment or for some other reason, don't want to make the product themselves. Sawgrass takes care of all the money and the customer designs the product so all you do is make it and ship it out.

For more information, see Part Six of the "Introduction to Sublimation" at the front of the book.

WORKING WITH FRAMERS

Picture framers usually want only a small tag or plate to mount on a customer's picture. Although these are most often engraved, they can also be sublimated.

Requests will come in a variety of styles: Often, they will want to cut a hole and mount the plate behind the mat with double-faced tape. This will require making the plate about ½" to 1" larger in each direction to allow space for the tape.

Other requests will be for plates that mount on the face of the frame. These usually require two #4 screws for mounting. Obviously, you will need to buy a die-cut plate with holes or have the ability to cut your own plate and punch the holes yourself. A look at the chapter on "Additional Equipment", Section One, Part 19 should give you a good idea of what you will need: A shear, a hole punch and a corner cutter is optional. I'm especially fond of the 3 in 1 Maxi-Press from Main Trophy Supply.

Die cut brass plate suitable for sublimation

Fortunately, we do have both gold and silver metal available and some dealers also offer brass plates. With the right tools, you can make your own plates in any size needed.

Many framers are small one- or two-man shops much like yours probably is. This makes them especially easy to work with and you may even be able to send each other work. Think of all the metal panels, acrylic and glass photo panels you can offer to make for them on a wholesale basis. In return, they might be willing to help you with your shadow boxes.

What can I say about professional photographers? They can be a challenge to work with because their eyes are trained to see details in image quality I can't see. With the introduction of ChromaLuxe however, the quality of sublimated images has become so good that even the professional finishing houses are selling the ChromaLuxe panels, and at incredible prices.

With this in mind, you can feel pretty good about approaching the pros with images on ChromaLuxe. Use really good professionally shot images, however. Otherwise, you are taking a chance on the photographer tearing it apart for things you can't even see.

If you can, ask for one of his or her images in a high-resolution digital form and print that as a sample. If you have to change the size of it, be sure to retain as high definition as possible. Resolution is everything when dealing with a professional photographer.

Beyond the photo panels, you can offer him anything in your arsenal – cups, shirts, anything. Chances are, they will be open to selling all the various products using their photographs.

This means you will be selling wholesale so they can mark up the price. Don't be surprised if they make more than you do. Set your price at a fair wholesale level and don't worry about what they charge.

Bride on ChromaLuxe photo panel.

Keepsake box with photo on UNISUB tile.

TIP: Photographers are very touchy about people who duplicate their images and sell them. Although it is hotly debated, most photographers feel they own the images and although you probably won't get sued for scanning an image and reproducing it on a cup, etc., you may make an enemy of the photographer. Be very careful about duplicating anyone else's image. It may or may not be illegal but so far as the photographer is concerned, it is certainly unethical.

SELLING AT SHOWS
CAR, MOTORCYCLE, HORSE, SPORTS, PET, WEDDING, FOOD, GUN, AND A HUNDRED MORE

Every week, there are hundreds, if not thousands of shows held in the United States. There are shows for everything from cars to hot rods to fishing to weddings and more.

Car shows usually give a "Dash Plate" to each car owner.

To be part of these shows, all you have to do is rent a booth and go there. Using a light heat press like the J14 by George Knight, a Sawgrass SG500 printer, a laptop and your smartphone, you can make hundreds of products right on the spot.

Most shows welcome vendors to come and offer their products for a meager price of $10 to $50 for a six-foot table and a little real estate you can claim for your own.

You can get as fancy as you like by adding backdrops, table covers, signs and even give-a-ways, but all you have to have are some samples and electricity.

George Knight JP 14

Whatever your interest might be, there are probably shows held close by that focus.

Oh, and one more place you can set up is the State or County Fairs. Almost every county in the country has a fair. It's a big deal and thousands of people go each year. Booths are usually not expensive, and they can be a lot of fun. Most last several days and booths are often under roof so you can work rain or shine. Those areas that don't have a County Fair, probably have a State Fair. These are more expensive, but the people who come to them want to buy just about anything that will remind them of the event.

Not only does he have a sublimated plaque, note that she

Dallas State Fair. Notice the booths on the left.

Hunting & Fishing Expo, Charleston WV.

196

Artwork by Dashplak.com. Not to be duplicated.

DASH PLATES FOR CAR SHOWS

One nice little market that is perfect for sublimation is the Car Shows/Motorcycle Shows that take place in nearly every US town and city every weekend during warm weather. Some of these are just little meets where people who have old cars, restored cars, trucks, motorcycles or hot rods, get together in the parking lot of a local eatery and let people stop by and check out their cars. On the other end of the spectrum are the major car competitions where each car is on display and judged for a host of criteria.

To be sure, you can go after the trophy end of this hobby if your business is so inclined, but you can also go after the "Dash Plate" part of this hobby.

A dash Plate is a small piece of metal with the name and year of the show printed on it. These are often collected and displayed with the vehicle to impress the judges with the number of shows the car has been displayed. They are commonly given to every participant just for bringing their vehicle to the show.

For many years, these car plates have been screen printed in one or two colors and occasionally even in four colors (that is very different from full color or four-color process which is more like what sublimation is). A few are engraved as well, but not many.

This is perfect for sublimation. Even though all the plates are identical, we can offer things no one else can (or should). For instance, most screen-printing shops will only do a quantity of 100. We don't care, we can do any quantity, although you should charge more for small quantities than you do

There are thousands of car, boat and motorcycle shows all over the country every year. Photo by cruiseincalendar.com

for larger ones. Screen printers generally cannot do full color. They can do multiple colors but blending them is another deal altogether. We can give the customer full color. I don't really know how many colors are in the pallet, but I tell people there are 275,000 colors. I doubt anyone will really take me to task on that but if they want to count them, I'll show them how. This means we can actually print photographs. We don't have to restrict ourselves to generic pictures of cars or motorcycles, etc., we can print a photo of last year's Grand Prize Winner or of a custom design, if they have one.

You'll probably not get rich making Dash Plates but still, it's a nice little piece of business. Especially after you gain the trust of a dozen or so car clubs. In my area of the country, the most I can get for a Dash Plate is about $1.50 in a quantity of 100. That's $150 for 100 pieces of metal measuring the size of a business card. The bigger the size, the more it costs, etc. Broken down, this job will require the best part of four sheets of metal. With metal costing between $6

Conde & UNISUB offer several dash plates precut and ready to imprint. Typical size is about 2.5"x3" but custom sizes are not uncommon.

and $9 per sheet, or quality metal (UNISUB, Dye-Sub, etc.), depending on what you use, this will mean I will at least make a 400% profit on my material. Of course, labor has to come out of that, and my experience tells me it takes about an hour to make 100 dash plates from start to finish. If you count your labor to be worth $50 an hour, you still about double your money, which isn't too bad.

A couple of notes: You will need a metal shear to cut your metal ($200-$1500) and I like to round the corners on mine, which requires two additional machines: A corner rounder ($85-$300) and a miniature belt sander ($50-100) to sand off any burrs left by either the shear or corner rounder. If you don't do this, the corner rounder will leave sharp edges that can cut fingers or scratch other dash plates.

I print a third or half sheet of metal at a time, depending on what printer I use. These go very fast since it only takes about 1 minute to press metal. Then I cut them apart and round the corners if needed. To sand off the burrs, I just touch the back side of the plate to the belt sander for just a second and the plate is ready. Like the baker's dozen, I always throw in a few extras in case one gets scratched and so I never have to worry about a customer coming back saying I miss counted and only sent 99 plates.

PART THREE
SECTION 9

"Just because something doesn't do what you planned it to do doesn't mean it's useless."
-Thomas A. Edison

MARKETING IS THE KEY TO SUCCESS

Most people starting up a business are least concerned and most scared of the word, "Marketing". Yet, it is the key to whether or not the business will succeed or fail.

Most young businesses don't invest in marketing (or they invest in the wrong type of marketing), because they think they can't afford it and, in many ways, they are right. TV, radio, newspapers and the like probably are terrible ways to market a new business because they are so expensive.

There are, however, many other ways to market your products without significant expense. In some cases, there is no expense at all! Ironically, these free or low-cost methods are often better than those that are super expensive. That is what this section will focus on.

In the pages to follow, several marketing methods will be introduced. Not all of them will be your "cup of tea" and that's fine. What isn't fine is brushing off this vital part of business because you either don't have the time, the money, or you just don't like marketing.

Being in business, any business, depends on marketing in one form or another. You may find one method works well for a while and then dies out. That's okay. Just pick up another method and keep on going.

Don't try to do them all at once. There are hundreds of ways to market yourself and your business, but if you try to be like the cowboy who "jumped on his horse and rode off in all directions at once", your marketing won't work. Pick one or two methods and focus on them. If they work, keep going, if they don't drop them and move to something else. You may find the ones that don't work for you now, will be your best performers later.

Finally, it is important that you continue marketing – even if your cash flow seems not to allow for it. Remember, it's marketing that got your business started and it is marketing that will keep it growing. As you develop your business plan and create a budget for your new business, be sure to include some percentage for marketing. Big business often reports spending about 10% of their total business on marketing. That's a good place to start. Early on, that won't be much money, but it will grow right along with your successful business.

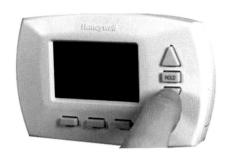

STEPPING OUT OF YOUR COMFORT ZONE

For an existing business or even a new one, your strategies will determine your success.

Henry Ford once said, *"If you always do what you've always done, you'll always get what you've always got."*

The brother of Sigmund Freud, along with Albert Einstein and about 100 other people, have been given credit for saying, ***"Insanity is doing the same thing over and over again and expecting different results".***

We are all guilty of getting stuck in a routine. Just as many routines are not healthy for our bodies, they are also often not healthy for our businesses. Step outside your comfort zone and try something new. Don't be afraid of change. Just because something seems to be working in someone else's business doesn't mean it is right for yours. Experiment. Try new products and technologies.

This is especially important for a new business as you try to make decisions about:

- What products will you sell?
- Will your business be a store front, on-line or a home business?
- What should you do with Social media?
- Will you use a catalog, a website or some other way to show your products?
- Where will you obtain your artwork?
- What will your business focus on?

The decision as to what to sell is usually done with little planning and therefore, often leads to loads of mistakes. Likewise, I have seen many existing businesses with a very stale product offering. I recommend that you step out of your comfort zone and test loads of new products to see what your clients prefer. Ask questions, do surveys. People like giving their opinions. Learn to ask and then to listen. Most companies have a warehouse of products the owners "just knew would sell" but didn't. Learn the art of testing new things, asking lots of questions and constantly trying something new.

Take a Picture of what You Make

Products and photo by M. Hodge

"Why?" You might ask. It takes time and it's a lot of trouble. Yes, it does take time and it can be a pain but here's the logic.

Most people have no idea what sublimation is or what can be done with it. They will have trouble catching on to the fact they can use most any photograph they want, add the text they want, use the colors they want and still, only make ONE of whatever they want. Communicating those facts can be difficult.

Likewise, many people will have no idea what they actually want on their cup, shirt, tray or whatever. Having a bunch of photos of actual products can save a lot of time when helping the customer to decide what they like. Call it, "inspiration".

There are a number of ways you can use those photographs and some of those are discussed in the pages that follow. This is a very inexpensive way to obtain photos for Facebook, Etsy, eBay, Amazon (Amazon requires a white background).

They don't have to look like they were taken by a professional. In fact, it is often best if they don't. Just take a picture of whatever you make.

As best you can, be sure the object takes up most of the screen. Be sure it is well lighted and avoid glare as much as possible. Perhaps most important is to be sure the object is in focus. Out of focus or images too dark to see detail are worthless.

Products and photo by Emerald Coast Novelties.

You don't have to buy an expensive camera to do this. In fact, your cellphone will do just fine. When you save your picture, save it at the highest resolution possible. This makes it adaptable to almost any application you come across.

One final comment. When you go to store your photos, save one in the same folder you store your customer's individual artwork. This way, you will always have a photo of the jobs you did for that customer and that can sometimes be extremely helpful!

Going Mobile

Wouldn't it be nice to be able to pack up your heat press, computer and products and go out where the action is?

This is a true story: I once was driving from West Virginia to Nashville, Tennessee to teach a seminar about sublimation. On my way, I kept seeing Corvettes – lots of Corvettes. Now, it isn't unusual to see the occasional Corvette on the Interstate, but I was seeing dozens – all clean and shiny, too. Then I passed the Corvette factory

1991 Corvette.

(which I had no idea was near the Tennessee line). There were hundreds of Corvettes parked in the lawn surrounding the plant (this was before the floor collapsed in the showroom). Every color and model and each one had a proud owner standing next to his or her most prized procession.

Had I realized this was the 50th Anniversary of Corvette and they had invited all the Corvette owners to bring their cars back to the place of their "birth", (and if I had an ounce of brains), I would have dragged my sublimation equipment down there and made shirts and key chains and whatever else I could carry. There was the opportunity of a lifetime and I missed it. There wasn't a single person there who wouldn't have wanted a shirt with a picture of him, her or them, beside their Corvette.

Granted, taking a big 100+ pound heat press and a big Epson 3000 printer wouldn't have been much fun, but making $20-$25 profit on every shirt I sold would have made up for it!

That was a decade ago. In today's world, going mobile is a lot easier. Sure, you can still struggle with that big heat press if you want, but there are easier ways. First, today's laptops are more than adequate to handle all the graphics you can throw at them. Second, the little Virtuoso 400 is so light and portable; it travels well – no need to take out inks – just keep it relatively level in transit. As for the heat press, George Knight builds a press that is very portable. It is called the JP 14S. Don't think

George Knight JP 14 Heat Press weight is only 65lbs.

this is a lightweight, however. It still weighs about 60 pounds – enough to be tough and versatile, yet at only 5.4 amps, it won't blow every circuit breaker in town. This press is adequate to do shirts, phone covers, key tags, mousepads and many other FRP products.

These components along with design software, a few samples and some paper and you can have an entire sublimation operation on a standard six-foot folding table.

With the ability to transfer images from cellphones to your laptop, using Condé's Kiosk system and an app for your phone to allow for the use of green screen, you are ready for just about any kind of event. If you want to be self-contained, a small generator will be enough to provide power to your computer and heat press.

I once knew a couple who loved horse shows, so they took part of their RV and converted it into a sublimation workshop and travelled all over the country selling to horse people. They already had a Class A motor home, so the investment was minimal, and they were getting incredible markups on their products.

Class A RV used to visit horseshows.

Of course, you don't need a $100,000 RV to go mobile. If you have an SUV, you probably have all the transportation you need to get started. At best, you might want to invest in a small trailer to carry your equipment and inventory.

It doesn't take a lot of room for a travelling sublimation setup.

Suggestions to consider: Horseshows, car shows, motorcycle rallies, skating competitions, shooting competitions, archery competitions, swim meets, gymnastic events, county fairs, eating contests, 5K runs, bicycle races, sporting events, graduations, craft shows, church homecomings & other events, Christmas bazaars, events in State and National parks, beauty contests and special events of all kinds.

There's no limit to the number of places you can go to offer personalized products. Some will do well, and some may not. You will quickly learn what works and what doesn't. You may even find event promotors inviting you to come to their events.

Tents like this one make a nice place to setup your equipment and avoid the rain or sun.

USING SAMPLING AS A SALES TOOL

Tell someone you do sublimation and don't be surprised if you get a blank stare. Most people have no idea what sublimation is and most who think they know, are wrong. That's why I call it Digital Imprinting rather than sublimation.

Regardless, for people to understand what we do, you have to put something in their hands – a real, live sample. All the pictures and discussion in the world will not convince them of the quality and versatility of sublimation.

This is doubly true when you are trying to pick up an industrial or corporate account. Busy purchasing agents are not interested in looking at your catalog of mostly residential products or listening to your lengthy explanation of what you do. After about ten-seconds, their minds go back to the work stacked up on their desk.

When approaching a corporate type, you want to identify some problem he has and solve it. If you can solve a problem, you have a customer. Otherwise, it's all pie-in-the-sky. So, how do you tackle this situation.

First, you have to speak the same language. That is, he has to understand something about sublimation. You know already, he isn't going to listen to a long speech, so you will have to get and maintain his (or her) attention some other way.

Here is my suggestion. I've seen it work lots of times, so hang on.

First, call the company and ask who the Purchasing Agent is. You don't want to talk to him, you just want to know his name and how to spell it correctly. This is usually easy to obtain.

Second, ask if he is the one who generally buys all the materials for the company. Some Purchasing Agents have a team who do their buying and he just watches the budget.

Third, make a product with his name and company logo on it. Nothing more expensive than a desk easel. This is not a gift. It is a sample and it must not exceed $25 in value. You can do a key fob, coaster, name badge or coffee cup; whatever you think is most appropriate for him or her.

Use Priority Mail to get the customer's attention or create your own package that is unique and says "I'm important. Open me first!"

204

Fourth, wrap the sample in in a nice box or envelope. Either use Priority mail or make it look really important by marking it "Personal". This is to try and get the package past the secretary without being opened. Along with the sample, enclose a letter telling who you are and what you can offer to solve some problem such as labels, safety awards, signage, customer appreciation gifts, etc. Tell him you will call his secretary in a few days to set up a meeting. In most cases, he (she) will call you. If they do, you don't need a meeting, you have already started a relationship. If they don't call, follow-up as promised. Who knows, you might walk out with a nice order. In any case, you have shown him what sublimation is, who does it, the quality of your work and that you do what you say (you called and followed up your letter).

Fifth, keep in touch. Even if they don't order anything, touch base in some fashion about once every quarter. Don't overdo it. Send something through the mail, drop an email with your quarterly specials; it doesn't matter, just stay in the background but where he is reminded you're there. Sooner or later, something will come up that you can be of help.

GOOD PRODUCTS FOR SAMPLE MARKETING

Coasters

Luggage Finders

Phone stands

Mouse Pads

Mugs

Name Badges

ig Tags

.ey Chains

Water Bottles

PROMOTING YOUR PRODUCTS IN BUNDLES

Like salt and pepper, some things just go together. The same is true with sublimation. Sometimes, it is only logical that some sublimated products be grouped together or sold as a set or bundle.

Obviously, things like coasters and napkin rings would commonly be sold in a set of four but grouping goes further than that. For instance, why not display one of the Condé tins along with a sublimated puzzle? Don't they belong together? Or what about a coffee mug? Shouldn't you include a coaster with it? A glass cutting board and an oven mitt might be another.

But it goes even further than that. Consider a bundled display for firefighters: Why not a shirt using with their favorite fire truck along with a personalized coffee cup, coaster, travel mug and plaque with the Fireman's Prayer? Other items could also be included such as a phone cover, notebook and mousepad. Don't forget a trailer hitch cover and personalized key fob and license plate – all with a matching image that ties them all together.

A good line of products to display is for first responders.

Actually, a mix like this one could be used for almost any group or subject matter: A church, fraternal organization, sporting group or school. It is almost always easier to sell multiple items if they are displayed in groups like the one above. It is a matter of engaging a buyer's imagination.

Stop by a good gift shop and look around. Notice how they might have some dishes or tea sets in multiple colors, and each is displayed as an entire group. It's almost as if they were trying to paint a picture of what these might look like if they were in your home.

This is the greatest problem with selling sublimation – getting the customer to visualize and understand all the possibilities of sublimated items. Customers tend to think only about what they actually see and that's a problem because there is no way you can display all the products necessary to convey all the ways that product might be decorated. That's why we recommend using TV monitors in your showroom.

Of course, by making products that use the same image or basic design, it should take less time to actually design the product and that justifies a small discount for buying multiple items – say 5 or 10% - you need not overdo it.

The theme here is anything related to babies.

Let's think of some other combinations: Pet tag, collar, leash, pet bowl and pet matt. Don't forget a shirt using the pet or a license plate or cutting board for the kitchen. A purse can include a glasses case, checkbook cover, phone cover and matching travel mug. A desk easel might include a pen holder, notebook, coaster, coffee cup, phone cover and name badge. And finally, a wedding couple might be interested in a tray, matching phone covers, matching travel mugs and coffee mugs, "Just Married" license plate and keepsake box.

Creating your own combinations is easy and fun – let your creative juices flow.

INSTALL A FLAT SCREEN TV

Perhaps one of the most difficult things to do in the sublimation business is to communicate to your customer what you are capable of doing with sublimation. It is difficult for the average customer to understand that the mug with a coach's picture on it can also be made with a company logo, birthday wishes, or one of a thousand other things. You have to show them! But how do you do that? It's impossible and too expensive to make dozens of samples of the same product and try to display them in your showroom. What can you do?

If you have a store front, I recommend you install a flat screen TV (or several) and use it to show folks what they can buy from you.

First, get a TV that is fairly large with a USB port. You can then place content on a USB flash drive and just plug it into the TV and let it run your pictures over and over like a slide show. The more pictures you have on your flash drive the better. As time goes by, you can add new pictures and new products to your show. It's as fast and easy as copying a picture from your computer to the flash drive.

Until you have a library of your own products, pictures are available from a variety of sources, including Condé. Just contact our Support Department for assistance. You will find hundreds of high-quality shots of Condé products on their website.

Electronic photo displays like this 8x10" display work great for small spaces.

In a previous tip, we suggested you take photos of all the products you make - preferably with the client for which it was made. These photos can be placed on the flash drive individually or you can fashion them into a slide show. You can even create a slide show every month.

In addition, you can play the unbranded videos available for free download at www.Condé.com.

These photos will serve at least two purposes. One, they will stir up excitement and plant seeds. Folks will see what you have done and share it with others. Since you have a limited amount of showroom space, the photos serve as additional counter space for additional themes. For instance, remember the dozens of mugs we talked about earlier? Using the monitor, you can show as many virtual mugs as you want with no investment except for a little time.

TVs like medium resolution jpegs. To make your own, you can import a picture (any picture), into CorelDRAW, size it, resample it (change the resolution), add text to explain what the product is or how much it costs and even group several pictures together to make an interesting collage. Then export it to your flash drive as a jpeg. Simple, fast and fun.

In my shop, I have two 24" TV monitors. One plays the unbranded videos from Condé while the other shows products and their prices. I also have several of the 8x10" digital picture frames scattered around running pictures of sublimated products or slides about other products offered. With the super low cost of TV monitors today, it doesn't cost a lot of money and promises a big payback. As time has passed since I bought my monitors, the prices have fallen even more making 32" TVs about the same price as 24"; so you might want to buy larger. I mount mine on inexpensive wall swivel mounts so they are high and out of the way and don't take up any shelf space.

REFERRALS BEAT A PATH TO YOUR DOOR
(WORD OF MOUTH ADVERTISING)

There is considerable debate about what is the best form of advertising – especially if you don't have any money. Some say it is word of mouth, and they may be right, but there's a couple of problems with that.

It's true: If someone tells a friend about your company and how great you are, there probably isn't a more powerful form of advertising. Getting customers to say something to friends and buisness associates is the problem. People don't usually go around bragging on your company for no reason. You have to do something to cause that to happen.

Art by edublogs, www.blogs.brighton.ac.uk.

One of the common mistakes made by new start-ups is their confidence that word of mouth advertising will carry them, and it won't. Oh, after you have been in business for 20 years, it might, but it takes a long time to generate enough happy customers for word of mouth to be that helpful.

Don't misunderstand. Word of mouth can make or break you, but it is more likely to break than to make – especially in the beginning. Here's what I mean:

Out of ten happy customers, one *might* tell a friend. Should you have a problem with a customer, he or she is *almost guaranteed* to tell ten friends what a jerk you are. See the problem?

To generate good word of mouth, there are at least four rules a business must follow:

1. *Deliver the job on time.*
2. *Quality, quality, quality.*
3. *Do it right the first time.*
If something does go wrong, do everything in your power to correct it IMMEDIATELY.

There is no excuse for not delivering a job when promised – NONE. As for quality, only your very best is good enough and do the job right the first time. Three simple rules you must live by if you ever hope to develop good word of mouth. As for the fourth, that is where most companies seem to break down, and I don't understand why. If you make a mistake in an order – perhaps spell a name wrong or get something mixed up. Don't debate it. Don't question whose fault it is. Just fix it – IMMEDIATELY – before you do anything else. If you can do it while the customer waits for it, that's even better. If not, perhaps delivering the product free to their home or business might be in order. Take responsibility for your mistakes. Mistakes do happen. When they do, make it an opportunity to show what you are made of. This alone will do more to generate positive word of mouth than anything I know.

Start-ups need to be very conscious about good word of mouth to be sure, especially in the day of Facebook, Tweets and the like; but to be successful, a new company needs to have a plan that goes far beyond word of mouth.

How are you going to reach your intended audience? There are, of course, a hundred ways, including radio, TV, newspaper advertising, etc., but these are usually out of reach for startups so what are some ways that work and are affordable?

There are inexpensive ways to advertise. Good signage on your building is one. It doesn't have to be illuminated or have digital readouts or even be on a pole fifty feet in the air. But it does need to be easy to read, tasteful and have an air of quality about it. A painted sign is fine if it is professionally painted. Vinyl signs are fine, just make sure they are easy to read and look good. I once saw a sign shop that was operating from someone's house. No problem there, but the sign he put up in his front yard was a full sheet of plywood painted white with yellow letters. You could not begin to read it from even twenty-five feet away! Did I mention it was for a sign shop? The sign stayed up for about a year that way. Finally, he changed it and did the lettering in black. Now, the question is, "Would you buy your business signage from that company?". I should hope not.

The same applies to you. Being in the sublimation business, you are also in the "sign" business in a way and you must display your ability and judgement in your signage. You must have some kind of exterior sign anyway, why not make it nice?

Show off your products whenever possible. For example, wear sublimated polo shirts as work shirts and wear them everywhere you go. I don't think T-shirts are professional enough for business, so I would recommend your shirts have a collar (but that's just me). Whatever you do, make sure it is a quality design. This goes for your staff as well as yourself.

Carrying a cell phone with a sublimated cover is a must! These generate a lot of questions just about anywhere you go. Add to that a sublimated key fob, notepad, license plate on your vehicles, a sublimated travel mug when you are on the road and coffee cups when you are in the shop and anything else that comes to mind. Sublimation sells itself, but only if people can see it, touch it and understand it.

Nice business cards are also a must. With companies like Vistaprint, there is no excuse for not having a nice, full-color business card. Remember, you are in the color business so everything you do should scream "color"! If you don't use very many cards or want to make your own, you can make nice cards from metal or better yet, Condé's Dye Flex plastic-like material. You can cut it with a paper shear or razor knife.

Use sublimation catalogs. Condé sells a great full-color catalog very inexpensively. You can also generate your own full-color flyers using artwork from the downloadable catalog on the Condé website. These can be printed on any color printer for only a few cents each or by your local office supply store.

Do open houses both at your shop or in your home. Invite some friends and neighbors over to your house and tell them about your new venture while serving refreshments. Don't try to sell anything, just educate. Sublimation will sell itself given the opportunity.

Join your local Chamber of Commerce. This usually isn't too expensive and affords lots of opportunities to meet other businesspeople in your community through mixers and other Chamber events. Don't forget to go after the Chamber's award program business. They might turn out to be one of your best clients.

Look for speaking opportunities at local Lion's Club, Kiwanis Club and other business-related meetings. Talk about the challenges of starting a new business in their (your) community and ask for their support. These groups often have occasion for giving awards as well.

Look for opportunities to become a wholesaler. Talk to local gift shops, tourist locations (and the like) to see if you can put your products in their shop. How you work out payment is up to you, but you can do it on consignment or sell it outright at a reduced price. Decorate the products you sell with local landmarks or things of interest to the community.

Look for businesses that might want to sell your products for you. Again, this is a wholesale type relationship so you won't make nearly as much profit, but you will probably be selling products to people you would never have the opportunity to sell to otherwise. Consider talking to awards and trophy shops that don't do sublimation in house, framing shops, photographers, pet store and hobby shops.

Talk to local organizations such as Knights of Columbus, Daughters of the American Revolution, VFW, etc. to see if you can make their name badges. Also, consider local military related activities such as Army or Naval Reserves. These groups often give annual awards and always present outgoing commanders with a plaque. The type of activity will vary according to your location but ask to talk to whoever is responsible for their "coffee fund". That person will most likely be responsible for ordering plaques, coffee cups, etc.

Some areas of the country have a cable TV channel that runs business ads either for free or very inexpensively. I'm not sure how business these really generate but if it's free, it's worth a try.

Trade can be very profitable, especially with a local radio station. Offer to supply them with a certain number of plaques, trophies or coffee cups in exchange for free airtime. Try to get them to do a live interview with you about your business or have a local DJ visit your shop and then report what he has seen on the air.

Show your products on Social Media sites like Facebook and Instagram. Talk about how your spouse uses the product or about the organization that gives something away at an awards banquet. Talk about products from the perspective of a news or gossip report rather than a sales perspective. It really works.

Websites can be very expensive and time consuming, especially if you create a really nice one. They don't have to break the bank, however. A company called iPersonalize can help you create a website that allows the customer to design his own products and even include a full credit card processing system for very little money. Check them out at iPersonalize.com.

Vistaprint (and others) print whatever you might want on Post It® notes. A company called Bebco also does this on a wholesale basis. Consider printing these with your company name, explanation of what you do and a full-color background showing products; and when you are out in the community after business hours, just stick one of these on every door you pass. It's a funny thing about Post It notes, is they hang around for a long time. One multi-million-dollar Canadian company built their entire business using nothing but Post Its to promote their business!

Referrals in exchange for credit or a gift is another way to promote your business. This involves giving each customer a coupon they can pass to someone else as a referral. When the coupon is brought in, it is exchanged for a discount to the new customer and a credit or gift for the person who gave the coupon away. The beauty of sublimated products is that most have a large enough profit margin that you can offer discounts without cutting into your profit margin too badly.

There are probably a hundred more ways to advertise your business without spending a lot of money, but this should get you thinking. Although most startups open their door with no plan at all, you are assured a much quicker ramp up if you have a business plan that includes getting the word out any way you can afford.

GREEN SCREEN

BEFORE   AFTER

Green Screen is a great way to have some fun and involve customers in ways you won't believe. Even the most strait-laced can get caught up in playing dress up with their friends. Suddenly, they can be any body and be any place (so long as you have the right props and backgrounds on your computer).

This is usually done at fairs, carnivals, various shows and sporting events, but it can be done right in your own shop. Outside of your shop, you will need a printer, small heat press, laptop and cellphone (don't forget electricity) and something green you can hang up. A green bed sheet or piece of cloth will work fine.

You will also need a "Green Screen" App for whatever phone you are using to take the pictures. These are free and there are several to pick from. Download several and try them out. Keep the one you like and practice with it so you can use it quickly.

Although you can place the person in front of any photo you have on your computer, limit your options to about a dozen. Otherwise, people will take too long to choose the one they want.

Here's a couple that went all out with the dress up part. They had their picture placed on 20 oz. travel mugs.

Have a bag of old hats, scarves, coats, dresses – anything you think might be fun (secondhand shops are a good place to find items). Let people mix and match all the items to become anyone they want to be – flapper from the roaring 20s, cowboy, superhero, etc. Take their picture in front of the green screen using the green screen app, transfer it to your laptop, add the background you want and print it out. It's as simple as that.

Images like this one from www.freepik.com make great backgrounds.

On a more serious note, you can also use green screen to take pictures of products, pets – just about anything – and sublimate the image over whatever background you like.

Backgrounds are available from lots of sources. CorelDraw includes lots of photos with their packages. You can buy collections of photos online or take your own. Look for high resolution images of 200-300 dpi at the size you will print them and of course, watch copyrights. Don't steal someone else's work and then sell it. Images of famous places such as New York City, San Francisco, a ball field, etc. or in front of famous buildings like the Eiffel Tower, the Empire State Building or the World Trade Center are good. A stormy sky background or one with a tornado in the background is fun. Most of the images will be free.

PART THREE
SECTION 10

"A (show)room should never look as though everything arrived on the same day." -Beuluh Miles

TURN YOUR SHOWROOM OR WEBSITE INTO

A CANDY STORE

A nice showroom should be like a candy store of old. If you are old enough, you probably have fond memories of a "real" candy store. Perhaps there was one you frequented near your elementary school or on the corner near where you lived. Memories of peering over the edge of the display case at the wealth of two-for-a-penny candies you filled your pockets with – and don't forget the full-size candy bars for a nickel or the nickel snow cones – it was a sweet lovers delight! That is exactly the description of a good sublimation showroom except it is for adults and fortunately, no sugar is involved. Showing actual products is a must to sell sublimated products. Even if your showroom comes out of a suitcase or is online, a nice showroom is a must.

This candy store is for adults and even if it isn't very fancy, it should display enough choices that it seems like a candy store of old.

Showrooms come in all sizes and types. If you have a storefront, a nicely lit, carefully decorated showroom is a must. It doesn't have to be fancy or expensive, but it does need to be a place where both men and women feel comfortable and welcome.

Carefully thought out lighting, carpeting (or other flooring), with lots of natural light (if possible) and lots of samples to look at will make the difference between selling and not selling your products.

Here are a few hints about making and showing samples in your showroom:

1. Try never to put a date on the sample. Dates mean the products get old and have to be replaced.
2. Try to display your products in groups or themes. If you are going to show a product with a fireman's theme, do a series and display them together. For instance, you might show a shirt, a cup, a plaque, a key fob and a license plate – all with the same graphic. The reason for this approach is that people have a difficult time understanding that they can put anything they want on any product. The general public has, through the years, been taught that color is expensive, that it requires a big setup fee, they have to buy hundreds of identical products at a time and takes a long time. Now, we try to educate them to think just the opposite. There usually is no setup fee, they don't have to do hundreds of identical items at a time and it isn't expensive. It is a total mind-shift to what they have been trained

to think. Showing this visually by showing products in groups seem to help communicate what is obvious to us and seemingly impossible to them.

DISPLAY SUBLIMATION PRODUCTS BY THEME

SPORTS

CHURCHES

SCHOOLS

FIRE DEPARTMENTS

NEW BABIES

Here are some examples of Theme Displays. Show several products using the same basic theme to try and convey that any image can be used with any product. This is perhaps the most difficult concept there is to convey to a customer.

When selling to companies, and if you have time, create something with the customer's logo on it before you try to sell them. A key fob is enough. Anything to show them what you can do with their logo or company name. If you are going to call on the customer at his or her office, take it with you and present it immediately upon introducing yourself.

A simple name badge is a great way to display a logo.

If you want to introduce yourself by mail, your showroom can be that single gift item. A key fob with the company logo and the customer's name will "wow" the customer. To make the biggest impact, send the sample, along with a letter, either by Priority Mail or make up the envelop to look like it is Priority Mail and mark it "Personal" so it gets past the secretary who is told to trash any and all solicitations. A few days after you send the envelop, follow it up with a phone call or personal visit. Selling to most companies isn't hard if you have a product they need. Getting past the secretary is what's hard. That's why you always address your mail to the recipient by name. Sending it any other way is a total waste of time and money.

Have an Open House. If you are just starting and you have a storefront, hold an Open House and Ribbon Cutting. Make a big deal out of it and personally invite those people you want as customers. During lunch or just after work seems to be a good time so people can stop by on their lunch break or on their way home makes it more convenient.

The town's Mayor and his new granddaughter cut the ribbon.

Don't display your mistakes! If you make a product that has a misspelled word on it, you will be tempted to use it as a sample – after all, who will notice? Everyone, that's who. Don't show anything but your very best work.

Take advantage of the holidays. From New Year's Eve to Christmas, there are lots of holidays and special occasions you can dress up your showroom for. Customers will look forward to your new displays and decorations. It's also a great time to offer special discounts such as 25% to veterans at Veterans Day or 10% on Mother's Day gifts.

The holidays are a great time to draw in new customers with decorations.

Price your products so the customer doesn't have to ask. Don't play games with pricing. Customers talk to each other. They do research. They know when you price a product differently to one person than another. Set your price and stick with it.

Try offering specials such as "2 fers". Buy one product for $15.95, get two for $30. This encourages people to increase their orders and allows you to take advantage of the time it takes to design the product.

Eliminate clutter. Keep your showroom clean, uncluttered and dusted. It takes a lot of time to keep a nice showroom, but it pays off. A sloppy showroom tells the customer they may get a sloppy product.

Not everyone will have a physical showroom. Some will carry their showroom around in a suitcase. Nothing wrong with that. Just remember to follow the rules above that apply to you. Keep samples fresh and in perfect condition. When one becomes a little worn, replace it. When you are going to visit a client and you don't have several samples that are appropriate to his or her needs, make some. Calling on potential clients is hard. They are busy people and getting into see them can be exasperating. It takes patience and perseverance. Try to know who the right person to see is before you go. Call ahead and ask for the name of whoever buys products for that company and go prepared.

Others will sell their products online through a website or social opportunities like Facebook or Twitter. In this case, the website is your showroom and there are lots of rules to make your website attractive and functional.

Here are some tips and suggestions about creating your own website:

Keep it simple. Tell the customer exactly what you want them to do step by step. Not to sound Condéscending but every successful web designer says the same thing. Treat the visitor to your website like someone who can barely read. Big arrows saying, "Click Here" leading them through your site is not a bad idea. If customers think your website is too slow or too complicated, they will just go somewhere else.

Keep it up to date. Out of date information, sales notices, etc. are death to a website. Check your site regularly to make sure everything is working properly, and all dated material is removed.

Keep it fresh. Change pictures on your site often. Keep text short and to the point.

Keep it accurate. Spelling and grammatical errors are murder to a customer. It says you aren't careful.

Shipping charges are a big problem for websites. You can handle this in two ways: One, you can offer free shipping on all orders or all orders over a specific amount, or you can try and set shipping charges that don't scare the customer away. Amazon Prime has taught many shoppers to expect free shipping and if you are going to offer this, you must be sure to incorporate it somehow into the price. Shipping is never really free.

The same issues occur with Facebook. One suggestion is to take pictures of your products actually in use for your Facebook posts. For instance, if you make a purse for your wife, show her carrying it on a shopping trip and talk about how much she likes it. Don't try to "sell, sell, sell" on Facebook. It doesn't work. If you talk about a product however, and include a link to where they can buy one for themselves, that seems to work very well.

Another way to sell products is through eBay, Amazon or Etsy. These, and other services offer you the

opportunity to show your products to a larger market than you could ever attract on your own. The services are not free and they take considerable time to create postings, but they do work for many people. Postings are created by inserting your information into a spreadsheet like the one below. Inventory and changes can be made in seconds.

The problem with websites and all web related sites for that matter is "How do you get people to visit your sites?". This can be a complex and expensive problem to which many people have never found a solution. True, there are scores of people who promise they can solve that by positioning your link high in the search engines or other such pie-in-the-sky promises. Maybe some of them can, but which ones? For most, this is an expensive learning experience that results in only one person making money (and it isn't you).

Search engines like Google offer strategically placed links on their front pages and in search results, and although these may work, they can be very expensive. A recent check showed the word, "plaque" cost over $5 every time someone clicked on it. Although that may bring a lot of traffic to your site, you must ask yourself, "At what price?". If 20 people click on your site and only one actually ends up buying a $35 plaque, you have lost over $100 in the process of selling a $35 product! Of course, not all search words are this expensive, but the cost is based on the popularity of the word being searched, making it very difficult to win at this game of roulette.

Don't forget the obvious. Condé offers full-color catalogs of their products in PDF and "Flip Page" formats free for the

Also available as a "Flip Catalog" you can use on a tablet or include on your website.

Available in PDF so you can print your own or use it in a digital form.

downloading. Just add your contact information and you're in business. Although catalogs are not necessarily the best way to sell sublimation products (nothing is better than the customer holding the actual product in their hand), it does help when it isn't possible to have the actual product isn't possible. You should always have a few of these catalogs handy to give away when the opportunity affords itself. One thing you will need to do if you use the catalog is to develop a price sheet. This is no easy task but is easier if you use the suggested prices available on Condé's Pricing Spreadsheet (available free from your sales rep). Be sure all your prices are the same across the various selling platforms you offer (website, Facebook, physical showroom etc.).

Always remember, your showroom is a direct reflection of you, your work and your company. Taking pride in it (regardless of the type), is extremely important. And remember, when you see a customer's eyes glaze over like a kid in a candy shop, you know you have the right combination in your showroom. It's when a world of possibilities begins dancing through the heads of your clients that you can know your showroom is doing its job. The days of two-for-a-penny candy is gone but not the thrill of finding a whole new world of visual delights that can still be created.

PART THREE
SECTION 11

"If you don't value your time, neither will others. Stop giving away your time and talents. Value what you know and start charging for it." -Kim Garst

WHAT SHOULD I CHARGE FOR MY PRODUCTS?

That's the most commonly asked of all questions in sublimation. And rightly so. Learning to sublimate products is easy. Even learning CorelDRAW is easy compared to learning how to price products. Charge too much and people won't buy. Charge too little and you go broke.

Most retailers never have to learn how to price their products. It is done for them either by their products having a MSRP (Manufacturers Suggested Retail Price) sticker, giving you an amount that everyone is going to use as their "retail", or by an old process called "Key stoning". But sublimation products don't come that way and because you actually manufacture the product, is entirely up to you.

Most new businesses, and many old one, must stretch every dollar to make ends meet.

Ordinary retail and gift shops have for decades used something called "key stoning" to price their products. Key stoning means whatever you pay for the product, you charge double that as retail. But they aren't actually making the products and don't have to deal with the cost of waste, buying and maintaining equipment and labor. All they do is take it out of the box and put it on the shelf. Consequently, key stoning isn't usually the best method of pricing for sublimation.

Manufacturers who make products for gift shops (and almost everything else), often use a percentage to set their MSRP. In the case of gift items, that percentage is often 600% above their cost. That means if it costs $1 to make a widget, it should sell retail for $6. Sound like too much? Well, by the time you figure in the cost of equipment, overhead, labor, shipping, etc. it comes out pretty much on the money, and often, that number works well for

Keystone Pricing example:

Manufacturing Cost		Wholesale Price		Retail Price
$20		$40		$80
	2x markup		2x markup	

sublimation. Sometimes however, it puts the price so high, no one would ever buy our product. This means that although this method might work for some products, it won't work for all; so let's consider another method.

Some people in the sublimation business just look to see what other people are charging for their products and copy what they do. That's not a bad practice if you have competitors in your area but what if they aren't charging nearly enough? What if you have to pay more for your raw materials than they do? Those who want to use this method or use this method to check to see how their prices compare, might price products, on the Internet with companies like CafePress. Even so, this method might work for some products but certainly not all.

Yet another way, and sometimes the only way, is called "perceived value". In other words, "what would a customer see the product as being worth"? Anytime a product is priced below a person's perceived value, they see it as cheap (junk). If the product is more than what they perceive its value to be, it is overpriced and they will probably walk away. This method carries with it many pitfalls, not the least of which is the fact that everyone will see the product differently. Still, this is a viable approach to pricing, especially if you can be objective.

What keeps most sublimators from being objective is the fact we know what the product actually costs. Our minds immediately go to the base cost of the product and fails to factor in all the other costs associated with making the product (rent, electricity, labor, design time, etc.). In our minds, doubling or tripling our investment seems like a good thing (and it might be for some products), but more often than not, it will lead us to grossly underpricing our products.

If you haven't guessed by now, there isn't one single way to price sublimation products. It has to be done partly with percentage, partly with common sense, partly by experience and sometimes by trial and error. For example: If you offer a cup for $19.95 and it doesn't sell well but it does sell at $15.95, you have found a "sweet spot", so you reduce the price accordingly. Sounds simple but it usually isn't.

Here is an example: One of the most common products sold is a sublimated cup. For our purposes, we'll say a basic, no frills cup costs about $1.50 to buy and about 15¢ to print. That means our cost is $1.65. If we use the key stone method, retail would be $4.95 – a ridiculously low price. After all, you had to spend time designing the cup and then buy a device to make the cup, and provide electricity for the process; and (don't forget), in order to sell the one cup, you had to buy a case of 36 and pay the shipping (which can easily be as much as the cost of the cup) and if you made a mistake and applied the transfer upside down (don't laugh, even the experts do it), that wasted a cup. Now, what is it worth?

Is it worth the 600% markup we talked about earlier? You bet it is and more. So let's do the math:

$1.65 for the mug + $1 shipping=$2.65 x 600% = $15

So, now we must ask ourselves two questions:

1. Is this reasonable? Can you make money at this price?

2. How does this compare to the perceived value of the product?

If the answer to both questions is "yes", then you have found a basic price for the product. The price is reasonable for a custom made cup, based on what it costs to make, including something for overhead, labor, etc. It is also acceptable since the perceived value of a full-color, personalized cup should be seen as being worth about $15. This doesn't mean we can't "massage" the price a little to make it more enticing, however. Because of our culture of pricing everything as $4.95 or $5.98, etc., I would then price it at $15.95. But what am I going to offer for $15.95? Here's the problem with $15.95: If someone wants to order ten cups, the first thing he is going to ask is, "Do I get a discount for quantity?". And the answer should be, "yes, of course"; but wait a minute. If $15.95 is the base price, where do you go to get a discount? In reality, what you will be doing is giving away your profit in order to sell more cups. Here is a better solution: You know you want about $15.00 minimum for a cup, so ask yourself, "will the market stand $19.95 for a cup?". Chances are, it will. After all, this is a custom made, highly personalized, one-of-a-kind cup. If that is the case, you have lots of room to offer a discount for quantity without cutting into your profit margin. With a 10% discount or even a 20% discount, you are still making more than your base price for each cup. You're happy and the customer is happy. It also leaves you room for larger discounts for larger quantities. In fact, you can go as high as 25% and still sell your cup at a 600% margin ($15).

Another way to both offer a discount and encourage more sales is by offering "Two-fers". A "Two-fer" is when you offer two products that use the same basic design for a reduced price. For instance, using the cup above which sells for $19.95, we might give a "Two-fer $35" or if you sell the cup for $15.95, you might offer a "Two-fer $30". The logic of this is based on the fact that the most expensive element of any sublimated product is probably the time you spend designing it. Therefore, if you can take advantage of that by selling multiple products using the same design, it costs you less to make the product.

As mentioned above, the most expensive element in most sublimated products isn't the product or even the overhead. It is the time spent designing the product. That is why making multiple products with the same graphic are so profitable that they merit offering discounts for quantity. Think about it: How many hours could you spend designing and re-designing the same coffee cup to find your very best graphic? The answer is hours. Trying multiple backgrounds, searching for just the right piece of clipart, trying various fonts, etc. all go together to cost you money! This is not to say you shouldn't do the best you can to create a nice graphic, but keep in mind what you are investing into this one product. The gross profit of a coffee cup might be $12-$15. If you spend an hour designing it, what is your time worth? It is surely worth more than $15 an hour so if you spend an hour, designing the cup, it would actually be cheaper for you to pay the customer to go somewhere else to buy their cup.

Design time must be controlled. This is why it is best to sell products where either the design can be reused, or sell to customers who keep coming back for additional copies of the same basic design. Granted, while you are just starting to learn design, you will spend far too much time designing products, but this should be written off to experience. It will take a while for you to become comfortable designing products, finding clipart, etc. Don't be too hard on yourself in the beginning. Even the most hardened expert had to learn.

Let's look at pricing another product. One of the most common products is a name badge. A badge, with the finding (findings are the pins, magnets, etc, used on the back of a badge), including shipping, will cost about $1. If we use our trusty 600% formula, that means a finished badge should retail for about $6. Although I would consider that pretty low for a single badge because of the time it takes to design it, it's about right for a badge that has already been designed, so let's look at it this way:

Badges in quantity or remakes: The price starts at $6

For new designs or single orders: Increase the price to 10.95-15.95 to cover design time.

Although some companies charge for design time, and you may too, some don't. This allows them to advertise "No setup fee" or "Price is all inclusive". Customers don't like it when you nickel and dime them to death with hidden fees.

What about a shirt? Shirts vary in price but can be the most expensive product we sublimate. An expensive shirt might cost $9. If we use our 600% rule (9x6=$45), we end up with a figure few people will be willing to pay. So, in spite of the fact that shirts are one of the easiest products to mess up, we find ourselves in a dilemma. Do we reduce the price and hope for the best, or hold our price and cut deeply into our sales? Of course, each individual must answer this question for themselves, but if you want to sell shirts, you reduce the price – but how much?

In this case, sell the product for "as much as the market will bear". In other words, the perceived value. A T-shirt's value might be seen as $20, and maybe a bit more since it is personalized. That is enough for us to double our money, IF we don't have any waste. For every shirt you have to throw away, you break even on two good ones. This is further complicated in a market where screen printers often sell shirts for just a few dollars each (of course they might have a minimum of 144 shirts and they likely only pay a dollar or two for each shirt). You can see the problem. If you want to sell shirts, you will have to take less profit and take more risk than with most other products. Here, pricing is strictly "whatever the market will bear".

To help with pricing, Condé Systems offers a free service to help you price sublimated products. It is a downloadable spreadsheet that shows suggested prices for all the products Condé sells along with the ability to compute profit margins by percentage. Ask your Condé representative for a copy.

INTRODUCTION TO PART IV

The Fourth element of Sublimation success is perhaps the most challenging. That is starting, building and running a business all your own. We have talked extensively about designing and making the products and that should be the secret to success, but it isn't – not by itself anyway. Before all that success can happen, you have to actually "be in business". That means taxes and insurance and leasing property and so much more.

What is your starting point going to be? Are you a new business or an already existing one looking to expand into a new process?

If you are a new business, you have some exciting times ahead. True, there will be many difficult decisions and probably some frustrating days but hey, you will be working for yourself where there is no one to take the credit for a job well done but you. Of course, the same can be said for the responsibility of making mistakes, but if you follow the guidelines in this book, there should be a minimum of those.

If this is an add-on profit center for an existing business, you have picked a good one: Low costs and high profits are all but guaranteed. I don't know of any business anywhere with a lower startup cost and a higher profit margin than sublimation. All you have to concentrate on is grow, grow, grow!

In the pages to follow, you will read a great deal about how to grow a business. The focus of these will be the two ways to grow a business: Number one: Sell more products to your existing clients or Two: Find new profitable clients. We shall explore both.

This is the section you should read with a highlighter in your hand. Mark the statements you want to remember and come back to over and over. Growing a business is easy in principle but can be very challenging in reality. The guidelines presented here will help you avoid the mistakes countless others have made who have gone before you. Mark them, remember them, they will save you much time, money and grief.

Now, let's get started....

"You jump off a cliff and you assemble an airplane on the way down." -Reid Hoffman

BEFORE YOU BEGIN

THERE ARE SOME THINGS YOU NEED TO KNOW

Reid Hoffman's quote sounds a bit ominous, even careless, yet as the cofounder of LinkedIn, that is pretty much what he did. He jumped into the unknown without a parachute and built an airplane on his way down. It worked for him but for most, such a reckless decision would be just short of foolish. You don't have to go into your venture as one who has never ventured there before. Many have gone before and created a path you can follow.

Hopefully, you are already excited about starting your own business. That's great! Before you begin however, there are some important things you should take care of – namely Uncle Sam.

Although every state is different, there are some things you will need to take care of before you start selling products. In most states, these are not complicated, but they are vital.

The one thing you must NEVER do is shortchange Uncle Sam. I have known more than one business owner who cut corners and spent six months in some Federal prison as a result. Get started on the right foot.

Decide what kind of business you are going to have: Sole Proprietor, LLC, S Corp or C Corp. Most small businesses select either a Sole Proprietor or LLC because of the simple tax structure and the low cost of setting it up. If you have questions, consult with an attorney. You will eventually need an attorney anyway, so you might as well begin building a relationship with one now.

Get a business license if your state requires one. This will also set up a system for paying sales taxes that you collect, usually on a monthly basis. In most states, this is easy to do and, in some states, it is even free. Contact your State and City Tax Departments for instructions. Be advised that most states require a business license as do many counties or parishes and most cities or towns. Be sure to check with all these that might apply to you and your location. Be sure to display your business license(s) where the general public can view it/them.

If you are going to have employees, you will need to register your business with the Federal Government and obtain a Federal ID Tax Number and make monthly deposits at a local bank to cover any funds you deduct from your employee's pay, plus your portion of their Social Security.

If you are going to have employees, you will need to buy Unemployment Insurance. States differ as to how they collect this. Some states do it through your business insurance while others bid it out to a specific company that specializes in this type of insurance.

You need to obtain insurance for your business. Don't confuse this with your Unemployment Insurance above. This insurance will include fire, theft and liability coverage and can vary greatly depending on the size of your business and number of employees. Most major insurance companies cover small businesses, so shop around. They can vary wildly in cost and coverage.

Rent a facility if you are not going to work out of your home. This can be complicated and should be entered into carefully. Most landlords will require a lease that can run from one to five years. Obviously, you will want to try and obtain a one-year lease since all new businesses are precarious at best. If you have never signed a commercial lease, there are some things you need to understand: Commercial leases are different from residential leases. In a residential lease, the landlord is responsible for repairs, the roof, air conditioning, etc. In a commercial lease these responsibilities are often shifted to the tenant. This means that if the roof suddenly needs to be replaced, you can be stuck with the bill! Read the lease before signing.

Prepare your facility for your business. Be it a storefront or your garage, basement or bedroom, there are some things that need your attention. Not the least of these is the electrical system in the building. Heat presses draw a lot of current. Safety demands that each press be on a 20-amp circuit by itself. Printer, lights and computers should never be on the same circuit as your heat press. Avoid using extension cords of all kinds. If you have to use an extension cord with a heat press, be sure it is made with #12 wire. Do not use outlet strips with heat presses, as most are not safe above 15 amps.

Ensure that you have good ventilation. Heat presses put out a lot of heat and will raise the temperature of an ordinary room to over 100 degrees very quickly. Fans, windows, central air conditioning and vents all can be used to exhaust heat and fumes. Fumes are minimal with sublimation, but heat presses do put off fumes and these should be vented as much as possible for obvious reasons.

Mount your heat press(s) on strong sturdy tables. These presses weight in at close to one-hundred pounds and should one collapse a table, it is likely someone will be injured. The ideal height of a table for a heat press is debated but most agree it is somewhere between 20" and 24" tall.

Build or obtain a good workbench. I prefer something long and about 36" tall. You can have storage underneath and I prefer low pile indoor/outdoor carpeting covering the bench.

You will need to build some way of storing your inventory. The more inventory, the more shelves you will need. Remember that although most sublimation products are fairly light, things like cups and plaques can count up in weight.

Lighting is essential to a good work area and showroom. It helps greatly to have lighting that doesn't alter the color of what you are sublimating. Incandescent bulbs cast a yellow light while florescent tubes can be white, yellow or blue depending on what color you use. The new LED light strips are my favorite since they put out an intense white light. Showroom lighting is usually track lighting. It is inexpensive and easy to hang. New LED versions are expensive but worth it both in energy savings and eliminating the heat put off by other types of lighting.

Will you need a security system? Some areas of the country are still crime free, but they are becoming smaller and less common. Go ahead and have a basic system installed if you think you need it before something happens. There are lots of options to choose from so do some comparative shopping. ADT, Brinks and others will even install a basic system in exchange for an annual contract for monitoring at $25 to $35 per month.

You will also need Internet access. This can be obtained in several ways, but you will need a good broadband connection to save both time and frustration. If you ae really on a tight budget, you can even use your cellphone as a Hot Spot to drive your computers to the Internet. It isn't exactly convenient, but it works.

Of course, you will need to set up accounts with all the necessary utilities including gas, electric, water, trash pickup and sewer. These often require a fairly hefty deposit, so be prepared. Sometimes you can get around the deposits if you put them in your name while you also have your home utilities in your name.

Have an Open House. If you are working out of your home, ask some friends and neighbors over to get things rolling. If you have a storefront, invite the Major to come and cut the ribbon and take lots of pictures for publicity shots later.

If you aren't good with construction or don't want to build your own benches, this wood bench from Harbor Freight is a good place to start. I cover the tops of my benches with a low-pile carpet.

Although some may disagree, this type of bench's only advantage is that it is cheap.

Metal units that are a combination of storage and a workbench are very nice. Harbor Freight is an inexpensive source.

George Knight offers a stand for their heat presses that is strong and on wheels. If you opt to build your own, it should be about 24" tall for best leverage.

This type of LED light is great for general lighting but doesn't work well over a workbench because it aims the LEDs into your eyes.

"Shop Lights" with side fins are much better for over a workbench because you can keep the light from shining directly into your eyes.

Track lighting is all but a must for any showroom. Many styles are available. LEDs are a must since they save electricity, can be gangged together in much larger numbers and produce no heat. This showroom belongs to Cornwall Trophies in Pool, Reduth.

"There are no shortcuts to anyplace worth going." -Beverly Siles

BUSINESS PLANS...WHO NEEDS THEM? YOU DO!

If you go to a bank and ask for a loan to start a business, one of the first things they will ask for is a Business Plan. Since most of you reading this book won't go to a bank, that's something you won't have to do but you should just the same.

A business plan makes you think. It forces you to create a working budget, a projected Profit and Loss Statement and a realistic look at what it costs to be in business. There are two types of business plans: The first is what you might offer a bank showing your projected expenses, investment, cash on hand, projected sales, overhead and salaries and, of course, your projected profits. It should include your Mission (which should not be listed as "To make money") even though it really is, but something like, "To serve the public by offering quality awards, gifts and other personalized items along with exceptional customer service".

If you are starting up using your own money or with credit cards, as most people do, you won't have to create this document for anyone but yourself but that doesn't lessen the value of it. This lesson I didn't learn until I started my second business.

Now, let me brush away some of the misconceptions you probably have about business plans:

MYTH: When a person goes to a bank asking for startup money, the bank will require a business plan. Since the person has probably never been in the sublimation business before, they really have no earthly clue how to do this, so they just make it up. They hope to sell so many items at such and such a price and with the cost of doing business being this or that, a profit of x amount of dollars will be the result and that is sufficient to live and pay off the bank loan. Actually, the bank only cares about your paying off the loan. They couldn't care less if you live beyond that or not.

FACT: Well, that is *not* what we are talking about here. That kind of research may be great for a Business Major in college, but our plan needs to be much more practical and far less theoretical.

MYTH: Once created, the typical business plan should be stuck to like glue. To vary from that plan or to change that plan is an admission of some kind of failure.

FACT: Not true with our business plan. In fact, just the opposite is true. We want our plan to be dynamic, capable of change, open to new ideas and flexible enough that good advice or life experience can be inserted, and unrealistic expectations removed as it matures.

Because our business plan is *alive*, it invites change, and is always looking for opportunities to grow.

MYTH: A working business plan doesn't have to be written down.

FACT: Just as no bank would ever accept a business plan that is just in your head, I won't either. A business plan needs to have structure (we will talk more about that in a minute) and be available for you and everyone else involved in your enterprise to see and understand.

MYTH: A mental image of what you want your business to be is a dream.

FACT: Before that dream can become a reality, there must be a transition. Putting it on paper, in detail, is the first step to turning that dream into reality.

MYTH: You must set accurate, realistic goals from the very beginning.

Wrong! You can't set accurate goals and objectives for something you know nothing about. Sure, you should set some goals, lofty goals, but the problem with goals in a new business is that when they aren't met, it is translated as failure. When a goal of $100,000 for the first year is set and you only do $98,000, somehow that is a failure. In spite of the fact you did $98,000 more this year than last year, that somehow doesn't measure up.

FACT: Goals are vital. They are often our strongest motivator when things are hard. Someone once said, "A mortgage is the best motivator there is.". Well, that's true. Paying that mortgage and keeping your house is an excellent motivator and so are goals but....

Anytime you do a business startup, there are going to be a lot of obstacles you don't expect. And, there may very well be some pleasant surprises along the way as well. One businessperson I know says that "a business startup is success when 3 things are present: A good plan, a lot of hard work, and luck". Take any one of these out of the equation and the business will struggle. Notice the last one, "luck". I don't know how to define that term, but we all know what it is. Sometimes it is being in the right place at the right time. Sometimes it is knowing the right person or having the right connections. Sometimes it is just grace that falls from the sky and hits us squarely on the top of the head. One thing for sure, I have seen a lot of businesses fail through the years in spite of a good sounding plan and hard work. I don't know what to attribute those failures to other than just plain old bad luck – the owner got sick, had an accident, some natural disaster occurred, legal problems arose for some reason or most common of all, they just ran out of money.

MYTH: A business plan is all about money.

FACT: Not true. A business plan is about action but make no mistake, if you enter any business venture undercapitalized, you are probably going to struggle. That doesn't mean you will fail but you will have to be doubly careful about each and every financial decision. There will be little, if any, room for mistakes.

If you are going into a new business underfunded, I will give you three pieces of advice:

Don't do it.

If you are determined to do it, do your homework. Find people who have lots of experience under their belts and beg for their help and then listen to what they have to say.

Don't do it.

Somewhere I read that 90% of the businesses that didn't survive five years failed because of underfunding. I can't say if that is true or not, but my experience says the numbers are probably right.

MYTH: A business plan is only about the business.

FACT: Wrong again. If you are the sole owner of a new business, your business plan needs to be about both you and your company. Businesses don't spring up and immediately start paying dividends. It takes time to grow a business. Some people start up while working another full or part time job. Others wait for retirement. Still others use their life savings to get started. This isn't just about *your business*; it has everything to do with *you*. While you are waiting for your business to grow to a point it can pay you a salary, how are you going to live? Are there car payments, mortgage payments and other commitments that need to be met? How are you going to meet family responsibilities? The inability to meet these commitments brings on stress – stress that can harm your health, your interpersonal relationships and the way you perform in your new business. It is hard to be excited about anything when you can't pay your bills!

If you are not already in an established, successful business, include yourself, your family and your business in your plan. Until you have crossed the point where your business can actually support itself and you, there is no way to separate your needs, the needs of your family and your business.

 Have a contingency plan.

I don't think I have ever seen this in a business plan offered to a bank, but it makes common sense. If everything goes wrong, what then? Remember, even though it may seem like it most of the time, the only reason for building a business is so it can work for you. Too often, we end up being slaves to our business when the reason we started the business in the first place was to get away from all that. OK, so luck isn't with you. What will that mean? Will you lose everything? Your home, your investments, your dignity, even your family?

No business venture is worth all that. The risk is just too great, so build into your contingency plan a safety escape hatch. At what point are you going to pull the plug and do something else? Having this pre-determined means the difference between success and failure. I know of too many business owners who wait until they have lost everything before they admit defeat. If it is part of the plan, it isn't defeat. How many highly successful men and women do you know who started over and over again before being really successful?

Now some will say this section is negative. No, it is anything but because it ensures future success. Starting a business is a risky deal – always. Anyone who tells you different has never built a business. Always plan for the best and prepare for the worst. That's why we buy insurance – just in case. Some of us are insurance poor because of that, but that's a story for another time.

OK, it's time to begin to develop your business startup plan. Step one is to run out and buy all that fancy equipment, right? Wrong again. We are still a long way from spending money so relax and let's spend some time getting excited about the possibilities.

Already, we have talked about many applications for sublimation. You probably have no real idea just what you on want to focus. A few things are pretty sure: You probably aren't going to make car interiors and draperies, but what are you going to make?

The basis of one business plan model goes like this: Before you buy any equipment, determine these three things:

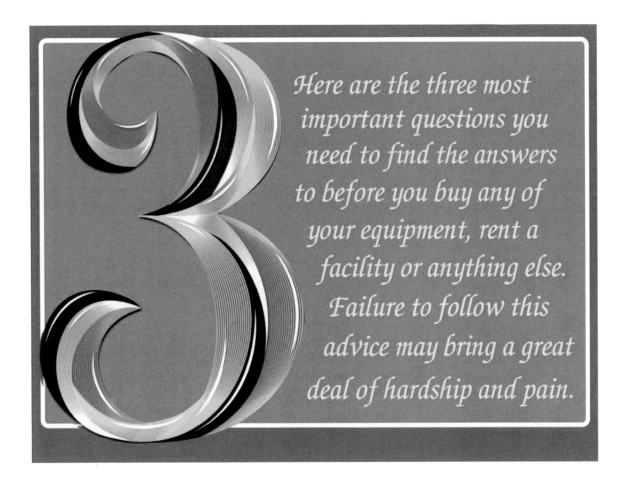

Here are the three most important questions you need to find the answers to before you buy any of your equipment, rent a facility or anything else. Failure to follow this advice may bring a great deal of hardship and pain.

What are you going to make with sublimation?

Are you going to make wearables, drinkware, home décor items, photo panels or something else? Do a little test marketing in your area to see what the interests are.

To whom are you going to sell it?

Are there customers in your area that want the products you plan to make? You can always expand and add new products but if you can find in immediate market for your products, you will be way ahead of the game.

And how?

How are you going to reach your potential customers? Face to face, through the Internet, by way of a selling site such as Amazon, eBay or Etsy?

"The secret to success is to do a common thing uncommonly well." -John D. Rockefeller, Jr.

WHAT DOES IT COST TO BE IN BUSINESS?

What does it cost to be in business? That's a good question and this is just the right time to ask it – before you actually start. The short answer to this question is, "a lot more than you think".

The long answer is a lot more involved, but understanding your "real" cost of having a business is crucial to staying in business.

Statistics are constantly being waved around that between 75% and 95% of all business startups fail in the first year. And it's probably true. Whether it's 90% or 75% or something in between, however, isn't important. What is important is that new business startups understand *why* so many businesses fail.

To be sure, some fail because the owners make too many mistakes, or it was just a bad idea from the start, but sublimation has been around for a long time and has a proven track record of being a sound business investment. Still, sublimation businesses sometimes fail too and the reason is usually one of two reasons: Under-capitalization (that is, they didn't have enough money to carry them until their business could stand on its own, or the owners didn't know what it cost to be in business and didn't adjust their prices and business plan accordingly). Simply put, when there is more going out than coming in, the business is going to fail.

So, what is the cost of being in business? Unfortunately, those costs differ with each company and often, the costs are hidden and difficult to identify accurately during startup. Expenses are far easier to determine accurately after being in business for a year or so.

In a nutshell, the cost of being in business is the grand total of everything you spend. Below is a chart to help gather your thoughts about your cost of being in business. I suggest you try to enter your estimates on an annual basis.

FORMULA FOR DETERMINING THE COST OF BEING IN BUSINESS

Rent or mortgage for building:

    Repairs on building (most repairs will be your responsibility):   _____

    Electricity   _____

    Gas   _____

    Water   _____

    Insurance   _____

    Security Deposits   _____

    Security (Alarm system, etc.)   _____

Employees:

    Your salary: _____

        Insurance (health, life, retirement):   _____

    Employee's wages: _____

        Your share of their Social Security (7.2%):   _____

        Medicare (3.4%):   _____

        Unemployment Insurance: _____

        Employee Benefits (health insurance, vacation, etc.)   _____

Equipment:

    Sublimation equipment (Printer, heat press, etc.):   _____
    Computer(s):   _____

        Software (Drawing, accounting, Word, etc.)   _____

    Shears, heat wraps and other related equipment: _____

    Equipment repairs & depreciation: _____

Product Cost:

    Ink & Paper: _____

    Blank products (initial inventory):   _____

Advertising:

    Yellow Pages: _____

Showroom (Samples, fixtures, etc.): _____

Catalogs & Other Sales Aids: _____

Website: _____

Business cards: _____

Exterior signage: _____

Outside advertising (Yearbooks, newspaper, etc.): _____

Transportation:

Cost of vehicle: _____

Mileage (55¢ per mile): _____

Insurance: _____

Repairs: _____

Taxes: _____

Shipping:

UPS/FedEx fees: _____

Postage: _____

Shipping materials (bubble wrap, etc.) _____

Taxes:

Property taxes: _____

Business & Occupation Taxes: _____

Tax preparation costs (accountant): _____

Banking:

Cost of checking account: _____

Loan payments: _____

Interest on loans: _____

Credit card processing: _____

Communication:

Telephone: _____

Cell phone: _____

Internet service (WiFi, etc.):   _____

Dues & Memberships: _____

Organizations (Chamber of Commerce, etc.)   _____

TOTAL   _____

These may not reflect everything you might encounter in your first year and some you may not encounter at all, but it does provide a realistic worksheet for you to plan your business's health long before you actually spend a dime.

As time goes on, more and more things will be added to the list. It is amazing how easily and quickly things add up. For example: Once you are established, who is going to wash the windows or cut the grass? You might take your trash home with you while you are just starting up but eventually, you will have to pay someone to haul it off. At what point do you provide company shirts for all your employees or have to put a new roof on your building or new air conditioning? How much inventory are you going to carry and how are you going to pay for it? And what about that well-deserved vacation? As you can see, things can get out of hand very quickly.

After you have been in business for a year or so, it becomes much easier to get a snapshot of what is really happening in your business. This is easiest to obtain when you are doing your Federal Income Taxes for the business (Schedule C).

Abbreviated Cost of Being in Business

DIVIDE THIS AMOUNT by 12 to get what it costs you to be in business per month: _____

DIVIDE THIS AMOUNT by 52 to get what it costs you to be in business per week: _____

DIVIDE THIS AMOUNT by 2080 to get what it costs you to be in business per hour: _____

(Based on a 40-hour work week):

You can do the same thing with your GROSS INCOME from your Schedule C to find out how much you are grossing per month, week or hour.

SUBTRACT the expenses from the Gross Income to find out how much you are really making in PROFIT per year. Don't be surprised if these numbers are sobering. That's why it is important you understand how much it costs you to be in business, even before you make a dime!

The 5% to 25% of startups that do make it in the real world are the ones that understand these numbers and how much they influence everyday business. They help us keep our perspective on what we should be charging for our time and products and help us look beyond the number in our checkbook before spending money irresponsibly.

If you watch and understand these numbers, you will be much more likely to be successful.

Good Luck!

NOTES

BUSINESS BASICS 4

"The absolute fundamental aim is to make money out of satisfying customers." -John Egan

DON'T MAKE THIS MISTAKE WITH PRICING!

Many of you are going to start your business out of your home. Perhaps a garage, basement or even an extra bedroom and that's fine; many people do just that. Some grow into a storefront and others build very successful businesses right out of their homes and stay there.

There are both positives and negatives with either arrangement: storefront or home based (and you have probably discovered some already). Storefronts are expensive and confining – you have to set working hours and hold to them. A home-based business is far more flexible and usually less expensive, but there is one major drawback to a home business that almost never gets attention until it is too late and that is setting prices.

Setting prices is always difficult (has you will see in the chapter dedicated to that topic) but this is a slightly different problem and it comes up with almost everyone who tries to start their business at home; and in too many cases, it causes them to fail as soon as the business starts to have some overhead, such as employees or you grow into a storefront.

Let me guess. I'll bet I know what is in the back of your mind. Perhaps you haven't said it out loud yet, but I'll bet you think that because you are working out of your home and don't have all that overhead storefront owners do, you can charge less than they do. Through some magic attraction, that is going to cause people to beat a path to your door and you will prosper.

The truth is, you won't, and neither will your competition. It is a foolish notion and should be discarded the instant it comes into your mind. Here's why:

It is true that you can sell for less when your only overhead is a little electricity and ink but why would you want to? Why would you want to leave all that money on the table?

The day will come, and perhaps much faster than you think, when you will want to hire employees, move to a storefront or retire from your present job and depend on your sublimation business to take up the slack (or perhaps support you and your family completely), and it can.

The problem is, you lock yourself in once you set your prices. It is very difficult to raise prices for repeat customers or even for new customers who happen to be friends with people who are already customers. Do you think they won't talk and compare prices? They surely will and then, what do you do?

You may have little to no overhead now, but overhead will come. It just has a way of doing that. Updating equipment, utilities, Internet, interest on loans, employees, commissions, advertising, websites and on the list goes. At some point, you may want to lease a vehicle or move into a storefront where you have to pay rent; and then you have to maintain a showroom where you have to install lighting or replace carpeting and the list goes on.

You may think you will just deal with those things when they occur, but it doesn't work that way. If you don't lay the groundwork for them now, you will not be able to afford them when the time is right.

In short, set prices the same as if you had all these things and enjoy the benefits brought by the extra income. That way, when expansion does come, you won't have to make an increase in your prices and the transition will go smoothly. Too many companies have made this mistake and found that when they had to increase their prices to survive or grow, they lost most of their customers because "they charge too much".

People don't know what sublimated products are worth until you tell them. Then they must decide if they are worth that price to them. When you start out too low and then increase the price drastically, you have told them what they are "really" worth; and suddenly "increased costs to pay for that fancy storefront, etc.".

Be smart and set your prices according to what you learned in the chapter on pricing and don't be influenced by what I call "the Walmart mentality" of constantly lowering prices. Just remember the owners of Walmart are some of the richest people in the world. They didn't get wealthy by selling cheap – they only make it sound that way.

APPENDIX I

RESOURCES

Education is, without a doubt, the most important element in the success or failure of a sublimation business. Understanding how the process works, how products work, and business basics, are essential to the success of any business - especially sublimation. Condé System is here to help you but there are many other sources for information as well. Education can come through trade magazines, blogs, tradeshows, Facebook pages, Twitter and websites. Like most industries, the more you can learn, the better off you will be. Even if you hear information that isn't accurate, (and there is plenty out there), you will be growing in knowledge as to what works and what doesn't; who you can trust and who you can't.

Archive of Articles by David Gross and Others from A&E Magazine: Go to https://a-e-mag.com/features then type in "David Gross" in the Search window.

Archive of Articles by Steve Spence and Others from Engravers Journal: Go to the website www.engraversjournal.com then select "Articles".

CONDÉ TV: Need to learn how to do something? Forgotten how to make a product? Have printer issues? Trying to learn CorelDRAW? All these, and many more are all covered in detail at CondéTV. Just go to YouTube.com and type in what you need to review.

Templates: Did you know there are templates for all the sublimation products available – FREE? They are, just go to the Condé website and click on "Templates" on the left-hand side of the page.

Instructions: Don't know how to make a product? No problem. You could go to CondéTV and watch it made or you can see the written instructions available online. Just pull up the product you are making, and you will see a tab below the product marked "Instructions".

Artwork: Artwork – tons of artwork. Every kind of background you can think of with more being added all the time. Sold at very reasonable prices, you can stock up on the kinds of designs your customers want and not break the bank doing it. Just go to the Condé website and click on "Artwork" on the left-hand side of the screen. It will put you in a wonderland of designs.

Sample Designs by Various Sublimators: At a loss for how to create a design for a particular product? No problem. A wealth of ideas are available right on the Condé website. Just select the product you are going to decorate and check out the options at the bottom of the screen. One will be "Gallery", which contains pictures of what other sublimators have done and were willing to share with others.

MAGAZINES:

A&E: A publication of NBM (National Business Media). Although no longer published, it was a monthly magazine for the awards and engraving industry and archives of articles are available online. In 2020, it was combined into a combo magazine called "Graphics Pro" that included the old Printware and Sign Business magazines. www.nbm.com David Gross was often a contributor to this magazine.

Engravers Journal: A publication of Davis Publishing. Offers an annual subscription, online access and a 3-month free trial. www.engraversjournal.com Steve Spence is often a contributor to this magazine.

Insights: A publication of the Awards & Personalization Association (APA). This magazine is free with an annual membership to the APA ($210).

Printwear: A publication of NBM (National Business Media). A monthly magazine for the Printware industry for many years by NBM. In 2020, it was combined into a combo magazine called "Graphics Pro" that included the A&E and Sign Business magazines. www.nbm.com David Gross was often a contributor to this magazine.

BLOGS:

Condé Blog: Open to customers, staff and sublimation experts. Answers to hundreds of questions along with product suggestions. Free, www.Condé.com

ORGANIZATIONS:

Awards & Personalization Association (APA), Trophies, awards, sublimated gifts. www.awardspersonalization.org

Advertising Specialty Institute (ASI), Promotional product organization. www.asicentral.com

Promotional Products Association International (PPAI), Promotional product organization. www.ppai.org

International Print & Imaging, www.ipiphoto.com

SAGE, Technology Supplier for websites and marketing. www.sage.com

TRADESHOWS:

APA Shows: Both a National annual show and regional shows sponsored by the Awards & Personalization Association. The annual show is held at the Rio Hotel & Casino in Las Vegas while regional shows move from city to city, www.awardspersonalization.org

NBM Shows: Sponsored by National Business Media, these shows target sublimation, laser engraving, screen printing, the print-ware industry and the sign industry. Most years they offer at least six shows held around the country. For an up-to-date list of show locations and venders, go to www.nbm.com.

PRINTING UNITED (Formerly the SGIA Expo): The Specialty Imaging & Technology group does a series of shows related to the printing industry. www.sgia.org

ISS Shows: Imprinted Sportswear does five shows per year around the country that are solely about imprinted garments, including sublimation.

ISA Show: Held in Orlando, Florida each summer, this tradeshow involves everything about signage. www.signs.org

IPI Shows: The International Print & Imaging Conference is held in Las Vegas each summer, www.lpiphoto.com

WEBSITES:

www.Condé.com for access to blog, CondéTV, products, sample designs, backgrounds, webinars, video downloads, new products.

www.color.adobe.com For advanced designers who want to better understand the use of color and the types of colors that complement each other.

www.geoknight.com for information about heat presses.

www.koolplate.com for information about the KoolPlate and what it can do to help you increase production.

www.pantone.com for Pantone™ swatch books, apps and other support.

www.sawgrassink.com for information about Sawgrass products, phone numbers for technical assistance, stock designs, business support information, articles and access to Creative Studios.

www.unisub.com for UNISUB products and templates.

PRINT SERVICES:

Don't have time or the right equipment to sublimate an order in-house? No problem, Condé can do it for you. This service is especially helpful because it allows you to include things like car mats, carpet squares and ceiling tiles to your inventory. Check it out on the Condé website.

OTHER:

125 Ways to Make Money with Sublimation by J. Stephen Spence: A printed manual describing over 125 niche markets, how to approach them and what products to offer. Optional dual CD pack contains layouts for each market that are great for samples.

Successful Sublimation Video Series by J. Stephen Spence: Although somewhat dated, this four-DVD set covers sublimation from start to finish. Each disk can be purchased separately. Disk One: Introduction to Sublimation. Disk Two: Tips & Techniques. Disk Three: Introduction to CorelDRAW. Disk Four: Marketing.

 APPENDIX II

MY BEST 101 TIPS & TRICKS BY DAVID GROSS

GENERAL

David Gross

1. Document everything. Keep a sublimation diary of your print jobs, transfer details, and any problems you experience. This is the best way to minimize waste and get to the bottom of future problems. When you master a product, document in your own words what works. When you need to reprint that one tile from a particular mural, you'll be able to refer back to job details such as the file name, what kind of tile you used, paper used, press settings, etc.

2. Create a "Wall of Shame" that displays some of your past mistakes, e.g. an upside-down plaque or crooked T-shirt image. This will remind you not to make the same mistake again.

3. Test kits (available for hard and soft substrates) provide an inexpensive way to check quality and color without having to use your more expensive substrates.

4. Keep your sublimation instructions up to date. We revise our instructions every few weeks to keep up with new products, improved transfer techniques, and changes in substrates. Translate our instructions to your words and post these near your heat press. Also, watch our massive collection of free sublimation videos at www.youtube.com/Condésystems.

5. Don't turn away business you can't handle! Ask your supplier for help with printing large quantities and/or transferring to substrates too large for your existing equipment.

6. Have a backup plan for when you have equipment or personal issues. Do you know someone close by that could help in an emergency? If not, ask your supplier for help locating someone in your area that might be able to help out in a pinch.

7. If you lack graphic expertise, seek out a graphic artist at a local college or university. Clients will pay for quality work.

8. Take an Adobe Photoshop class! Even a little training will go a very long way. This is also a great way to meet new clients or find a new employee.

PRINTER

9. Install your printer on a very sturdy, level table that will not shake while printing. Connect a UPS (battery backup) to your computer and your printer (but not your heat press) to avoid potential major interruptions in production. Locate printers in a temperature-controlled environment and avoid low humidity. Use a humidifier if needed to maintain at least 25% RH.

10. Keep a log for your printer. Documenting when the ink cartridges are replaced in relation to the printer's page count can help keep tract of ink costs. Also, documenting error codes and nozzle-check issues will greatly help in solving problems yourself or with the help of technical support.

11. Buy plastic airtight containers for your sublimation papers. This will prevent the paper from absorbing moisture, as well as keeping things organized by size and type.

12. Choose the right media for the right application to ensure superb transfer quality. Choosing the right paper depends on the type of substrate being transferred. Standard paper provides superb image clarity and color on hard substrates such as ceramic tiles, award plaques, name badges and coffee mugs. High-release paper is designed to release more sublimation ink in the transfer process, resulting in incredibly vibrant transfers on soft (thirsty) substrates, including T-shirts, mousepads, towels and tote bags. Also consider pre-cut mug paper. This simple change can help digital decorators at all levels of production eliminate paper waste and drastically reduce the time and effort involved in producing mugs in an oven or traditional mug press.

13. All inkjet printers have a waste ink tank that will eventually become full. An Epson printer's message reads, "parts are near end life". For printers that do not have replaceable tanks, a software program is available from your supplier that will reset it (look on our website under support special utilities). For printers that have replaceable tanks, ask your supplier for available options.

14. Hide non-sublimation inks so that it is not possible to install one by accident.

15. Ask your supplier for advice on how to maintain the health of your printer, e.g. learning to clean a transport belt or a capping station.

16. Buy extended warranties for your printer(s) when possible.

17. Raising the printhead on an Epson printer to its highest position will prevent ink smears – especially on larger paper sizes. This is not needed on the Ricoh or Virtuoso printers.

18. Ask your supplier how much your printers cost to print. A good way to reduce a printer's ink cost is to recycle empty sublimation cartridges, (as we provide a $5 credit per cartridge).

19. Call your supplier (before calling Epson or Ricoh) when your printer appears to be dying. There are often simple fixes that can help bring a printer back to life. Your supplier should be highly motivated to get your printer back on track.

20. Consider purchasing a backup/spare printer. This is a great way to get back on track when your primary printer fails. If you wait until an emergency occurs, you may not be able to find an exact replacement for your printer, (as models become obsolete over time). Be aware that changing to a different printer will always introduce slight variations in spot colors.

21. Perform a nozzle check at the beginning of each day and when printed transfers have visible banding problems. The printed test pattern checks the condition of the printer's ink nozzles. When the test pattern is complete, then the printer is ready to print transfers. An incomplete test pattern represents clogged nozzles and should be followed up with a head-cleaning and nozzle check. If the head-cleaning fails, call your supplier's tech support department for assistance. Don't waste ink by performing repeated head-cleanings!

22. Get a copy of "Harvey Head Cleaner". This inexpensive software utility for Windows will automatically send a nozzle check to your printer once a day to help keep it healthy.

23. Leave your printer turned on. Turning your printer off and on only serves to waste ink.

24. Prints should always be transferred within a few days to ensure superb image clarity and color vibrancy.

COMPUTER

25. Use the ‹shift› ‹Print Screen› command to document important settings and printing preferences, including CorelDraw's "Tools/Color Management" and "Print Preview" screens. These "screen captures" can be pasted into Photoshop or CorelDRAW for saving and printing. Since a picture is worth a thousand words, you'll be very thankful to have these easy-t-reference images when you have to reinstall your software or move to a new PC.

26. For PC folds, go into the Printer's Properties, select the "Advance" tab, and check the "Keep Printed Documents" box. This hidden treasure allows you to re-print any job from the print folder without using your application. Great for repeat jobs.

27. Use Windows' restore feature to overcome major computer problems. This feature returns Windows to a point before the problem occurred. This has saved me many times.

28. For future orders, remember to archive all artwork and important files on an external USB hard drive. Rotate drives for off-site storage in the event of fire or theft. The Cloud is a must have for backups.

29. Should you go with 64-bit windows? I say a qualified "yes" to those with new computers that do not need to run old software applications. It has a much higher RAM limit and delivers better performance. ArTainium and Gel ink customers are all set since we can use our ICC profiles with the native printer drivers. Those with very old Epson printers and those that use PowerDriver should check first. For instance, Epson 3000 folks are out of luck as there is no 64-bit driver. No problem for Epson 4000 series printers.

30. Max out your RAM on your PC or MAC. This is the least costly performance booster.

31. Of course, everyone should install virus/spyware/firewall software. I like Microsoft's Security Essentials and its *free!* Visit www.microsoft.com/securityessentals for more information.

32. Don't bother buying monitor calibration equipment or software unless you have a nice new monitor like a Sony brand. If you think you have a nice monitor, then install and use the ICC profile for it.

HEAT PRESS

33. Keep your press area clean, organized and well ventilated. Have a place for all your transfer accessories and know what the power requirements are for each press. If possible, have a dedicated 30-amp circuit for your heat press (multiple presses may require additional circuits).

34. Always use protective paper on the top and bottom of a substrate while it is being pressed. I recommend a roll of uncoated, white butcher paper (available at Sam's Club and office supply stores). The paper, thrown away after each use, protects your heat platen, bottom pad and substrate from ink and other debris. I seldom recommend Teflon sheets as it traps moisture and will transfer sublimation ink to the next substrate. I do, however, recommend it for products with adhesive backs such as Rowmark's MATES material and our fabric patches.

35. Used as a "buffer" between the heat platen of the press and the substrate being pressed, heat conductive rubber pads distribute heat slowly and evenly over substrates. A must when pressing glass products.

36. Heat insulating felt pads have excellent insulating properties and help keep the heat next to the item being transferred to. Placing a substrate between the heat platen and a felt pad will contain the heat, therefore reducing pressing time. A must when pressing ceramic tiles.

37. Lubricate your press every month with high-temp grease to ensure smooth operation and long life.

38. Pressing small, medium or large quantities of substrates requires a clean, flat and appropriately sized cooling table counter located near the heat press. Several un-imaged glass floor tiles or a sheet of aluminum can do the job for most products; and a filing cabinet makes an excellent surface for cooling flexible magnets.

39. Check that your press closes evenly by cutting a sheet of paper into four squares and placing ½ of each square under each corner of the press. Then close with light pressure. Verify that each square pulls with the same resistance. If not, the press may need to be adjusted.

40. Check to see if a shuttle attachment is available for your press. This is an awesome productivity enhancer that allows you to press a product while prepping for the next.

41. Remember, a bigger pot boils slower. When pressing several items at a time, you must (in most cases) increase the overall transfer time. Document your times. You might also want to increase your pressure slightly to insure even contact.

42. A small convection oven and an assortment of dye wraps (a dye wrap holds the transfer to the substrate) can produce multiple mugs, shot glasses, latte mugs, large steins and dog bowls easily and inexpensively. I like the Cuisinart Brick Oven that's good for up to six 11 oz mugs. Place a thermometer in the oven to accurately set the temperature. Only use this oven for sublimation, not for food preparation.

43. Use a lint roller to remove loose fibers and debris from T-shirts and other fabric products before pressing. This usually removes the blue lint that sometimes shows up after sublimation. f you have major static issues, wipe the substrate with an unscented drier sheet before pressing.

44. Heat tape and Dye Trans Pro Spray make it easy to align and secure the printed transfer to hard and soft substrates for consistent, ghost free results. Ghosting is a result of the printed transfer shifting/moving

during the heating process. When applying Pro Spray, it's wise to spray over a large trash can or dedicated cardboard box to prevent a sticky work area.

45. Most fabrics will shrink in the heat press. If this occurs with a transfer attached, a ghost-like image will result. Pre-pressing (pressing the fabric for a short period of time without a transfer attached) will get the shrinking out of the way and provide excellent transfer results.

46. Ceramic mugs retain heat very well and can stay hot long after being removed from a mug press or oven. Allowing a mug to cool slowly can result in a degraded image due to outgassing – the evaporation of ink from the mug's surface. Dipping an imaged mug into a bucket of room-temperature water (don't dip a hot mug into cold water!) will quickly lower the mug's temperature and prevent this from occurring.

47. Prevent unsightly transfer creases and marks on fabric by using a foam filled Teflon-coated pillow (available in a variety of sizes) or Vapor Foam Kit (13.5 sq feet of ready to cut foam). Placing a pillow or foam under garments with heavy seams or buttons allows even platen pressure during the transfer process.

48. Learn to use jigs for increasing productivity on larger orders. Ask your supplier which products can be produced using jigs.

49. Measure your heat press' temperature at least twice a year. I recommend a low-tech solution: a metal candy thermometer or a wired pyrometer. If you determine the press is out of calibration, ask your supplier which "magic buttons" will fix the problem.

50. Use a metal shear to easily produce your own custom aluminum pieces on demand and inexpensively.

CORELDRAW/PHOTOSHOP

51. To reset CorelDRAW to its default menus, press F8 as you are launching the program.

52. Learn to use CorelDRAW's Print Merge Wizard. The Print Merge Wizard can automatically generate name badges from a specified list of names – without having to create them individually! Detailed instructions are available on our website.

53. Resolution: I recommend a minimum of 200dpi for hard substrates and 150dpi for soft substrates. Let's say that you are scaling an 8"x10" photograph for the production of an 80"x100" tile mural. Scan at 2,000dpi (200dpi x 10). Once scanned, resize using the tip below and your image will be around 200dpi (Tip 54).

54. Resizing images: Uncheck the resample box in Adobe Photoshop under "image › image size" or for Elements "image ›image size › resize image". In Corel PHOTO-PAINT, check the box "Maintain Original File size". Used incorrectly, these features can really disturb your image. When resizing an image, you want to either push the dots closer or spread them out. Used improperly, these features cause the software to either add dots out of thin air or delete them by maintaining the current resolution.

55. Use Genuine Fractals to add more resolution when a higher-resolution image is not available. This inexpensive plug-in for Adobe Photoshop/Photoshop Elements is a great band-aid for adding more apparent resolution.

56. Yes, you really need both CorelDRAW and Photoshop. CorelDRAW is an excellent illustration (vector) tool, while Adobe Photoshop is a superb photo-editing (raster) tool. For most things I prefer Adobe Photoshop to Corel PHOTO-PAINT. Adobe Photoshop Elements is an inexpensive alternative to Photoshop that still gets the job done.

57. When printing black & white photos, be sure to convert the image to RGB before printing; otherwise, it will likely print with a strange tint.

58. Upgrade your CorelDRAW to a more current version. The cost is low and installing a newer version won't affect your old version. This is really necessary if your clients send you PDF artwork.

59. Check out Smart Designer from Digital Art Solutions. It is an excellent add-on for CorelDRAW that simplifies complex actions.

60. For Photoshop Elements users, I suggest Photoshop Essentials from www.ononcsoftware.com. It is an inexpensive bundle that includes Genuine Fractals.

61. Check out www.vectomagic.com for converting raster graphics to vector. This software and on-line tool work better than anything I have ever used.

62. Join www.istockphoto.com. This is the best collection of photos, vector art, and backgrounds.

63. A food design should always begin with an accurate software template. Available in a variety of file formats to ensure compatibility with your chosen graphics software package, templates give you an on-the-screen view of what the finished product will look like. Whether it's a heart-shaped mousepad, oval key chain, or a megaphone-shaped award plaque, designers can position photographs, graphics and text with confidence the first time, not through trial and error. We also have some excellent videos to assist you in using these templates.

64. For Photoshop users: When opening a file, I see the message "This file does not have an embedded profile". What should I do? You should assign SRGV and convert to workspace, which I suggest should be Adobe RGB 1998.

65. Why do my scans look so bad compared to my digital camera? Scanners cannot detect the correct white balance of the scan. You must do this step in PhotoShop under "Image adjust levels" or "enhance lighting levels". A quick fix is to try "Auto Contrast".

66. Verify that CorelDRAW's "fountain steps" are set to 256. Some versions are set to 64, which prints poorly. Look in "print preview > setting > Misc.".

MATCHING COLORS

67. For "no surprise color matching", print your color palettes using Corel's undocumented "create color swatch macro" feature. (See my articles from 2005/2007 Sublimation Almanac posted at www.Condé.com/support for full details.) Color matching is the No. 11 issue and this amazing free feature in CorelDRAW is the best solution I know. For other programs like Photoshop and Illustrator, drop me an email at dgross@Condé.com.

68. If you need to match Pantone colors, buy a Pantone swatch book. Most large corporations specify their colors with a Pantone solid-coated color. You must have the Pantone swatch book to know what that color should look like: then you can use Tip #67 to nail the proper shade.

69. Should I use RGB or CMYK colors? For photos, we really want to work in the RGB world since the devices that produce photos (like digital cameras and scanners) generate RGB colors. Both work for graphics, but you can achieve a much larger color space (color gamut) with RGB compared with CMYK.

70. In CorelDRAW, the Replace Wizard can easily convert all of the spot colors used in a graphic (Pantone, CMYK, etc.), to RGB for printing. When in CorelDRAW, choose Edit › Find and Replace › Replace Object. The Replace Wizard menu will pop-up. Select "Replace a color model or palette". Next, select "Find any color model or color palette" and next to "Replace with the color model", select RGB. A "Find and Replace" box will pop-up. Push the "Replace All" button. Depending on the image's complexity, it'll take a few moments for CorelDRAW to search the entire page and replace any non-RGB colors with their RGB equivalents.

MARKETING/SALES

71. Put your contact information on every product you sell, i.e., sublimating re-order info (your contact info plus the artwork filename) on the back of name badges or at the bottom of shirts. I suggest placing Rowmark MATES oval stickers on the bottom of mugs.

72. Sublimated products will fade outdoors depending on the ambient temperature and amount of exposure to direct sunlight. Always inform your customers that products will have a limited outdoor life (typically fading in 18-24 months). Do not install ceramic or glass tiles outdoors or in any environment that receives strong direct sunlight. For car tags and signage, be sure to use Unisub metal or FRP featuring the yellow peel coat. This yellow peel coat signifies an outdoor coating.

73. Also try to date your designs with the year, theme or other message that would promote new designs.

74. Sell name badges! Schools, churches, and businesses always need traditional or slotted name badges. Without a doubt, this is my favorite sublimation product...profits are excellent!

75. Always sell and promote product bundles. If the customer buys a mug, offer a discount if he/she also buys a mousepad.

76. Three things often determine pricing: to whom you are selling, the selling environment and what's on the product, i.e. including "Ask me about tax credits" on a real estate agent's name badge. It makes it more valuable to them and increases your volume as themes change.

77. Plant seeds! Provide targeted prospects with samples personalized for them. This is a great way to open doors to new clients. Join your local Chamber of Commerce and send a name badge or desk plate to selected members. Network!

78. Get involved with silent auctions for charities. This is an amazing way to get great PR for almost nothing. Give away something appropriate for the event.

79. Tap into event-driven opportunities like car shows, sports, hobbies, and pet shows. These provide great impulse buying opportunities.

80. Install a free tile mural for charity in a public or high traffic area and use this as your calling card to show others the beauty of sublimation.

81. Sell closing gifts and promotional products to real estate agents. This is just one of the tips in the great book "125 Ways to Make Money with Sublimation".

82. Use glossy FRP sheet stock and UNISUB metal as dry-erase boards.

83. Promote green products such as tote bags.

84. Use a digital photo frame to display samples of your products. Be sure to take a photograph of every product you produce to add to your photo frame.

85. Make sales calls to museum gift shops and other tourist attractions. You can provide these folks with custom imprinted products like mugs and mousepads. With local delivery and small order quantities, how can they say no?

86. Make a set of personalized mugs for the local TV morning show. Amazing PR.

87. Save your client's images, let them know they can come back for reprints.

88. Collect your community and Chamber of Commerce calendars and look for sales and PR opportunities.

89. Market to special occasions like weddings, Valentine's Day, First Communion, and graduations.

90. Expand your product offering. Ask your partner to automatically send you samples of any new products. This is a great way to keep your customers excited. In addition, add larger products such as ChromaLuxe panels, ceiling tiles, and floor mats. Have us create a PartnerNet (floor mat for you to promote our business).

91. Always ask photographers for permission to use their images. This is also a great way to build partnerships for wholesale business and referrals.

92. Display your samples. Show folks what you can do! You won't sell products your customers don't know you offer. Try all products, let your customers decide what products they like. Your goal should be to maximize the profit on every client. If you need a quick start, we can provide you a samples kit with imaged products for you to show immediately.

93. Download our free unbranded product catalog. You can customize it with your company's logo for printing, emailing and placing on your own website. It is excellent!

94. Get web images of products from your supplier partners for use on your website.

95. Plant seeds. When possible, include a sample product with a customer's order. Often that sample will find its way to someone new.

96. Display several different products using the same artwork/graphic, i.e. a ceramic mug, mousepad, T-shirt and key chain made for a major corporate or church event.

97. Remember what you can do: full-color, personalized, no minimum quantity and on-demand products!

98. Choose a supplier that will become a partner who focuses on your success. Look for phone support, email support, remote access. YouTube videos, instructions, templates, after hours and weekend support are a must.

99. Download, print and transfer our test image called "tweak image", the default RGB palette and your nozzle check. Then store this away. If you ever think your system is no longer working properly, you can print and transfer again to compare. You would be surprised how often colors get out of order, inks mixed, and so forth. Be sure to document on the back of the substrate your print and transfer settings.

100. Call your supplier for help and training sooner than later.

101. Keep reading trade magazines!

APPENDIX III

GLOSSARY OF SUBLIMATION TERMS

Accucutter: The company that makes shears, corner cutters and rollers for the awards and sublimation industry.

Acrylic: A thermoplastic material that when properly coated and of a specific type, can be sublimated.

Adobe: The manufacturer of PhotoShop, Illustrator and PhotoShop Essentials.

All-Over Print: Usually refers to garments with an imprint that covers the entire garment. Also referred to as "Cut & Sew" meaning the garment is sublimated before it is sewn together.

Aluminum: A relatively soft, silver metal commonly coated and used with sublimation. Multiple grades of coatings are available which can add vibrancy, UV protection or a texture finish to the product.

ArTainium Ink: An alternative ink from Epson to compete with Sawgrass ink for those who run printers 42" or wider.

Backgrounding: Usually only seen with laser sublimation. It is the presence of tiny specks of toner that have sublimated into a substrate. This may vary from light to heavy and cannot be removed. Usually doesn't show up on satin gold or silver metal but common on white substrates.

Banding: The presence of thin white lines across a sublimation image. Caused by a non-functioning nozzle in a printhead.

Beveler: A mechanical device designed for placing a bevel on thin plastics, wood or FRP when creating your own products from sheet stock.

Bison: A company that coats ceramic tile for the purpose of sublimation.

Bitmap Software: Software intended for working with photographs including PhotoShop and PhotoPaint and PhotoShop Essentials.

Brass: A metal alloy made up of copper and zinc. Commonly used in the engraving industry and can be sublimated if properly coated.

Bulk Ink Supply: A means to add large pouches of ink to a printer that is designed to accept only small cartridges. This greatly reduces the cost of printing. The idea came with many issues and except for a few Epson printers, is no longer available.

Carrier Sheet: Another term for the "transfer sheet" used in sublimation.

Cast Acrylic: A type of acrylic obtained by pouring liquid acrylic into a mold. Used in laser engraving and when properly coated, some high temp acrylics can be sublimated.

Ceramic: An inorganic nonmetallic solid material. Ceramic is typically the baked surface of a tile, cup or other product. When coated properly, it can be sublimated but the sublimation dyes only penetrate the surface coating of the product and do not go into the substrate itself.

ChromaLuxe®: A product from UNISUB. Highest quality photo-ready surface on a variety of metals.

Clamshell Press: A type of heat press where the heating element lifts up at an angle to allow loading of the stage. This type of press is commonly used for making T-shirts and can also make thin items such as metal or FRP but is not recommended for thicker items because the heating element closes at an angle presenting more pressure to the back than the front and thus, distorting the image colors.

CMYK: Stands for CYAN, MAGENTA, YELLOW, BLACK. The four primary colors used in a printer to produce a color image.

Cockling: A small wave pattern that the paper makes when it is too humid or there is too much saturation on the paper. Resembles rolling hills.

Color Chart: A series of color swatches applied to a sheet of metal, FRP or other material to show the actual end result of selecting a specific color in a software program.

Color-Filling: A process of adding color to a substrate that has been laser engraved. Typically used for adding metallic gold or silver to a name badge.

ColorSure®: Sublimation production printers by Epson. Intended to use Epson's own sublimation inks. Available in 44" and 64".

Computer Graphics: Graphic designs created using a computer.

CondéTV: A free service of Condé Systems available on YouTube. These short educational videos demonstrate how to make various products, service printers, etc.

CorelDRAW™: A graphics program for working with vector images with some ability to manipulate bitmaps. Used by most people in the sublimation industry. Available for purchase.

CornerMate: A mechanical device intended to notch or round corners on thin plastics or metal.

Cover Paper: Can be newsprint, butcher paper or copy paper. Must be an uncoated paper that is applied over the top of a substrate and its transfer when placed in a heat press. The purpose is to ensure stray ink does not find its way to the platen of the heat press.

Cut & Sew: Usually refers to garments with an imprint that covers the entire garment. This is accomplished by sublimating the garment before it is sewn together.

Designs 4 U: Discontinued product. Was once sold by UNISUB dealers and contained hundreds of templates, layouts and images that could be used for making showroom samples or altered and used as actual products. Several CDs were available. Now available from the Condé website.

Desktop Printer: Typically refers to small printers that can sit on a desk. This sometimes refers to printers that are under 24". This includes most of the Epson and Ricoh printers currently being used for sublimation.

Disks: Disks are commonly used in the awards industry and can be sublimated when properly coated. These include 1" and 2" metal disks and can include disks used for specialty products that include 1.625" and .9375" disks. Disks are commonly available in white, gold and silver. Disks can also refer to tokens (poker chips) made from a sublimatable compound.

Dithering: The presence of squares in a monitor image or dots in a printed image. These squares or dots are individual pixels. They appear when the image is of too low resolution to produce a smooth edge on an image.

DPI: Dots per Inch. DPI refers to the number of ink droplets a printer can place on a substrate. Commonly used interchangeably with pixels per inch which is the number of pixels a monitor can display per inch. The higher the DPI, the higher the resolution of an image and the larger it can be printed without pixilating.

Dwell Time: The length of time a heat press is closed.

Dye Sublimation: A process of transferring a full-color image from a transfer to a substrate using heat, pressure and special inks. A process where dye changes from a solid to a gas without going through a liquid state.

DyeFlex®: A very thin plastic-like material brought to market by Condé Systems for sublimation. It is a single-sided, 1/64" thick, high flexible plastic.

DyeTrans: A brand name for many Condé products.

DynaSub: A type of sublimation metal available in white, silver and gold. This high quality, high resolution metal is a cheaper alternative to the UNISUB metal but does not contain UNISUB'S UV protective agents.

Epson: The brand name for many sublimation printers, present and past. These printers are somewhat unique in the marketplace because they use Piezo printheads which are suitable for sublimation inks. Until the introduction of the Ricoh printers, Epson was the only brand used in the desktop format.

FRP: Fiberglass Reinforced Plastic: A UNISUB product that appears to be plastic but is actually fiberglass with the UNISUB coating applied to one or both sides. This material is 3/32" thick and is available in both sheet stock and a wide variety of premade products.

Full-Bleed Printing: When the background or photograph extends beyond the edges of the finished product.

Ghosting: Usually caused by moving a transfer too quickly after opening the heat press. Can also be caused by opening a heat press too quickly and thus moving the transfer while it is still at 400° F. Ghosting is also called "shadowing" and is a shadow image making a sublimated image appear to be repeated on the same substrate.

Glass: Tempered glass is a commonly used sublimation substrate when properly coated. It is commonly used for tile and cutting boards.

Gloss: Highly reflective.

Graphic Design: The process of creating an image suitable for printing or sublimating on a substrate using a computer graphics program.

Green Heat Conductive Pad: A special rubber pad (usually green and usually 1/8" thick) used to disperse heat across uneven surfaces in a heat press.

Hardboard: A common material in hardware stores but also used as a sublimation substrate. Usually 1/8" thick, it can also be ¼". Hardboard can be coated with a sublimation receptive coating for use as a clipboard, picture frame or any number of other products.

Harvey Head Cleaner: A software program that automatically runs a nozzle check on sublimation printers.

Heat Press: An electric-mechanical device intended for heating sublimation transfers and their substrates to 400° F using a consistent temperature and pressure.

Heat Tape: A special single-sided tape used to hold sublimation products in place while pressing. These tapes will withstand over 500° F without failing. Tapes come in several thicknesses and colors.

Heat Transfer: Although it is commonly mistaken for sublimation, it is not. A heat transfer is an image that melts into fabric or lays on top of fabric much like screen printing. Sublimation dyes the fabric permanently rather than clings to the face of it. Heat transfers are commonly used on cotton while sublimation is always used on Polyester.

Heating Element: Usually the upper portion of a heat press. Also referred to as a Platen. Some heat presses have multiple platens that allow both the top and bottom of a substrate to be heated equally and simultaneously. Other have side by side platens to allow one stage to be loaded while the other is being pressed.

ICC Profile: A color management tool (software) promulgated by the International Color Consortium (ICC).

Illustrator: A graphics software program by Adobe intended for working with vector images. A direct alternative to CorelDRAW. Not available for purchase. This program is Cloud based and must be rented monthly.

Image Resolution: Also referred to as DPI (dots per inch) or PPI (pixels per inch). Used to determine the quality of a bitmap image and how much that image can be enlarged before pixilation occurs.

Jig: A device designed to hold multiple products so they can all be sublimated at once. Most jigs on the market today are made by UNISUB and intended for UNISUB products.

KoolPlate™: A device that uses multiple fans and thermodynamics to accelerate the cooling of sublimated products. Sold exclusively by Condé Systems.

KrinkleSub®: The name given to a type of aluminum that is both coated for sublimation and given a texture to make it more interesting. This metal can also be laser engraved.

Large Format Printer: Although there is no fast rule about this, most people agree anything larger than 44" wide is considered wide-format. Some, consider the 24" printers to also be wide-format.

Laser Cutting: The ability to use a laser engraver to vector cut your own products from hardboard, rubber, leather, Neoprene, wood or FRP.

Laser Sublimation: A type of sublimation that uses a b/w or color laser printer to produce sublimation transfers. Very popular at one time, it is rarely used today because of problems obtaining suitable printers and backgrounding.

Layout: A design, text, image or photograph to be applied by sublimation to a product.

Leather: Some light-colored leather can be sublimated.

Lightroom: A software program by Adobe that is excellent for working with bitmaps of all kinds. This is primarily a cataloging program, but it also allows manipulation of a photograph without damaging the original. Allows storage to be done in multiple locations. Makes for easy posting of photos on Facebook or converting to a print book of photos. Available for purchase or grouped with PhotoShop on the Cloud for a monthly fee.

MATES®: A highly flexible self-adhesive film that can be sublimated. Available in white, gold and silver.

Matte: Flat or satin finish. Non-reflective.

MDF: Medium Density Fiberboard. This material is actually made of many very thin sheets of paper pressed together to form what appears to be a wood board. It can be cut, routered and painted just like wood. It is strictly for interior use and can be coated to be sublimatable. It is used to produce picture frames, plaques, clocks and other UNISUB products.

Media Street: A paper manufacturer that produces sublimation transfer paper.

Medium Density Fiberboard: Also referred to as MDF. This material is actually made of many very thin sheets of paper pressed together to form what appears to be a wood board. It can be cut, routered and painted just like wood. It is strictly for interior use and can be coated to be sublimatable. It is used to produce picture frames, plaques, clocks and other UNISUB products.

Micro-Fiber: Another name given to synthetic fabrics such as Polyester.

Migration: Migration in sublimation is when the dye (ink) tends to shift or move from where it belongs in a image to either something laying on top of the sublimated piece or to a place where it does not belong in a sublimated image. Usually caused by too much heat or pressure being applied for a long period of time. Can also occur when products are stacked on top of each other too soon after being sublimated.

Mirror Image: For most sublimation (except glass and acrylic) the image must be mirrored on the transfer sheet so it will appear "right" on the substrate. PowerDriver will perform this function or you can do it manually in CorelDRAW or other graphics programs.

MorphMugs®: A type of ceramic coffee cup that changes color when a hot liquid is poured into it. This is commonly a black mug that can be sublimated but the sublimation only shows up when hot liquid is poured into it and turning the surface of the cup white.

Mouse Pad Material: A piece of Polyester fabric glued to a rubber backing. Rubber backing can be various thickness including 1/16", 1/8", ¼", ½" and 1".

MouseMates®: A product made for Rowmark and distributed through dealers like Condé Systems. It is a mousepad on a rubber 1/8" thick backing with a Mates film over the surface that provides a washable surface that accepts a high-resolution image. Available in white or silver.

Mug Press: A specialized heat press for making 11oz and 15oz ceramic mugs.

Mug Wrap: A flexible rubber wrap that can be applied to a coffee cup so it can be sublimated in an oven. Each wrap must be made for a specific object. These can include an 11oz cup, a 15oz mug, steins of various sizes, shot glasses, drinking glasses, pet bowls, etc.

MugMates®: A product made for Rowmark and distributed through dealers like Condé Systems. It is a coaster on a rubber 1/8" thick backing with a Mates film over the surface that provides a washable surface that accepts a high-resolution image. Available in white or silver.

Multi-Pass Tray: A mechanical device that can be attached to printers like the Ricoh 7000 and 7100 to allow paper up to 13" wide to be fed through a printer that otherwise would only accept 11" paper. Also works with the Sawgrass SG800 and SG1000.

Mutoh: The manufacturer of wide-format printers commonly used for sublimation.

Neenah: A paper manufacturer that produces sublimation transfer paper.

Neoprene: The material used to make wetsuits for scuba divers. This material can be sublimated provided it is white in color.

Nomex Pad: A high temperature felt pad designed to protect areas of the substrate that you do not want heated. Heat Insulating Nomex Felt Pads are soft and heat resistant and most commonly used to press ceramic tiles. When pressure is applied the tile sinks into the transfer and the pad, allowing the image to coat beveled edges and provide a better product. This high-temperature resistant material is only needed for ceramic tiles and light switch plates for sublimation printing.

Nozzle Check: A test to determine if the nozzles in a printhead are functioning properly. Usually accessed through the print driver or PowerDriver software.

Nozzle: A single Piezo outlet in a printhead. It is an electro-magnetic device that vibrates when power is sent to it. The vibration causes the nozzle to flex which fires a speck of ink.

Okidata: Manufacturer of printers commonly used for heat transfers and laser sublimation.

Page Layout Software: Layout software can be almost anything from Word to CorelDRAW. In the sublimation industry, it is almost always CorelDRAW but almost any program can be used to create a design that will then be printed and used for sublimation.

Pantone®: The color standard of the industry.

PartnerNet: A special status of Condé customer who is given a pass to material which non-customers cannot access.

Pennant: As in baseball pennant. These felt shapes can be sublimated to reflect whatever type of pennant a customer might want. Typically used for a child's room.

Performance Fabric: Another word for Micro-Fiber or Polyester. This specific variant of Polyester allows the fabric to "breathe" and thus keeping its wearer cooler. Commonly used in sports apparel.

Perpetual Plaque: A plaque that holds 12 or more "engraving" plates. Specially made brass or aluminum plates can be sublimated and used to make a perpetual plaque.

Pewter: Pewter is a malleable metal alloy traditionally 85-99% tin with the remainder being copper and trace amounts of other metals. Although not sublimatable itself, it is often used as a frame or holder for sublimated disks, tiles or other products.

Phone Cover: Perhaps the industry's most popular sublimated products. These specially made plastic or rubber devices hold a flat metal or DyeFlex insert that can be sublimated.

PhotoPaint™: An alternative to PhotoShop. This is a bitmap software program that interacts with CorelDRAW. Available on CD, this program comes free with CorelDRAW. It contains an excellent cut out plug-in for sublimation (formerly called Knock-Out).

PhotoShop Elements™: A bitmap software program by Adobe intended for working with photographs. This program, available for purchase, is an abbreviated version of PhotoShop with some important additional programs. This software contains the best program for enlarging a photograph or increasing the DPI of a photo. A must have for making murals.

PhotoShop™: A bitmap software program by Adobe intended for working with photographs. A direct alternative to PhotoPaint. Not available for purchase. This program is Cloud based and must be rented monthly.

Piezo: A type of nozzle used in a printhead that uses electromagnetism to vibrate and move ink out of the nozzle. A necessary element for ink-jet sublimation.

Pixel: A single dot of light on a computer monitor or TV screen.

Platen: Usually the upper portion of a heat press. Also referred to as a heating element. Some heat presses have multiple platens that allow both the top and bottom of a substrate to be heated equally and simultaneously. Others have side by side platens to allow one stage to be loaded while the other is being pressed.

Polyester: Another word for Micro-Fiber or Performance fabric. This is a synthetic fabric that accepts sublimation dyes.

PolyMug®: An 11oz cup made from an unbreakable material that feels like plastic.

PolySub: The manufacturer of the PolyMug product.

Porcelain: A ceramic material baked at 1,200° to 1,400° F.

PowerDriver: A special piece of software referred to as a "driver" that is an alternate to using an ICC profile(s) for sublimation.

Pressure: The amount of pressure applied to a substrate in a heat press. Some presses have a gauge to measure relative pressure but most people use an approximated pressure of light, medium and heavy.

Printhead: The collection of multiple nozzles arranged to produce an image on paper.

Pyrometer: A special type of electronic thermometer. When used with a special contact probe, this allows the measurement of a heat press.

Raster Image: An image made up of dots or pixels. A photograph or type of bitmap such as a jpeg, gif, tiff, etc. This type of image cannot be broken apart like a vector image.

Refillable Cartridges: A type of ink cartridge used in high production, wide format printers to allow additional ink to be inserted while the printer continues to run. This is not recommended unless there is a high production environment since ink exposed to air has a shorter life than ink sealed in a cartridge.

Reveal-S: An experimental paper designed to allow sublimation printers to be used to make heat transfers that can be applied to cotton fabrics. The paper was printed with sublimation ink and then transferred using a heat press. Listed here for informational purposes only.

Ribbon: Sublimatable light colored Polyester ribbon that is generally used as an award ribbon or bookmark. light colored Polyester ribbon can be sublimated.

Ricoh: The brand name of many sublimation printers still being used. The manufacturer of the Sawgrass Virtuoso printers currently being sold for sublimation.

RIP Software: Special color management software used in connection with wide-format printers. Its purpose is to adjust the output to match a printed color standard.

RIP: A raster image processor.

Roller (Metal): A mechanical device used to roll metal into a curved shape. For sublimation, it is used to give a curve to flat sublimatable metal after sublimation. This adds character and allows the product to stand up on its own. Made by Accucutter.

Rowmark: The manufacturer of engraving plastics and distributor of the MATES® product.

Sandstone: A stone-like material used for making coasters that absorbs moisture and when properly coated, can be sublimated.

Satin: Flat or matte finish. Non-reflective.

Sawgrass Technologies: The manufacturer of the Sawgrass sublimation inks and creator of the Creative Studio software.

SG500 & SG1000: As of this printing, these are the current models of Sawgrass sublimation printers. Replaced the Virtuoso series SG400 and SG800.

Shear (Metal): A device used to cut thin metal.

Spacer (Tile): The tiny ribs on the edges of ceramic tile.

Spectrum Marking: The manufacturer of the MATES® material.

Stage: The lower platform on a heat press.

SubliGlass®: The name given to many of the sublimatable glass plaques currently being offered.

SubliJet: Brand of Sawgrass inks. Includes several variations such as Sublijet-R, E, IQ and HD.

Sublimation: A process by which a solid turns to a gas and back into a solid without passing through a liquid stage.

SubliSlate: The name given to black slate, cut and coated with a white sublimatable coating. Used as wall hangings or products to sit on a shelf, these ½" thick plaques come in a variety of sizes and shapes.

SubliWrap: A sublimatable, self-adhesive white film that is sold by the roll or dye-cut into specific products such as phone covers and face plates for printers.

Substrate: The base or product being sublimated.

Swatch book: A printed book of sample colors, (usually Pantone™ colors) that are used as a color standard so printers, painters and others can refer to a single source and know the actual color. Used in sublimation by running a test strip of colors and manually matching them to the swatch (PMS) book to find a match.

Swing-a-Way Press: A heat press that contains a pivotal joint, allowing the heating element to swing 180° so it is out of the way when loading the press. Allows for perfectly vertical pressure on the substrate.

Synthetic Fabrics: This can include many fabrics and most will sublimate; with Polyester being the most common. (Polyester, Micro-fiber, Performance Fabric, Dacron, Olefin, acrylic, Nylon.)

Tacky Paper: A special paper used to sublimate large sheets of fabric with a wide-format printer and heat press.

Teflon Sheet: A brown sheet used to protect a heat press from stray sublimation gas. Commonly recommended to be placed over the rubber pad on the stage of a heat press. Two sheets are often used when printing self-adhesive films.

Template: A computer design that shows the actual size of a product and an extended area for full-bleed printing.

TexPrint: A specialty transfer paper for sublimation.

Textured Metal: Aluminum with a pebble-like surface. Offered by UNISUB and others.

Tumbled Stone: Tile made of compressed sandstone.

UNISUB Metal: An aluminum sheet with the UNISUB coating applied. This is the only aluminum containing a UV inhibitor. Has a slightly yellow cast to it prior to sublimating. Considered by most to be the highest grade sublimatable available.

UNISUB: Brand name for most of the products made by Universal Woods. The other brand is ChromaLuxe™.

Universal Woods: Maker of all UNISUB and ChromaLuxe products.

Vapor®: Manufacturer of most of the Polyester garments used in the sublimation industry.

Vector Image: An image made up of lines and shapes that can be taken apart when opened in a graphics program. Any image you create yourself starts out as a vector image.

Vector Software: Software like CorelDRAW and Illustrator intended for creating line type drawings.

Virtuoso™: Brand name of the first generation of Sawgrass printers. Included the SG400 and SG800 models, now discontinued. Replaced with the SG500 and SG1000 Sawgrass printers.

Wasatch SoftRIP: A brand of RIP software designed for wide-format printers.

 APPENDIX IV

TIME & TEMPERATURE CHART

Most people just beginning with sublimation become somewhat obsessed with all the times and temperatures used for the various products. Actually, it isn't all that complicated since the vast majority are the same: 1 minute at 400 with medium pressure. Only the more unique products like tiles and glass require a drastically different setting. You may want to photocopy this page and hang it over your press for quick reference.

All FRP (Fiberglass Reinforced Plastic)	60 sec	Medium	Face Up	400
	120 sec	Medium	Face Down	400
All Metal (Except ChromaLuxe)	60 sec	Medium	Face Down	400
ChromaLuxe	90 sec	Medium	Face Down	400
All UNISUB Hardboard	60 sec	Medium	Face Up	400
All UNISUB MDF Board	60 sec	Medium	Face Up	400
MDF over 10x12"	120 sec	Heavy	Face Up	400
Adhesive Film (Mates)	34-45 sec	Medium	Either	400
Fabric, including shirts	35-45 sec	Medium	Face Up	400
Dye-Flex Plastic	60-90 sec	Medium	Either	400
Mousepads, except MouseMates	60 sec	Medium	Face Up	400
MouseMates & MugMates	90 sec	Medium	Face Up	400
Leather	60 sec	Medium	Face Up	400
Flip Flops	60 sec	Medium	Face Up	400
Towels	60 sec	Medium	Face Up	400
All Ceramic Tiles*	7.5 min	Heavy	Face Up	400
Glass*	7.5 min	Heavy	Face Up	400
Porcelain Tiles*	7.5 min	Heavy	Face Up	400
Porcelain Christmas Ornaments*	60 sec	Medium	Face Up	400

*Tiles and glass require the use of Nomex™ and/or a green rubber pad. Check CondéTV for instructions.

How to Judge Heat Press Pressures Without a Gauge

How to measure pressure with a George Knight heat press is fairly simple, and although it is anything but scientific, it is quite adequate for our purposes:

LIGHT PRESSURE: Assuming someone with normal upper body strength, you should be able to close the press with virtually no effort with one hand. If you don't encounter or hear the press latch down, increase the pressure slightly until you do.

MEDIUM PRESSURE: Assuming someone with normal upper body strength, this should require considerable effort to close the press with one hand and is the pressure setting most commonly used.

HEAVY PRESSURE: Assuming someone with normal upper body strength, this setting should require considerable effort with both hands.

People with less upper body strength than an average man, will need to adjust these tips accordingly.

 APPENDIX V

BASIC SUBLIMATION TROUBLE SHOOTING

Now that your system is installed and operating, let's review how our support system goes about assisting you. This insight will give you an edge to solving problems faster.

First, it is critical that you document your sublimation process steps. I use a sublimation journal for this. I tend to document each job and evaluate my results. Some new operators put a job number on the back of the transfers that can also be used to assist your clients in reordering your products. This number would be detailed in your journal. As you are just beginning, I suggest documenting all your successes, failures and of course, questions. If you call for help and we ask for details and all you can say is nothing is working, that will be difficult to trouble shoot.

Problems generally are first related to learning the process, very much like learning to cook or drive. There are three areas of focus for sublimation. Computer, printer and heat press. Sometimes it is difficult to determine where to focus.

Computer:

Computer issues come from two sources. It is either a settings issue or an issue with your artwork.

Settings can be further broken down to printer and application settings. These simply need to be correct for proper color and quality. Sometimes during major windows and Mac OS software updates, these settings can be deleted. So, you should check before printing that these settings are being used. A great way to remember these settings is to take photos of the various computer screens with your smartphone to document your driver and application settings. These can be printed out and included with your sublimation journal.

I recommend that once your system is configured, you print some test images of your own and also print our calibration image. These images should confirm if your system is good to go!

Artwork:

Artwork trouble shooting can be simple for the experienced but can often be perplexing for new operators. One thing to remember is that the colors on the paper or the screen will not reflect what happens when the inks are heated.

A. Image quality

See the section on image resolution. As the saying goes, "Garbage in, Garbage out". I have received many calls from new operators that download images from the internet only to find that when printed they look terrible but seem just fine on the screen. This is because there are not enough dots in the image to print with good quality. Most images on the internet are 72 dpi at screen size. We need 200 dpi or more at print size, in general. So, if you are having quality issues, I recommend printing a known good image like our calibration image, or an image you have taken from your smart phone or digital camera.

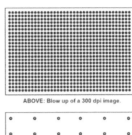

ABOVE: Blow up of a 300 dpi image.

ABOVE: Blow up of a 72 dpi image.

B. My colors look fine on the monitor but sublimate differently

Every monitor is different and so you cannot use your monitor to select colors. Instead print and sublimate a color chart and then pick your color from it and go back and choose those colors in your graphics software.

The first step is to make sure your graphics program is set up properly and you are using only the RGB color pallet in your drawings. Corel offers many pallets you can use but only the RGB pallet will produce the type of color you want.

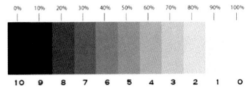

Generic gray scale.

The next step in trouble shooting color issues is to verify that your system is working correctly. One of the best ways to do this is to print and transfer our calibration image or one of your digital camera or smartphone photos to something like a piece of white UNISUB metal or FRP. First view the grey scale. If it is not grey, then something may be wrong.

C. Colors look good to me, but client says they are wrong

This is a great lesson. When you are expected to match colors for a company logo or school colors, you must have a tangible example with which to compare. You should not guess at colors – you will _always_ be wrong! If your client specifies colors using the Pantone® system, you must buy a Pantone® book so you can see what the color looks like.

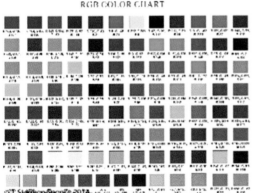

RGB COLOR CHART

Your color charts make the magic happen.

Pantone color chart.

Unfortunately, you cannot use the codes in the book, you must print a color chart and match them by comparing one with the other. For a less precise color match, (like a school color), you need an example you can compare to your color chart.

Printer:

Printer issues also fall into two categories. Printer or paper related. For the printer, you should verify that the nozzle check is complete. Beyond that, there are a number of other things to check at the printer but before you do, give your support team a call. We can direct you to the next step.

TexPrint R comes in a variety of sizes.

It is critical that you print with the proper sublimation paper for your printer and that you print on the correct side. Often our instructions will recommend the proper paper for the substrate and printer/ink. For example, using the TexPrint XP paper in a Ricoh based printer will cause vertical dotted wheel marks as the ink will not dry fast enough for the fast print speeds. You should be using TexPrint-R unless instructed otherwise.

Heat Press:

Starting with a great heat press is a big help in sublimation. (See my chapter on heat presses). Most new operators believe that there is some sort of magic in cooking stuff at the heat press and that you must go to extreme lengths to have great results. Most substrates are straight forward and have what I call a "large sweet spot" meaning that like cooking, just add the right ingredients and cook hot enough or long enough and you will have great results. Here are a few of the most common issues:

- Did you build the sublimation sandwich in the correct order?
- Did you press long enough for your heat press?
- Is the temperature really correct?
- Is the pressure heavy enough?
- Is most of the ink gone from the paper after pressing?

Generally, if you press something too long, black turns brown. Not enough time and the transfer is incomplete.

Make it easy on yourself:

How did we each learn to drive a car? Well, we didn't get on the interstate day one; we learned to drive around the neighborhood. So, with sublimation, practice on easy substrates like white polyester fabric, Unisub metal or FRP until you get the hang of it. See the magic!

Never hesitate to call us:

We can't be successful unless you are successful. We are a team. Don't understand something? Call our Technical Support Team at 1-800-826-6332.

APPENDIX VI

"Success is not the key to happiness. Happiness is the key to success. If you love what you are doing, you will be successful." -Albert Schweitzer

QUALITY PROBLEMS AT THE HEAT PRESS

Sublimation, when done correctly, is absolutely stunning. The colors are not only accurate but sharp and brilliant. Some say it has a "WOW" factor and they are right. You will often hear your customers exclaim, "Wow" when you give them their products. I dare to say there is not another color imprinting method on earth that is any better.

Best of all is the fact that obtaining these mind-blowing results is easy and you *can* do it. Many people accomplish it with their very first try.

But what if you don't? What if the colors are all wrong and it has a ghost like shadow over it and it isn't straight or even upside down and backwards? All of these are possible, but they are easy to correct and once you understand the cause, you will be able to troubleshoot any problems that might come up in just seconds, and if you can't, Condé offers free telephone support for anyone doing sublimation. Just call, and an expert will walk you through the steps to find out what went wrong and tell you how to fix it. The other day, I heard David Gross say, "You can do sublimation in the dark" and that's just about right. It is that easy but things can, from time to time, go astray and when they do, check the list below. If that doesn't help, pick up the phone and call Condé Technical Support.

Ghosting (double image): This is almost always caused by movement of the transfer sheet just after or during the time the press is being opened. The easiest way to solve this problem is by using heat tape to securely attach the substrate to the transfer and to open the press gently and slowly. Don't jerk the press open as it causes the transfer to stick to the heating element and then drop off. This often causes the transfer to shift slightly. One other trick is to wait for 10-20 seconds after opening the press to touch or move the transfer or substrates. As long as the transfer is above 350° F, it is going to continue to transfer dye to the substrate.

Sizzle or Popping Noise When Closing the Press (Steam coming from press): If you hear sizzling noise when you close your press, it is probably because there is too much moisture in your transfer and/or substrate. This *usually* doesn't hurt anything but it can, especially with garments. You will likely also see steam rolling out from under the platen of your heat press. This is also the result of too much moisture. To eliminate this potential problem, you should take the following steps just before sublimating your item: One, if the substrate is fabric, link roll the garment that will come into contact with the platen and close the press lightly for about 5 seconds. Two, lay the transfer on top of the garment and allow it to sit there for 10-20 seconds with the platen hovering over it (don't close it!). These two steps will remove most of the moisture from both the transfer and the garment and should solve the problem. For hard surfaces like metal, dry the transfer as described above. Make the transfer immediately after drying the transfer or it will just absorb moisture again. Most hard substrates really don't need to be dried like fabric, but with a few, like the self-adhesive films, it helps.

Blue Specks on fabric: This is a very strange phenomenon that can occur with fabric. It is caused by stray fibers embedded in the fabric that are invisible to the naked eye. To eliminate this problem, roll a lint roller over the entire area of fabric that is going to come into contact with the heating element. This should eliminate the problem.

Wisps of Color Around the Edges of a Transfer: In most cases, you should always have your transfer larger than the substrate you are imprinting. This will eliminate this problem. Where this isn't practical such as with fabric or ceramic coffee cups, you should know the wisps are from escaping gas from the transfer and caused by too much moisture in the transfer. Drying the transfer by laying it under the heating element for 10-20 seconds with the element hovering over but not touching the transfer should solve the problem. Once this is done, make your transfer as quickly as possible since the transfer will rather quickly absorb the moisture back into the pores of the paper.

Image from a Previous Transfer Reappears: This is a very common mistake caused by failing to place a cover sheet (not a Teflon sheet) over the back of the transfer. When heated, a small amount of dye migrates through the back of the transfer sheet and onto either the heating platen or the stage where the substrate rests. Once this dye makes its way to either the rubber pad or the heating platen, it can be very stubborn to remove. Rubbing alcohol can be used to clean the heating element (Platens can be cleaned hot or cold but be careful, 400° causes an instant 3rd degree burn, so Be sure to wear the proper protection when cleaning it hot.). The rubber base is more difficult to clean but Simple Green seems to do the best job. For an immediate solution, place a sheet of newsprint over the rubber pad and on top of each job to protect your project. This should be a habit you do each and every time you sublimate something! Failure to do so will cause painful consequences.

FRP Products Warp: FRP products, especially the larger ones like license plates, will warp if they are allowed to cool on an uneven surface. The best solution is to remove them from the heat press and immediately place them on a KoolPlate™ or flat surface to cool. In some cases, you may need to place the item face down and put a weight on the back of it but if you use a KoolPlate™, this should not be necessary.

Blotches on White Metal: We don't see this much anymore since there are so many good metals on the market but inferior metals will imprint with blotches or even streaks showing in the image. This is usually the fault of the metal and the only solution is to buy a better grade of metal. In some cases, however, this can be caused by too much moisture. Drying the transfer as described above will eliminate the moisture, but more often than not, the problem will be the metal itself.

Trouble with Self-Adhesive Films: Self-adhesive films are an animal of their own. When making small items, you will have few problems but when working with larger sheets (8x10" or larger), problems seem to multiply. Films are really easy to print if you just follow the rules: One, remove as much moisture as you can from both the film and the transfer. Two, if you use heat tape, place two pieces (and only two pieces) of tape on one side of the transfer. Leave the other sides loose. After pressing, you may see considerable curling. This is normal. Cool your product on a KoolPlate™ if possible by laying it face down with a small weight in the center of each sheet. This will help flatten the sheet but will not do so completely. Over time, the film will relax but being curled does not hurt the quality of the product as it will work properly, even if it is curled.

Indentations On My Hard Substrates: This is common with fabric and there are easy fixes for that (see below) but it can be avoided on hard substrates easily by always cutting your transfer the same size or larger than the substrate. When the transfer is smaller than the substrate, the pressure from the heat press actually pushes the transfer sheet into the coating on the substrate leaving an indentation. Placing heat tape over the face of the product can also cause this issue. Always apply tape to the back of a hard substrate, never the front.

Indentations In My Fabrics: This is a common problem that has plagued the industry from the beginning, but rest assured, there are several easy fixes. You may need to try a couple to find the one that works best for you. Here are three solutions I recommend:

1. If you aren't using a lot of pressure, you can probably get by with this little trick. Rather than cut your transfer with straight edges as you normally would, tear the edges by hand. Don't try to tear the paper straight, in fact, do just the opposite. This causes the paper to act as if the edges were feathered out.
2. Your local sewing center or hobby store carries all kinds of foam (like the stuff used to make pillows). You can probably buy a 2x3' sheet of 2" foam for less than $10. Cut various size pieces from the sheet in accordance with the size transfers you normally use. When using the foam, make sure the transfer is larger in both directions than the foam. This causes the transfer to hang over the edges of the foam and behave as if the edges were feathered out. To use, place the foam under the first layer of the garment with the transfer on top of the garment. Press so the foam is squeezed about 50% but no more. The foam can be used many times before it will become hard and inflexible.
3. Condé Systems sells "Sublimation Pillows" for this very purpose. They come in a variety of sizes and are a bit more professional and easier to use than the foam above, as the foam is sandwiched between two sheets of Teflon. The same rules apply as in solution 2 above. The transfer must be larger than the pillow being used and don't squeeze the pillow more than about 50% of its thickness.

The Colors Aren't Right: Color management can be very difficult, but it doesn't have to be. If you reach a point where you are becoming frustrated with color management, call Condé Technical and let them walk through the steps with you. Chances are, they can solve your problem in just a few minutes. Below are a few of the problems that are common:

1. Color management is not turned off in CorelDRAW. Unless this is turned off, Corel tries to apply its own color solutions to your artwork. Then when the print driver tries to do the same, colors can shift all over. In Corel, go to Tools and then Color Management.

2. You are using the wrong color pallet in CorelDRAW. The default pallet for Corel is CMYK. For sublimation however, you should use RGB. To change this, go to Window, then Color Pallets, then check RGB and uncheck CMYK.

3. Selecting the colors you want must be done from a color chart that you make yourself (Condé will happily walk you through the process). You cannot select colors from the little swatches on the right-hand side of the Corel screen. Although these may be close, they might also be a "mile off". If you select all your colors from the color chart, your colors will be "right on" every time.

4. Pressing a product for the wrong length of time, temperature or with the wrong amount of pressure can alter the colors. Check CondéTV for the product you are making to be sure your times, temps and pressure are right.

5. Make sure you are using sublimation transfer paper and printing on the correct side.

6. Make sure your printer isn't low on ink.

The Image Is Barely Visible: This is a common mistake and usually ends up being the transfer paper. Not all transfer paper has ID printing on the back side so it is easy to load your paper with the printable side up. In the Ricoh printers (and usually in the other printers), the paper should be loaded printable side down. If you are hand feeding the paper through a slot on the back of the printer, the printable side of the paper should face you.

Too little pressure can also cause this problem.

Rough Surface When I Use ProSpray: The idea when using ProSpray is that it will burn away during the pressing process. If you spray too much ProSpray on the transfer, that doesn't happen which leaves a "rough to the touch" surface. This can be cleaned off with alcohol or Goo Gone. The word of the day when using ProSpray is "a tiny bit will do ya". Don't try to cover the transfer. You only want a light mist. We recommend spraying this over a trashcan or cardboard box since the overspray can build up on carpets, workbenches and floors.

Findings won't Stick to the Back of Name Badges: If you are used to using plastic welds to attach findings to badges, you will find it doesn't work with FRP. Although FRP looks like plastic, it isn't. We recommend using a good double-faced tape to attach findings, although some people like to use a glue called E6000.

My Infrared Thermometer Doesn't Read Correctly when Pointed at my Heat Press: There are only a couple of ways to determine if your press is set at the right temperature and Infrared Thermometers is one of them. Here is how the experts do it:

1. Digital Pyrometer with Surface Probe: This electronic thermometer is designed specifically for this type of application. They aren't expensive (about $85) and they should last a lifetime. To measure your press, place the probe in the center of your platen and take a reading. Then take several other readings about 2" in from the edges. If there is a difference of more than 15 degrees, there might be a problem with the press. It the average of your readings is high or low from the set temperature, check the manual that came with your press to determine how to adjust it. It isn't difficult.

2. Multiple Readings with a Pocket Thermometer: These are available from Amazon for $15-20. Just be sure what you buy will read above 400° F since that is really the only temperature we are concerned about in sublimation. After heating the press and allowing it to sit for a few minutes so the temperature can stabilize, place the probe of the thermometer in a corner of the press and close it tight. Once you have a reading, move it to the other corners and do the same. Additional readings add to your certainty of what the actual temperature is. If it needs adjustment, follow the directions in your manual.

Transfer Paper Sticks to Substrate: If your transfer sticks to the substrate, chances are you are using the wrong paper or have forgotten to remove the clear protective film from the substrate prior to heating.

FREE RESOURCES FOR THOSE WHO PURCHASHED THIS BOOK

www.TheSublimationBook.com/Resources

Made in the USA
Monee, IL
16 March 2021